LOVE AND FEAR

LOVE AND FEAR

Letters and Some Pages from a Diary

by ELIZABETH C.

Translated from the French by
GERARD HOPKINS

'... one day, ten years from now, I shall
write a book — and then everyone will
be able to feel this sense of anxiety —
this mingling of love and fear — in
which I am at present floundering ...'

JONATHAN CAPE
THIRTY BEDFORD SQUARE
LONDON

FIRST PUBLISHED 1952

PRINTED IN GREAT BRITAIN IN THE CITY OF OXFORD
AT THE ALDEN PRESS
BOUND BY A. W. BAIN & CO. LTD., LONDON

TRANSLATOR'S NOTE

A L W A Y S , when one half of a correspondence is published,
the reader is tantalized. So much, he feels, could be explained if only the letters from the other end had been
printed to balance and illuminate the replies to them. Here,
in particular, the absence of 'Yves'' side of the interchange
is to be deplored. Throughout the long, sad story, 'Lisou' is,
for the most part, reacting to stimulus and exacerbation. She
withdraws a scorched hand — what, we ask, caused that burning wound? She protests, she argues — and we long to know
why. The text is thickly studded with names. Who, we
wonder, were Sa. and Do.? — who Li. and T.? — and what
parts did they play in this developing drama of a relationship?
Mostly we can guess enough for satisfaction, but there are
passages which remain obscure beyond all hope of elucidation.
The references, the language, are only too often 'private'.
Where I have found myself up against a blank wall I have said
so. But enough remains clear and comprehensible to make of
these letters a moving record of frustration, misunderstanding
and passion.

On page 79, 'Lisou' quotes a passage which she says that
she had found in Byron's *Journal*. Prolonged search by more
than one pair of eyes has failed to trace it in either Byron's
Journals or *Letters*. It should, therefore, be made clear that
the words quoted here in English are the translator's and not
Byron's.

GERARD HOPKINS

FOREWORD

I HAVE given much thought to the question whether I should publish certain letters which Elizabeth wrote to me, together with a few pages of her Diary. Elizabeth C. was an extremely reserved person. It was seldom that she laid bare her feelings, and I could not but wonder whether she would have liked the most sacred intimacies of her life over a number of years to be thus exposed for all to see. But I knew, too, how ardently she had longed not to be forgotten, how she had always wished that some part of her should survive, and realized that what little she wrote apart from her letters — which were far more than mere communications to a single person — could give but a feeble idea of her true talent.

Remembering some talks we had had, I decided, at last, on publication. I was confirmed in this decision when, re-reading the notes she had left, I found several times repeated this wish of hers to write, this expressed eagerness of hers not altogether to vanish.

'I am frightened — terribly frightened — of achieving nothing beautiful or worth while; of dying before I can produce — like so many others — of being forgotten, as so many others have been — and I don't, oh, I don't, want that to happen....' (Letter to Jacques G., dated 4th March, 1944) or: 'I feel so strongly that the great question, as between T. and myself, is — which of us two will succeed? — succeed in every way, I mean — in our lives, and in work that might outlive us....' (Diary, under the date 13th June, 1944.)

She was in every way remarkable — gifted equally for drawing and for sculpture, and we all felt in her this desire to leave behind some work of importance. But that was not the whole extent of her ambition. She wanted, quite simply, life and happiness. We remember Elizabeth as we knew her in the years 1943 and 1944, tall, sturdy, always smiling, with hair

9

piled at the back of her head, an observant eye, a small nose, which she herself described as 'cheeky', and long, ravishingly lovely hands, which were scarcely ever still. She blushed easily, and we enjoyed nothing so much as saying things calculated to bring the embarrassed colour to her face. Her charm was of the frank and open kind of which even strangers felt the power. On one occasion, when Madame C. was buying some flowers, a complete stranger said to her: 'You must choose them carefully — they are for an extremely pretty young lady.' Everything about her was eloquent of purity and innocence, of gaiety and joy. But all could turn to sadness in a moment, if something ugly, something grubby, had hurt her.

She spent the whole of 1945 in bed. During the two previous years she had been submitted to various forms of treatment. These had had no bad physical effect upon her, but in January 1945 she underwent an operation which left her health seriously impaired. At the age of twenty, when her illness started, she had written: 'I want too many things. What I need is not one life but a thousand lives. There are so many moments I must experience to the full.' Often and often she had given expression to her love of life, to her ardent longing to know everything, and she never lost her faith in the future . . . She thought, as we all of us thought — *that* can't happen; it just can't!

Y. R.

1943

Diary

Monday, 8th February (Sèvres)

I have just been looking out of the window. Such a lovely day, with a sky of late summer, pale green and pink. But I don't want to do anything. Even reading and writing is difficult. The radio is burbling away so quietly that it's as though it weren't on at all. My bed, with the sheets turned back, looks white and cool. I have been up for the last hour. It's been a gloomy day — not a flicker of happiness, not the hint of a wish. The dog's started barking. Perhaps it's the postman — or the doctor whom I've been expecting to come every moment. Very soon I shall get back into bed, and the night — another night — will come.

I can hear a strange voice downstairs which sets my heart beating in the most odious manner. One ought to be able to choose the moment for other people to act. I feel very strongly that if I could sometimes have plucked up courage to say: 'Do this', everyone might have been happy. One does not feel one's own clumsiness, but only that of others. This morning I had some fresh, fat endives to eat, after which I recovered my pillow (I had pitched it into an armchair a good two yards from my bed). I got mamma to draw the curtains, and then reverted to my slave condition, lying for three hours with my eyes shut, not sleeping a wink.

Friday, 12th February

I can't breathe without making a noise. Something very odd's happening in my left lung, deep down. It's as though I were setting in motion a thick sludge full of bubbles.

Saturday, 13th February

I dreamed last night that I was back at the studio. The company was a curious mixture — people I had known at the

13

Beaux-Arts and in the lower forms of the Lycée, together with some of the professors. I told them I was ill, but felt ashamed of my pink cheeks and general look of radiant health.

This morning summer is here.

The radio blaring away in the house opposite, the happy slamming of doors, and the great sweep of pale blue sky — all these things give me the feeling of it. The houses on the hill are glittering with the night's dew. I love this opalescent mist. It hides the ugly features of the thickly populated slopes with their crowded houses, stations and bridges.

10 p.m. How ugly I feel this evening — ugly and stupid . . . The weather has been lovely all day, but I feel terribly discouraged. This illness of mine's never going to end. It has taken root, and I know that it will keep on for years. I've been in bed now for nearly three weeks. Oh God! what an age!

Monday, 15th February: 10 p.m.

I'm off tomorrow. I don't feel frightened — I am very happy to think that I shall see Dr. V. again and be in his charge. My back's hurting all over — it's nothing but one big ache.

Tuesday, 16th February

I'm going to get up. I've been thinking what I shall wear. We're travelling by car. I shall cross the Seine, see people walking, listen to the Paris sounds. My hands feel damp: I mustn't get excited . . . Mauricette is sitting on my chest, licking her paws. She spreads them out under her tongue. The soft pad is like a little black flower, shiny and resilient. She doesn't like one to touch it. . . .

4 p.m. (Paris: D . . . Clinic) Here I am. A fit of the blues clamped down on me as soon as I crossed the threshold. My room is tiny, at the end of a long, gloomy corridor. Coming along it, I saw to my right a woman on her knees, scrubbing the

14

floor. She raised her head and looked at me as I passed the door. Just a girl, she thought, and went back to her cleaning.

Papa's dozing in a horrible greenish-coloured armchair close to the radiator. He kissed my hand. Very soon he'll go away and leave me alone with all these red and black hangings. They're covered with a pattern of mulberries — leaves, blossom, fruit and branches rampant on a scarlet background. I found a hair on the coverlet. My stomach contracted, but I wasn't sick. Actually, I had a good laugh about it with mamma. I've got to put up with all this for ten days, or longer.

It seems that a 'pneumothorax' is not 'very' painful. I know what that means. Either I am full of courage, or completely flabby.

The nightmare that's just beginning will be very unpleasant to look back on. It's encouraging at times to realize how quickly things, people and words become mere memories.

I have brought some flowers with me. I've been asked, in the nicest way possible, not to let myself be seen in the corridors, on account of there being a number of young men here — that's just about the last straw!

— And no tea! A man's voice has just said: 'yes . . . precisely' — a nice voice. I wish he could come and see me. I shall have to spend nights and nights here. I'm having my pneumo tomorrow morning. I wish it was over. I shall sleep badly, or, rather, I shan't sleep at all. I've just discovered some patches of damp on the wallpaper, and the ceiling is black with soot — a rather delicate effect, as it happens, and there's a flamboyant decoration of plaster mouldings. Papa is getting terribly bored. He has just gone — to get a snack at a confectioner's, he says. He was fast asleep. The sound of a door wakened him. Mummy's off to the Champs-Elysées, on a hunt for photos.

6 p.m. Some children have had the happy idea of starting to roller-skate in the street. They're yelling and playing like a lot of lunatics. A moment ago a young man knocked at the door, pushed his head into the room, and asked whether nurse

15

was with me. Any excuse is good enough for taking a look at the new arrival.

8 p.m. I don't know how I'm going to get through this long night all alone . . . The time goes so terribly slowly . . . I feel frightened to the very marrow of my bones . . . I went into the corridor just now . . . Downstairs, they were having dinner . . . muffled sound of voices and the chink of china (what china!). I can't believe that any of this is true. The sinister atmosphere of the place is more than I can bear. It has suddenly come over me that I am in love with happiness — especially with happiness in others — in all living creatures that show a sign of it.

Is dinner over? I can hear a lot of different bells, and voices and shouting. These people seem to be quite happy. They're coming back upstairs. How many of them are there? Twenty-eight, apparently. Twenty-eight happy young men, almost cured. How wonderful that must be! There's a sound of music. Why can't I see them, talk to them, laugh with them, and then go to sleep comfortably tired after my little bit of fun? . . . Somebody is playing a cornet . . . a long way off, but I can hear it.

How marvellous! I've just heard the following: 'She's in Room 25' — then, two voices in unison: 'How bored she must be' — a voice further off: 'Mustn't she just!' . . . My gratitude goes out to those young men — it's quite true, I'm bored to tears . . . They went up to the next floor . . . But somebody in this house, where I don't know a soul, has been thinking about me — that's all I want.

The odd thing is that no one coughs here — no one except me — and I try to deaden the sound in a handkerchief. My feet feel cold — I shall never have the strength of mind to go to bed and switch off the light. But I'm not frightened — not of anything, not of anything at all. No one has come to fetch my tray. The dishes are all there — barely touched. They look disgusting on the black surface. I've got a feeling that my heart is all anyhow.

16

Dr. V. has just been to see me — with another doctor. They looked at my X-ray photographs, and then started to examine me. 'Cough — take a deep breath — cough.' I feel awful. The doctor said: 'A good deal of noise . . . badly affected . . . there . . . Hmm . . . give her gardenal to make her sleep. We'll do it early tomorrow morning . . . We'll try to make a good job of it, my dear.'

'Yes, we'll try. . . .'

I wish it was tomorrow evening . . . I wish the time would go quickly . . . I lie waiting for my gardenal . . . As soon as I've taken it I'll switch off the light and open the window wide so as to get rid of this horrible smell of soup.

Dr. V. calls me 'my dear' . . . I'm not frightened now. By the time mamma comes it'll all be over.

I can hear someone talking . . . talking endlessly.

Wednesday, 17th February: 8 a.m.

The gardenal made me sleep like a log. When I woke up I looked at the clock. It showed only half-past twelve. From then until morning I turned and twisted, but couldn't get off to sleep again. I watched the day breaking through the slats of my shutter.

10 a.m. All over — and I'm beginning to feel better. There are no words to describe what I went through. I shall never forget the operating table covered with a white sheet, the drip of the tap in the basin, and the nice kind face of the tall doctor. At the moment, I've got a bit of a pain and have been lying on my back for the last hour, supported by pillows.

It's a marvellous day. My breakfast tray is on the radiator. I'm afraid to cough. They brought me back when it was all over (Oh, how I fought against being helped upstairs!), and then left me alone. If anyone should come in! (Heavens! I just cry and cry for no reason at all!)

When they put the needle in, my chest felt just like a

cardboard box with a hole in it — and then that awful breath-lessness got worse and worse.

1 o'clock. Mummy has arrived with a bunch of splendiferous anemones. She had a talk with Dr. V. at the bottom of the stairs. I could hear a little of what they were saying — something about a suspicious patch high up on the right lung. That's something new.

Very soon now the sun will be shining into my room. My pulse is rather more rapid than it should be. I shut my eyes and think of the beach in bright sunlight — of myself being grilled — of the sea close at hand — of the gulls crying — oh, when?

10 p.m. They're not going to do anything to me tomorrow — that's wonderful! I shall be able to have a quiet day. They've taken another X-ray. The puncture seems to have worked — though there's one sticky patch. Fortunately, the good part is just where it ought to be.

I do so understand people committing suicide from sheer weariness — not that I feel the slightest inclination that way myself — jumping out of a window at night.

Two tablets of gardenal . . . Dark red curtains lined with yellow — what a thought!

I should like to get up, but it makes me feel so terrible after-wards. I lose all control, and just lie groaning to myself.

J.'s just been in. He's really very sweet. He says that if I feel ill in the night I've only to press the bell — I could faint ten times before getting to it, because it's right at the other end of the room . . . still. . . .

My eyelids feel as heavy as lead. My left lung is quite silent now . . . dead. I can feel my heart beating in my temples . . . If only I can sleep tonight.

Saturday, 20th February

Two visits this morning — two doctors. Two separate times I was asked the same questions, and two separate times I gave the same answers. I'm so hungry that I believe I could eat even kidneys. My left lung has been more and more inert since it was blown up yesterday evening.

8 a.m. Tomorrow's Sunday, and I've been here since Wednesday. I'm getting thoroughly used to it. What I like is that I can be alone whenever I want to be — and sometimes when I don't. I've finished *Barbara*. How could anyone say she's like me! . . . She's stupid, and I certainly am not that!

How odd everything is here. My cheeks are blazing, my hot-water-bottle's so hot I can't touch it, and my fountain-pen is completely out of control.

When, oh when, shall I walk again along the beach in the moonlight, beside a silk-smooth sea? . . . frr . . . the small sound of breaking waves clinging to the sand and dragging it back as they retreat, and millions of stars, and the dark, rounded, vague line of the hushed forest . . . the sleeping forest . . . the sleeping moon . . . the sleeping night . . . Ah! I am nothing but a wave in a world of waves. . . .

Sunday, 21st February

Very early this morning I heard bells and the melancholy hooting of tugs. The Seine must be quite close. I am cold. I can't think what to wear so as not to feel these icy little shudders down my back. I've tried everything. Here I am, under piles of bedclothes, with thick pyjamas and a hot-water-bottle. But I can't get rid of them.

9 a.m. Turned on the radio. It tells me that the Free Zone is to be suppressed from the 1st March. Communication will be re-established . . . I can scarcely believe it . . . It's so marvellous that all this should happen just as I'm leaving.

Dr. V. has been in to say 'so long'. He's off tomorrow morning to the Sanatorium at X — I shan't see him again till I get there. What an extraordinary person he is! He was wearing a sweater, and had one hand in his pocket . . . as simple as simple . . . It was a lucky day for me when they decided to put me in his charge. I know now that I shall feel profoundly grateful to him all my life long. And I can't be the only one. I wish I knew his wife — stupid, but there it is.

Monday, 22nd February

When I get back home, I shall miss these solitary hours. They are a blessing, and bring rest and richness.

Tuesday, 23rd February

The fog is growing denser and turning yellow. The air is like solidified oil.

At two o'clock it will be exactly a week since I came — and already my arrival has become a memory.

Wednesday, 24th February

How passionately I long for the sea as soon as I know it'll be an age before I can hope to be there. Not a day passes but I think of the beach, of the great expanse of air which I'd like to suck down in a single gulp, of the gulls. When the weather's overcast they settle down with a sort of cawing laughter on the glittering stretch of sand left bare by the receding tide.

The dog used to look at them from a distance — head up, nose twitching. Then suddenly, with flapping ears, he would dash along the sands and plunge in amongst them with his mouth open, barking at the sky where they'd all taken refuge. He'd go into the sea after them, till the water was up to his belly, following their flight with his eyes, and then come back to me looking thoroughly miserable, stopping every now and then to turn round for another stare at the mocking, untouchable birds.

Thursday, 25th February

All the windows of the buildings I can see, the chimneys, the walls, seem as though piled up in my field of vision for the specific purpose of watching me live. Everything is spying on me. I enjoy drawing my curtains under their inquisitive noses, and shutting myself away in this room, which I detest, but which, all the same, teaches me a little more every day. I feel that if I had leisure enough to spend six months in every year alone in this sort of setting, *then* I could do some writing. It is only since I have been here that I have realized that I've really got something to say. Everything about me is a spur to action — every sound is a revelation. It is as though a flower were opening in my heart as a result of contact with all this ugliness. I shall leave here rich in the possession of an entirely new form of wealth, glittering in my own eyes like a heap of diamonds in sunlight. I look at myself with amazement — my own personality shines with extraordinary brilliance. I feel, at last, that if only I could set to and work, I might make something of it.

When I lift my hand from this notebook it trembles as though I were in the last extreme of weakness — yet, I feel amazingly well, fit, tough, and absolutely 'fulfilled'. All this bubbling up of new feelings has a warming effect upon me. I want to run, and run, and run, and then stand still for a long time, leaning against a tree, with my head in the crook of my arm, listening to the movement of my heart — terribly alive, vibrant with happiness, longing to know everything — everything.

How I've wasted my time up till now — so much wealth thrown to the winds in the course of the last few years. But it was all lovely! I am fully aware of the wastage, just as I am going to be aware of delight at making the most of my time. I am overcome with awe — in the religious sense — when I realize that everything has a value, from the voices I can hear in the street, to the smells coming from the kitchen, and a small boy's laughter at one special moment of the day. It bursts like a firework on a dark night, showering radiance on all who hear it.

I am dying of thirst, though there are two taps within reach. I am finding it difficult to breathe. I have been sitting perfectly still for the last half-hour. My nightgown is warming on the radiator. What a relief it will be to get out of these flannel pyjamas, which scratch my skin.

Friday, 26th February

I want too many things. What I need is not one life, but a thousand lives. There are so many moments I must experience to the full. Many of them are duties which I have long determined to perform.

Tuesday, 2nd March

I have been thinking of my wonderful grandmother. One day this summer I went out of the dining-room — which opens, so delightfully, straight into the garden. I was wearing a flowered dress, my hair was drawn back, and I was feeling rather specially well because I had just had a bath. She got up, came straight to me, and, looking into my eyes, said so simply that for quite a while I could make no answer — 'You are as lovely as a summer's day' (what answer can one make to a remark like that?). No compliment, sincere or not, has ever so flooded me with happiness.

I've suddenly begun to feel so ill that I've got to lie down. Everything is going round and round and getting muzzy — the heat is intolerable, damp and odious, and I find it impossible to breathe deeply . . . You can't get away from it — there's something 'ridiculous' about illness.

Wednesday, 3rd March

In bed, with the window wide open. The air's got a delicious undercurrent of coolness. The pavements were swept this morning by a man dressed in brown — very conscientious, and absorbed in his task. Great beams of sunlight are thrusting between the clouds. I feel ill all over — battered, exhausted, breathless, and miserable. I've got my coat collar turned up, and I've been lying for a long while with my nose buried in it. Two fat pigeons have just perched side by side on an iron rail, after fluttering about. A small girl, with a large check bow in her hair, is running along the street. She has just fallen

22

down. She has picked herself up, looked at her knee, and re-traced her steps, limping a bit, but with her head held high. She is holding up her frock, and I can see a good deal of blood on her leg. As soon as she's alone she'll start crying.

Friday, 12th March

The fever's completely gone — I can feel it — and that's quite enough to give me back all my self-confidence. Dear God, *how* I love life — and, Oh, Dear God, how I love You! . . .

The South — Provence — olive trees — cypresses — the Pro-testant cemeteries (how lovely to be buried in one's own gar-den!) — the light — the trees in blossom (and lying all snuggled up in bed, with the pattern of the wallpaper repeated on all four sides, while the spring marches on through fields and woods that I have never seen).

Two clearly defined points of pain between my breasts. They feel like deep bites and seem to go right through to my back. They flare up and subside without any apparent reason. I love laying my hand on my breast (I'd give as much as two sous for it to be bigger — a real one, like a grown woman's) — and on my hip, too — the round, projecting bone, the smooth, warm flow of life. I say to myself — 'that's me — I'm glad it's me'. This illness is just a visitor with whom I've got to put up as cheerfully as I can, and make an effort to talk to. I'm much too interested to show her the door. — One of us will have to give way to the other — which will it be? If she goes first — then there truly is such a person as God, such a thing as Faith. — If I go first, if I yield — but it's no good thinking of that — With . . .

Saturday, 13th March

Sky not exactly blue — mist making painful efforts to rise and take to flight.

Lovely night — calm, gentle — no fever.

My skin was cool all over this morning. Morale 500 degrees

above zero. I wish my second puncture was over and done with. Then I wouldn't have anything more to dread.

9 a.m. Two exactly symmetrical areas of pain which wake each time I draw a breath. To feel a child moving inside one ('La Reine Morte'). I pity men because they don't have to go through the pain of having a child.

Sunday, 14th March

A month ago today (I shouldn't have remembered it un-aided). I've forgotten the pain, but shall get a reminder of it tomorrow morning. Odd that I shouldn't be afraid: I scarcely think of it.

Monday, 15th March

Oh what a mass of flowers! . . . my room smells like a wood-land glade. Since one o'clock I've become someone who's had two pneumo-punctures — the second operation longer and more painful than the first. The flesh is quite tough — as though frozen — to a depth of several centimetres, and the needle pushes through this hard, insensitive crust — this time I saw the instruments: on the previous occasion they were behind my back. Anaesthesia much too slow in coming on. I long to go to sleep in spite of having a good deal of pain. Find it difficult to keep my eyes open. I am alone to the depths of my being.

8.30. How wonderful to be doing nothing, and yet not to be bored.

Such an acute crisis of pain that I was within an ace of fainting. Mummy rubbed my temples with Eau-de-Cologne. Slowly the pain drained away, and now I don't dare to make a movement. I expect I shall forget how bad it was. I still feel utterly alone.

Impossibility of talking about anything but myself.

Tuesday, 16th March: evening

Intense pain again this morning — so intense that I longed to faint dead away — just so's not to feel anything.

All the same, I'm putting up a fight — trying to be brave. I don't want not to be in pain — but merely to have sufficient courage to bear the pain. Is that asking too much?

I *do* quite often suffer without complaining — it's a grand feeling to be able to say 'it's hurting' at the precise moment when the pain's so awful that everything belonging to me — eyes, heart, ears — seems just a confused agony — and not a moment before. Whenever that happened, I was always proud of myself afterwards, proud to think that I had managed to smile so that the people round me shouldn't be worried.

Trite and trivial reflections of a tired child. They make me want to cry . . . I look at the sky and keep my jaws clenched. Don't cry, Elizabeth . . . I *am* being brave . . . don't cry . . . it's going to take months and months. That's the kind of thing they say to me . . . don't cry — don't cry — I've been in pain — I am in pain — I shall be in pain . . . but don't cry. In a moment something infinitely sweet and soothing will moisten the hair just above my temple — each time I flutter an eyelid, a new wave, but hotter, pursues exactly the same course as the one before it.

They're not going to 'blow me up' till Saturday — what luck!

X . . . Sanatorium: Wednesday, 21st April

The little snow-covered trees look very white against the dull grey of the mountain — the sky is mauve, pink, blue, all at the same time, but blurred like a 'washy' water-colour, with all the tints running into one another.

Since the snow stopped falling there has been complete silence — but also a feeling of suspense — one keeps on expecting something to happen — but what?

The nurse, leaning against the wall, with her veil over one

shoulder, has been telling me about her walk this afternoon. I, too, should like to get to know the country girls who make such lovely party-gloves while they watch their cows.

How is the young girl who's been down with typhoid? Much better — she's beginning to talk.

Sanatorium: Friday, 21st May

The mountain drowsing under its cold peak, its contour continued by a scarf of blue mist.

The darting flight of a swallow.

The broken flight of wasps.

The noble agitation of trees.

The purity of the sky.

I feel as though the world around me had become contracted to the confines of this single valley — of the mountains I see before me — of the plateau on which I am living. But if I am to cling to my dream of courage and tenacity, I *must* be able to think of a wider world beyond.

The sky is a bright glitter, with a sort of damp shimmer where it touches the mountains.

The sound of masculine voices swaddled in sunlight — the scarcely audible purring of a motor — the thin dry twittering, somewhere, of a bird.

The light of my happiness moves upon your face, as the refracted light from the water of a lake, when the sun is on it, moves about the trees upon its bank — A cloud drifts across the sun, and the lake 'goes out'. The trees turn gloomy and my happiness is dead.

The fluffy look of distant pine woods: the shadow cast by the leaf of a tree upon another leaf.

I keep on thinking of the past.

I can hear the heavy footsteps of a man walking — the measured pacing of a tired farm-worker pressing the earth as though intent on leaving there an indelible print.

The tight circlet of your fingers round my wrist — almost no 'play' in it — I don't want to break away, but only to give you the other hand as well.

The mere fact of your being alive has made me feel I have ceased to belong to myself.

The edge of the bed, the empty chair, the crumbs of bread, the square of sunlight on the wall which lengthens as the afternoon draws on. I stretch my smooth, round arm, and my fingers make a great black pattern silhouetted against the sky.

Monday, 16th August

Memories of Sèvres. I keep thinking of L. It was a Tuesday, I think — a cold and joyless day. At 9 a.m., Marguerite, who was doing her ironing, called up that a great basket of white flowers of impressive dimensions had been brought for me. I had never seen so many flowers together outside a florist's window. There were solemn-looking arums, and tulips, too, I believe — all of them white — white and lustreless, as though moulded in candle-wax. There was a large card. My hands trembled a little as I took it from its envelope.

'Darling . . . happiness . . . soon . . . I love you . . . for the rest of your life . . .' Then still more flowers came, with small cards pinned to the bouquets. I soon didn't know where to put them all . . . I felt annoyed that no one had sent any but white ones — I'd have given the world for a red rose. I felt as though I were living in the room of a young woman who had died young.

I went back to bed until six o'clock. Then mamma came in and laid a black velvet dress on the bed, and a pair of very thin stockings. I dressed. I looked very pale and very beautiful. I stared at my hands — no rings — for several hours. I kept gazing at myself in the glass that evening, before they came, so as to fill my consciousness with the image of something that was passing away. For the rest of my life.

I had brushed my hair straight back — I found it restful.

He came. He was wearing a dark blue suit, beautifully cut, as always — and a handsome pearl in his tie. There was that

27

faint smell I always associated with him — lavender-water, tobacco, and freshly cut hair. I had got up for the first time in five weeks, and so much attention to his person made me feel slightly queasy. . . .

He kissed my finger before slipping on the ring. He said — 'Never be parted from it' — The champagne was good and very cold. Madame A. looked at me. Her eyes were shadowed by a great black feather. Through the lace of her dress I could see her rich, fair skin.

The ices took some time to melt in my mouth. Perhaps because I was cold.

I asked whether anyone had remembered Marguerite. I took her down a little of everything on a plate, and a glass of champagne — she drank it with her head thrown back and her eyes shut because 'it was strong'.

When I went upstairs again, I met L. He took me in his arms.

'Now you are mine — for ever.'

I didn't feel so sure as he did. I wanted to tell him so — but it was the wrong time to choose. I ought to have done it before — long before.

While I was going to bed I thought over what had happened. I slipped the dress over my head. Looking at my naked body in the glass, I longed for something quite different. Only a very great love could persuade me to give all that — I didn't want to give it to him. This wasn't how things ought to be.

I put some of the flowers out on the balcony, and then went and lay on the bed. The lace coverlet was still there. Something irked my hand — it was the ring. I took it off and put it on the table. With all those flowers I really did feel as though I were going to sleep in the bed of a woman who had died young.

Letters

If you knew what delight all you say about my short story gives me, you would feel very pleased with yourself. I have at once got down to writing again — it is one of the few things which, just now, make life seem worth living. I've been terribly depressed for the last fortnight — being in no condition to hold a pen . . . I have completely forgotten that I've seen you only three times (and then, for no more than a minute) in the whole course of my life — it really is all so marvellous — and I won't let myself think of seeing you again, because the possibility is too disturbing . . . I am glad you added all those postscripts to your letter, because without them it would have seemed a bit on the stern side. It kept me happy for three whole days and I very nearly slept with it under my pillow — that'll give you some idea how low my morale has fallen . . . You make me terribly nervous — I say that with one finger in my mouth and my feet turned slightly in. I am so pleased that you treat me like a little girl (the little girl is feeling rather sick, having gobbled down the whole of her chocolate ration). Why don't I write letters as I write stories? Frankly, I don't know, unless it is that I find it very difficult to write to you — you're so old, you see, much older than I am, I mean. When I heard that you were to be kept in bed, I had a pleasant sense of calm superiority. I should have liked to bring you piping hot tea, nuts ready cracked, some of Dubout's pictures, and anything else you might have wanted — a bird in a cage, a little boat I've got with a red sail, my wireless set. Unfortunately, that was impossible — which is a pity. Life is so badly arranged that one can never do what one wants to do. For instance, at this precise moment I should like nothing so much as to go for a stroll. It's such a wonderful night, so productive of sentimental thoughts. I've almost forgotten what it's like to go walking in

[1] Unless otherwise stated, all the letters here printed were addressed to Yves R.

the darkness, without bothering about the time. One walks so much better then, I feel. One seems to be so completely part of the night. It is in one's ears, and in the palms of one's hands as they hang down at one's side with the fingers turned slightly inwards. The breeze just lifts the hair at the back of one's neck — all that would be so lovely. I long for it with every fibre of my body. The night is so cloudless. I'd like to take it in my arms, or let it run through my fingers like cold sand.

Will you let me show you, a little later on, the story I'm just starting, or would it be a bore? I'm going to be kept in bed, too — probably starting from tomorrow, so I shall have plenty of time to work really hard — I may have it finished in a week. May I send it to you?

Thank you for liking what I've written! Nothing could give me greater pleasure.

Good night
Elizabeth

Tuesday, 19th October

Your long letter was a lovely surprise. I don't mind admitting that I wasn't expecting it. I had the impression last Sunday — I don't know why — that you couldn't cope with me, and felt very sad as I walked home through the rain. I had only one wish, to get back, to light the lamp, and to listen to some music — which I did. I adore the darkness, and detest daylight when there is no sun.

Your letter makes me feel very proud. It is heavy and smooth, and there are two words in it which I can't read.

I am listening to a tune which I'm mad about — Stormy Weather — though it's as old as the hills. I should love to dance to it with you. The last time I danced was here — underneath the stage, when that appalling company and its orchestra put on a show. How lovely it would have been if you had been there. I miss Paris. There are moments when I'd give anything in the world to be in a crowded Métro carriage. . . .

I'd have simply loved to go for a walk with you at half-past six, but, unfortunately, I can't. On the morning of the one day I might have managed it, the doctor informed me that I mustn't go out except for a quarter of an hour after lunch. Perhaps if this wretched pneumo-puncture works, I may be freer. All these damned rules and regulations make me feel as though I'm living in a nursery . . . No, I've not been seriously ill, only rather uncomfortable, especially when I'm on my feet. At the moment, I'm lying flat on my back, which explains this appalling writing. I wish I could go to the cinema on Sunday, but I don't know whether I shall be allowed to. What sort of a room-companion have you got? Mine is irredeemably stupid, but so insignificant that I sometimes forget her existence . . . I've never known any human being to compare with her for *bromides* — they just pour out . . . She and He are so utterly dim. I won't say that they give me a distaste for love, because my view of love is different from this daily routine of dullness. They're like a couple of gathered sores — don't you think? And the extraordinary part of the whole thing is that they're *devoted*. I get a great deal of fun out of watching them. All my room-companions, since I came here, have been married women. Consequently, I have been able to make an intensive study of marriage. What's really funny is to see them going off to C. for a week-end with their husbands, and coming back with a dreamy, languorous look in their eyes.

This is proper bridge weather. If I were at home, the shutters would be closed all day long, the curtains tight drawn, a fire blazing in the grate, bread toasting, and tea, lots of very strong tea. It's times like those that I regret more than anything else here. Have you got any brothers or sisters? . . . somehow, I don't think you have. I can quite well imagine you as an only child — and abominably spoiled.

5.30. Here I am, thoroughly down in the mouth again. It's really as though these damned doctors took a positive pleasure in carving one up. I feel pretty bad — and as stiff as an Englishwoman. Thank Heavens, I've got a radio. I really couldn't do without one now. It's lovely to have a bit of music in the evenings. The Italians have got some stunning jazz-bands.

There's something sad about a room when night falls. I feel so lonely. I'm always boasting that I can get along without the rest of the human race, but there are moments when solitude weighs on me terribly. What I need is another of your long letters — soon. But don't, I beg, send me a single word that you don't *mean*. Don't ever say anything merely because you think it will give me pleasure. I am very vulnerable, because I believe everything that people say to me. I feel an irresistible longing to cry — for no better reason than that it will soon be dark, that I'm sick, that the music I'm listening to is cloying, so cloying that I could almost die of it. . . .

I've been thinking of Sa. I've grown very fond of her, and I'm frightened about her operation. She's a more than usually intelligent girl, I think, and her hair's lovely. I wish I could see it hanging loose over her shoulders.

I'm on the ground floor — which is rather pleasant. My window is the one with a half-drawn blind. I can see a little tree which is losing its leaves more and more each day. Autumn is a melancholy season. There are days when I love it, others when I hate it. I should like to think that I shan't have to see it more than once in this place.

I'm working through Proust. Heavens! what an appalling creature! To me there's something really unclean about him, diseased, squalid, though now and again, when reading him, one comes on a phrase of the most exquisite beauty. All the same, I'd like to send him to the devil!

I hope this letter will get to you by this evening. It did me good to write to you, but I can't see any longer.

Goodbye for the present — Don't forget my existence — or that I'm beginning to expect a letter.

LIZBETH

32

Wednesday, 20th October

I'm all upset at having had nothing from you this evening . . . But you were right not to answer. This sort of thing might so easily become a habit — and a habit which I mustn't get into — whatever happens. . . .

I spent today gloomily staring at my nails. I'm so sick of being in bed. I wish you could see me eating — it really is an extraordinarily funny sight — I'm the Queen of butterfingers.

Somebody new has been moved into my room, and the stream of friendly visitors has given me a splitting headache. The place is becoming like a public bar.

Thursday morning. I wonder whether I shall get a letter from you this side of Easter. On Easter Day — 1944, that'll be — you shall go for a walk with me in the forest, and we'll have a nice serious conversation about the existence of God. Does that appeal to you? I feel that by booking you like this six months ahead, I ought to be able to 'hook you over in safety'.[1]

Oh, please, please, I should so like to have a letter from you before the end of this week. Aren't you a little surprised at my talking to you so . . . freely?

My heart accelerates in the most painful fashion when I think that someone may come in with a letter for me. All the same, waiting is a wonderful invention.

6 p.m. I had a present of some Cravens this morning — here's one for you. Merely to sniff at them sends me into ecstasies. For me, Cravens are the most perfect symbol imaginable oı those happy days when I used to go bathing at night — in a warm and phosphorescent sea, and, in summer, stayed out on the sands with the dogs up to two in the morning. Have you known moments like that? — and, if so, don't you agree that they are unforgettable? Nothing means so much to me as that kind of memory. The moon was so much brighter when I was a little girl — I'm sure it was — and the summers were ten times hotter. Everywhere one went one heard Bing Crosby singing. There were fireworks at every turn, and I hadn't yet

[1] In English in the original.

been allowed to have my meals with the 'grown-ups'. Those same grown-ups were always sending me out of the room when they were playing bridge and bribing me with lavish promises of ices, to lug huge bags of golf-clubs from one end of the beach to the other. I was much fonder of the dogs than I was of them — and I've no doubt that you find all this breath-lessly interesting — it was the Cravens that started me off. . . .

Eudoxie, the chamber-maid, and her vacuum-cleaner were almost knocked over when the Abbé P. ran into them on his way to see me. She was quite furious when she told me about it, and said — 'That there old Apostle'd climb a-top of me without so much as a by your leave!' Isn't that superb? Oh Lord! I've just been told that I'm to have a new room-mate — I know it'll be some frightful creature with skin-trouble, spots, steel-rimmed spectacles and a grubby dressing-gown. One's always running into women like that — and one's always told that they're 'regular characters' — or that they have sweet faces — or hearts of gold.

You may not know it — but Heaven's got a down on me. There you are, quietly playing bridge, while I'm biting my nails in a mood of sheer frustration. The day's over — and I'm not going to get anything to help me through the night. Last night I had no more than ten minutes' sleep. Doesn't that make you feel a bit sorry for me? — besides, I'm ill — very ill, though I hate complaining. I'm a pitiful and disappointed and utterly miserable little girl — and I haven't even the consolation of hating you.

Why are you behaving so badly?

Friday morning. I can't send you this — your silence makes me anxious. I have a horrid feeling that my letters just drop into the void. I no longer find waiting delicious.

I've got a magnificent bouquet of autumn leaves — all red and gold, and the wind's blowing right in on me. Sometimes this sheet of paper flutters so much that I can't write. I long to be swimming in a river millions of miles away from you — a very clear river, fringed with willows and poplars — there's

34

nothing more marvellous than a poplar with the sun on it, or a willow at night. The Tuileries must be quite wonderful just now, and Notre Dame, too. I expect the Seine is deep green and very smooth, and the trees are tufted with yellow above their intensely black trunks. The floating wash-houses are silent — There's a painter in brown corduroy, and a fisherman in blue overalls with a darn on one knee. All the book-boxes have got their lids raised — and their owners sit dozing on campstools in the sun. No one dares wake them — And the smell! — a mixture of leather and cellar-damp. Can't you get the feel of it in your nose?

Paris — Saint-Lazare — painted in red letters about half a mile before you get into the station — then a tunnel, and, at the end of it, a surging mob of people in a perpetual hurry. It is more than a year since I last strolled about Paris in a carefree mood, lunching off tea and toast just when the fancy took me. I'm longing for my ten days' 'leave' — but it won't be before the Spring. I'd love to be at home for my coming of age, just so's I could thump the table and say — 'Now I can do just as I please!' It must be wonderful to be of age — isn't it? I don't think I shall ever get tired of writing this sort of nonsense to you!

6 o'clock. I've just heard that there's going to be a concert again tomorrow. If you go, do please listen twice over, once for you, once for me. There's a marvellous Beethoven item on the programme — a song-cycle called 'The Distant Loved-One' — I'm quite capable of breaking out of here just to listen, if it weren't for the fact that I'm in such pain — I really have no luck at all, being kept in bed at such a time.

I'm wondering whether, having had nothing from you, I'll actually send you this letter — by all the rules I oughtn't to. All the same, I'd have to be terribly brave not to, and I've no right to blame you for keeping silent.

You must, honestly, tell me if I'm becoming a bore. You wouldn't know how much it would hurt me, so don't hesitate.

I'm trying very hard to put myself in your place, but can't,

somehow, see myself as tedious. I suppose it's lack of sensitiveness on my part, or what you will. Mercy, my good lord,
mercy. . . .

. . . I'll toss up . . . if it comes down heads I'll sign my name
at the bottom, and send it . . . if tails, I'll wait a bit longer . . .
Heads it is . . . well, here goes. . . .

I'm still waiting . . . it would be too mortifying . . . I'm going
to tell my fortune by the cards — the '48 hours' — I learned
that ridiculous game here (ridiculous, because I firmly believe
in it).

8 o'clock . . . It's nice and comfortable like this . . . but I
need calming. . . .

Yes, indeed, this wind makes one feel good for nothing.

I *am* sending you this, all the same, because it was written
for you and I don't want to keep it.

Aren't these cigarettes grand?

I'm going to get down seriously to my story.

Please don't answer this — it really is such utter nonsense.

Good night, and thank you for having spoiled two sheets of
superb paper just for me.

ELIZABETH

P.S. If you don't see me for some time, you mustn't run away
with the idea that I am afraid of seeing you. I really do think
I ought to stick in bed for a bit, because I'm still being doped
with morphine.

Why did you tell me that you enjoy reading my letters?

Sunday, 24th October

It's a perjured wretch who's writing to you today. I had
sworn not to send you so much as a word. I held your letter
between my teeth for ten whole minutes before reading it,
because I was cleaning out a honey-pot when it arrived. I
can't shower blessings enough upon you for having made my
Sunday in bed so gorgeous. I had resigned myself to spending

the Lord's Day in reading and looking out of the window (it's a lovely enough day to make one want to fall on one's knees), and now, suddenly, everything's changed, because I feel that I can write to you. What manner of man are you, who have this power of making somebody happy at a distance? No, it's a good thing you never did see me on the beach when I was exercising the dogs — because you'd have said — 'Really, some parents have no sense of responsibility! — fancy letting a young girl go out all alone at this time of night!' — and I should have been thoroughly upset at hearing you say any such thing — and, anyhow, you wouldn't have met me, because I always used to scramble among the dunes so long as anybody was within sight, and wait until they'd gone before I went near the sea again. There were always Smart-Alecs about who would call out — 'Here I am!' when I whistled to one of the dogs. It made me absolutely wild.

I'm glad the Beethoven was a rotten show — it'd have made me quite ill to hear it had been good — and anyhow, she didn't murder my darling *lieder*.

I'm not suffering any more — and I'd love to get out — go for a walk — see you. It would make me forget all about having had a bad spell. That's one of the things we needn't talk about. Your last letter was so hard, so icy, that I wanted to bang my head against the wall, just so's to punish myself for being so lacking in reticence. No, I certainly am not a grown-up person who has seen a lot of life. One's got to be a somebody to give that impression. I've lived nothing but fantasies — which are sometimes better than reality (by seeing a lot of life, I mean loving a great deal — which I take to be a fair statement).

You are perfectly right in what you say about illness. Personally I have always considered my being ill to reflect sadly on the wisdom of the Almighty. I'm the least fitted for illness of anyone I know. No one forgets it so soon as I do, no one suffers so abominably when it's there — at times. All the same, what it comes to, is that the whole business is a damned awful sign of decay! — to say nothing of all the time I have to waste

37

lying in bed when I want to be on my feet, miles and miles away from mattresses, and in a vertical position.

N. has told me that I shall be able to get up sometime round about next Sunday. You've no idea how violently I fought against the verdict. The only argument that really produced the slightest effect was my saying that my not sleeping was due to spending so much time in bed. I think that if I harp on that string every day, it'll end by doing the trick. It occurs to me that, at this very moment, you are probably performing your religious duties — are you a genuine believer, or is the whole thing just a matter of habit? I adore the chapel — I find it pretty and welcoming, especially when the priest is wearing his jade-green cope. The colours are quite staggering. I think it's really because of them that I go. So far as God is concerned I don't need any church, or priest, or Host in order to love Him. If you go to Paris in December, you may be at home for Christmas. Doesn't that prospect make you jump for joy? The idea of spending Christmas here is a nightmare. Of all days it is the loveliest — I fully intend to have a tree decorated from top to bottom, and to get them to send me my crèche. I shall sit on the end of my bed, waiting for midnight, and again on New Year's Eve. The only thing missing will be a clutter of children with moustaches of smeared chocolate, surrounded by parcels . . . and, of course, the horrible X will be of the company.

And now you can write me thirty-six icy letters — it's all the same to me — or very nearly, because I've got this one, and can read it over and over again as often as I like — I'm quite certain that my last letter didn't bore you. The sun's shining plumb on to me. I don't care, it's lovely. The paper is quite warm — can't you feel it? I'm sitting here imagining your hand, just to my right, holding the pages.

There's a handsome young man looking at me — he's always looking at me, no matter in what part of the room I happen to be. He's wearing a funny hat of a colour that's not very easy to describe — there's green in it, and blue, and violet — a yellow

38

jacket fastened at the neck with one button, and he's signed Van Gogh. He's a great pal of mine, the best I've got — and we are never separated. He accompanies me on all my journeys — and he always knows exactly what I'm thinking. When my conscience is uneasy I turn his face to the wall, but, think what you like, that's not very often.

It is late — that's to say, it's almost half-past nine, and I'm going to say good night.

So, good night to you. I've got my ration of gardenal, and ought to sleep well . . . all's as it should be.

I'm going to tip-toe out of the room now, and leave you to sleep.

LIZBETH

P.S. I adore life, don't you? I'm terribly tempted to do as I did last night — switch off the lamp and smoke by the glow of the tiny light of my radio set. My morale is much improved. I feel that I'm going to tell myself perfectly lovely stories: here goes — He came up to me and said 'Your nose is damned tiny and frantically cheeky' — no, he said — 'I love it when you laugh' — no, he said nothing at all — he looked sad, and I hesitated a long time before I asked him 'Why are you sad? — is there anything I can do?' Then he looked me in the eyes, and saw beyond any doubt that I was sincere.

You wouldn't believe all the things I make you do when I tell myself stories — you don't mind, do you?

You don't? — good! now I can do what I like with you, and with your words.

Good night

LIZBETH

Saturday, 30th October

After giving the matter a great deal of thought, I've come to the conclusion that being away from you bores me to distraction. Silly, isn't it, but then you see I'm still all of a tremble as a result of feeling your lips in the hollow of my hand — incidentally, I'd have you note that I played my part worthily: I'm sure no woman of 'experience' could have done better. I don't want you to think me a little goose, because I feel so marvellously *me* when we're together. I keep wondering whether you're so simple with everybody — or only with me, because that's the effect I have on people? I'd give a lot to know whether you knew what you were doing when you held my arm this evening — I'm quite sure you didn't realize all it meant to me. Oh, please, please, don't hurt me too much. You mustn't just amuse yourself at my expense: if you do, I shall never trust anyone again. I shall let my nails grow long and claw-like so as to scratch the nose of the first gentleman who tries to kiss my hand. You would have had a good laugh if you could have seen me at dinner — I've never before been quite so scatter-brained — I gave a jump every time I heard my name mentioned. You are well on the way to playing ducks and drakes with the little inner me — which up to now has been so snug and safe.

It gives me the horrors to think that quite a considerable number of hours must elapse before I see you again. It's terribly hard on me: one whole night — all of a breakfast-time — and half one treatment. If I got suddenly worse to-night, you would miss me a little, wouldn't you?

Good night, Yves — your name is as brief as a cry — till tomorrow.

Sunday evening. I love your way of existing. If you don't understand what I mean by that, it doesn't matter in the least. There are so many words that are untranslatable. The truth — it's terribly hard, sometimes, to put it into speech — much easier to write it . . . Do you want to know the truth?

All that follows I'm saying to you with my eyes shut. I'm clutching the lapels of your coat with both hands. My face is hidden, and I'm speaking very fast, so's you shall be able to remember nothing of what you hear.

I leave you at the door, turning to the left instead of to the right — I put down my overcoat beside the bed, instead of on it — I take the lift — I find myself once again having treatment, and wonder what on earth I'm doing there — I go downstairs again and take my place at the dinner-table. I look at all the other women, and decide that they are ugly, quite awful, and wholly intolerable — that they have frightful figures, malformed hands and shifty eyes, and I think of your eyes, which are the colour of rum and look me straight in the face — I think of your voice — I think how happy and simple I feel when I'm with you, and at once I become boorish. While the rest of the company is still busy with the vegetable course, I get up, say a friendly 'good night', and leave the room. I undress in the most commonsensical way possible, beginning, that is, with the outer layers — fill my hot-water-bottle — wetting myself from head to foot in the process, and run into Dr. I. — who tells me that I look, in my nightgown, like a young novice — to which remark I reply with an extremely absent-minded 'ah?' — then I go to bed. There, I indulge in a few moments of philosophical — and when I say philosophical I mean philosophical — reflection (don't you think Sophia is a lovely name? — I wish I'd been christened Sophia).

At this precise moment I feel that I should like to send everyone but you to the devil: then you'd have to put up with me. It's extraordinary how happy I'm feeling: it's as though I had capabilities for happiness till now unsuspected. But all this business of sickness and treatment has become quite intolerable to me. Never have I suffered so intensely from the mere fact of being an invalid — though it is something that you and I have in common. I'm being a terribly serious correspondent, and probably I'm boring you to tears — I'm sure you much prefer me to be an amusing little girl. I wish you could have known all the solemn truths I wanted my eyes to express when you took my face in your hands this evening and looked at me. But I am quite sure you did nothing of the sort. I love you so much — when I'm alone I keep up long conversations with you, but when we are together I am paralysed into silence.

How stupid one is when one is 20! You could hurt me abominably if you had a mind to. I'll try and explain it all to you tomorrow, instead of sending you this rambling letter.

Look me in the eyes and say — 'My ridiculous Lizbeth, you really are the most utter little fool that ever was! I should be infinitely obliged if you would behave like a grown-up person. Put out your lamp—roll over on your right side, and go to sleep.' But if I go to sleep, you won't hear the rest of the truth.

I *am* going to sleep: good night.

I wish tomorrow was here. There are at least 150 yards separating us. I should like to have a large hearth with a roaring fire, so that I might be able to look at something alive and gay before I go to sleep. Everything is marvellous when one is looking at flames or water.

LIZBETH

Tuesday, 9th November

It's quite unbelievable the way you have of making dirty cracks in so elegant a way and with so easy an air that one hardly notices that they are dirty cracks at all! Still, I prefer it that way. I hate the sort of easy-going people who always agree with one.

Oh God! — how the time is going to drag until this evening! I don't know whether you realize just how much it costs me to confess the kind of things I've been confessing, and to know all the time that the person I'm writing to is quite indifferent to every word!

My Friday widowhood is beginning to weigh heavy — what an interminable time of waiting between Thursday evening and Saturday morning. All that time you'll just go on having fun, and it won't occur to you that only a mile away there's a creature with an impertinent little nose thinking about you as she might think about the Messiah!

When I tell myself stories in my bed at night, I quite often imagine myself saving your life. I've already restored you to health at least a dozen times merely by laying my hand on yours — you, meanwhile, being delirious and therefore incapable of knowing that it's me. Then, as soon as I see that you have taken a turn for the better, I withdraw — unnamed, unknown, like all true heroes. In the far, far distant future, when you're an old man, with a white beard down to your knees, you may perhaps remember me, sweet little Lizbeth, whom, fifty years before, you taught how easy a thing it is to bring pain or happiness to those who love you . . . That knowledge opens wide horizons to my eyes, and I am smitten with remorse when I think how much suffering I may have brought to people I didn't care two hoots about.

What's going to happen to me when Sa. comes back? You won't abandon me at once, will you? She frightens me.

I do so wish Friday was over . . . I want it to be summer soon . . . I want to be cured . . . I want to stay young . . . I want to be a legendary beauty . . . I want, etc. . . .

I envy you for having so much to read this evening. If I had as much, parting from you would be less hard. There's a high-born lady in *The Possessed* who's for ever writing to a gentleman she sees constantly. That gives me a little encouragement.

Goodbye for the moment — I won't say another word — it would almost certainly be one too many. I hope you'll sleep better than I shall.

Your despotic Lizbeth (you know whom I mean — that skinny little creature).

Thursday evening, 11th November

You say the most upsetting things, and then you leave me. I walk back alone, and have to damp down all my emotions . . . I love you, Yves — I love you, and that's a terribly serious matter for me — I've never known it to happen before . . . The whole world is contained in my love for you. Nothing outside it is of the least importance. I'm no longer this, that, or the other, but simply and solely somebody who loves. Can you believe that nobody has ever loved you as I do? If only you could understand exactly how I feel.

Don't run away with the idea that I wanted this to happen. I've often longed for something of the kind, but never dared to hope that it would come. This I swear. I remember once, in one of the public rooms, looking at your mouth. It produced such an extraordinary impression on me that I blushed to the ears when you turned towards me. Now everything is all right because you take me in your arms, and say things that set my blood thumping, things that, as a rule, aren't said to ordinary young ladies, though they send this not-so-very-ordinary young lady full tilt into a world of dreams. I shan't see you tomorrow. I have a horrible fear that when you come back you'll be a different person — it's stupid of me, but I have. It's going to be a very long day for me. You know that, don't you? May I tell you just once more that I love you? — and I should desperately like to say 'darling', only once, in a very low voice, so's no one but I should know I'd said it.

Good night, darling.

Friday night, 9.30 p.m. Ouf! — this cursed day is over at last. I should like to think that you missed me — don't laugh! I spent the time exactly like a widow — stayed in and didn't go out once. I've done so much washing that the tips of my fingers are all shrivelled.

Doesn't it make you feel uneasy to know how much I love you? In your place I think I should find it a trifle irritating. You'll have to use all your weapons against me. I wonder whether you will? There may still be time. But I shall never forget you, no matter what you do.

Oh! — I long to see you! I long to touch your lips with my fingers. I long to hear you say fairy things to me in the darkness, while we lie together and you hold me tight. Life is getting lovelier and lovelier. I should like to think you had some little happiness because of me — the hundredth part of what I have because of you.

44

I've been thinking of what you asked me a little while back — about the young man who came to see me. I don't imagine, not for a moment, that you attach the slightest importance to the incident, but, all the same, I want to tell you about him.

In the first place, I am amazed that it shouldn't have occurred to you that he might be my brother — or a cousin. That's the first thing *I* should have thought in your place. Obviously, he's neither the one nor the other.

He's just simply a man with a one-track mind. He came all the way from Paris to prove to me logically that there was nothing for me to do but to become his wife in two days' time — just that, no more and no less. It never occurs to some people that they're not going to get what they want. I must say, it did take my breath away for a moment to see him arrive one evening full of determination, and bursting with arguments. But he didn't stay long. I can make people get fed up with me in next to no time! How awful to think that I mightn't have the right to love you as I do — completely — passionately!

I don't want to love you, but I can't help it. I'm feeling rather under the weather this evening — sad in a funny sort of way that goes deep. You probably think me an irresponsible sort of a person who is content to love what is agreeable in life. Unfortunately, I am a good deal more than that — I think of the disagreeables, too. But I have a horror of showing that I think of them — just as I have a horror of anyone knowing when I am suffering.

How I would love to lay my head on your shoulder and think of nothing at all — to be simply something that feels and experiences — something — and this especially — that never thinks, never anticipates, never fears.

I've got several old piano records. When I listen to them, I feel that all I want is to be carried along on the current. In a short while I shall see you again, and you'll find me just the same as ever — unless, that is, I can pluck up courage to tell you that I cry buckets' full when you're not there.

I've been thinking about your life up till now. I wish you had been born only when I saw you for the first time. Everything that went before makes me feel giddy. I wasn't lucky enough to be born not jealous — that can be rather tormenting at times. . . .

When I am with you, I have a marvellous feeling of security, not, let me be frank, about anything that concerns you, but about external things — floods, bombings, scoldings, rain, and things like that.

I must see you — I'm feeling terribly depressed — and full of every kind of sweet and indefinable desire.

Sunday. I know that the light may go out at any moment now: but I must say good night.

I am wondering whether you really think that I have had lovers. If you do, I feel as upset as though you had slapped my face. If I ever had had, even one, I should have him still. I should be loving him for ever, and not loving you at all. Perhaps you don't understand that? Men are extraordinary, and that's what makes me sad when you say that you want me, because I am quite sure that you could feel the same about any woman — and not only once, but a hundred times. My love for you is much more serious, because no one could ever take your place with me. When I lie in bed, at night, waiting for sleep, I go over in my mind all the things I've loved about you during the day just past, and I drop off long before I've reached the end of the list . . . What's so marvellous is that this is an entirely new experience for me — that I've got you to thank for everything. You have given me infinitely more than you can have any idea of, because I know now that the only truth is — not so much to be loved as to love. The certainty of that makes me feel rather desperate.

I am filled to the brim and flowing over, Yves — I ask for nothing but to be allowed to roll all that on my tongue. I must leave you now — though not in thought. I give you the hollows of my two hands to kiss.

Monday, 5.30 p.m. I was in a terrible hurry to have done with the silent treatment, so as to be able to write all sorts of things to you — and then I had to complete my move. It's only now that I have got a moment to myself, and there's nothing particularly nice to tell you, or, rather, I can't tell it as I should like to, in words that no one else has ever used. I want everything about me to seem new and young, as though all your illusions were freshly minted. Can't I give you something like that experience? But you probably don't find it particularly important. I have re-christened my Van Gogh. From now on his name is Yves — d'you see anything against that?

I love you — I've said that to you only once — but I put it down now in black and white, just so's you can be sure it's true. If it amuses you to do so, you can flourish this letter under the noses of all and sundry, and say that a child, a little girl, a woman — or whatever you like to call me — loves you as she has never loved anybody, and is ready to do anything for you. I feel so proud of myself that I could be almost happy — a rare thing with me. I'd adore to be crushed in your arms till my bones cracked. That would be terribly, but deliciously, painful. Why do you let yourself be loved? It's a fearful responsibility, you know — but you've never done a thing to stop me. So, what has happened is largely your fault. I hope you realize that.

I love you. When I think of you, and of certain things you have said to me (have you forgotten all the things you have said? — I'm afraid you may have), and, especially, when I think of your lips, it's as though a great wave had broken over me. It's nothing short of a disaster that we can't see more of each other. I hate these aimless moments. Have you ever tried to knock a nail in with a shoe? It is a sad and disappointing experience. Lots of things happen all round the nail, but never on it.

I shall be seeing you in a moment. May all good fortune be yours — I love you.

L.

I have been thinking about so many things since yesterday evening, that I am feeling a bit dazed. My ideas are not as clear as I should like them to be.

There is only one thing of which I am quite certain, and that is my love for you — it is a shining splendour. I say that with pride. It is the only thing that matters so far as I am concerned, and I know that my sort of love doesn't come to anybody twice in a lifetime. If you went away now, or a little later, when you'd had enough of me, I know that the whole of the rest of my life wouldn't be long enough to remember you in. I don't want to speak of all you mean to me, because it is somewhat excessive, and you might not believe it. You mustn't think that I am afraid of giving you too much of myself. I want you to know that I belong to you body and soul, and that you can do anything you like with me. From the first moment that I was sure I loved you, I put myself, morally, in your hands — but I'll take back the gift whenever you want me to.

I believe utterly the marvellous, the unforgettable thing you said to me yesterday evening. Now, it belongs to me, and nobody in the world can take it from me, not even you. You can't possibly realize how much I hate hearing you talk about your age, your duties, and all the hundred and one things that seem to stand in the way of your loving me. I have only the vaguest idea of what you mean, which is probably why I hate that kind of talk. Never forget that I worship you, and believe in you.

Monday evening, 9.30 p.m. I am feeling profoundly happy. I never before imagined anything remotely resembling this rather serious happiness, but now I can't do without it.

I think you must be feeling that one day you may make me suffer — because you said this morning — 'Poor Lisou'. I'm not afraid of that, and you oughtn't to be either . . . I am quite sure that I could die for you, if that was what you wanted — so, most certainly, I can suffer. It is wonderful to feel oneself so stripped and simple, so wholly at one with an emotion. I can never thank you, and worship you, enough for having revealed all that to me, and there are so many good and lovely things that you can still, could still, make known. You are the one and only person in the world for me (I love writing those words — they have an extraordinary weight and solidity. I feel that when I talk to you I give to words a value which they have for nobody but me, and, perhaps, for you).

There is something, don't you think, quite definitely *wrong* in our not being together this evening? A great hearth — and no light but the flickering of the flames. That there should be a storm raging outside is not absolutely indispensable — a bitter cold will do, and snow falling silently, each flake a miracle of peace. But the great, thick, heavy curtains must be drawn. All around us furniture twinkles in the firelight. I am wearing a black dress down to the heels, with very long, very close-fitting sleeves — something highly proper and very distin-guished. I am lying on the floor with my head on your tummy, and, because you have made me drink champagne, I am doing all the talking, while you are saying nothing. 'Yves, my well-beloved', I remark (don't laugh, there's nothing conventional about the phrase: on the contrary, it is quite superb) — 'my well-beloved. I have often imagined a moment like this, but never, never, did I dream that it would be within my power actually to experience it — and now, here it is! I love you' (you squeeze my wrist in your fingers). 'Don't you feel that you were born for the sole purpose of meeting me? For my own part, I am sure that I was born to love you, to tell you so, and to prove it. I have been a long time looking for you, and now at last, here we are — our hands tight clasped on the carpet. There are great shadows under the ceiling, and I am feeling rather frightened at the knowledge that soon we shall be closer, much closer to one another — that a mystery is waiting of which, as yet, I know nothing . . . the prospect is terrifying but wonderfully delicious. I love you' (you lift my hand to your lips). 'I love your mouth — I love every part of you — you are the best-loved man in all the world. I should like you to watch me while I sleep: I should like to watch you while you sleep, so as to be sure that you are thinking of nobody but me.'

I don't want to say any more — I am contented — I am happy — I should like to stop living.

Tuesday evening, 10 p.m. Why did you decide to leave me, just now? — it was hard to bear.

It'll take hours and hours for me to thaw enough to tell you more about myself and my thoughts. I always have to leave you when I most want to stay — but I know you can do nothing about it — nor can I.

How lonely and far from you I feel! I keep thinking what it'll be like meeting you when we're both back in Paris. I have so often imagined the scene — you with a woman, I alone — having no right to speak to you, scarcely the right to smile at you — and turning away. I see so vividly the sort of night I shall have afterwards, biting my pillow in a fit of jealousy and despair. For the moment I find courage in the thought that if you love me (you've said you do, Yves — one doesn't love much or little, one either loves or detests — and you've told me you love me) you can't love someone else at the same time. That is true, isn't it? The thought that it is fills me to bursting with a sense of happiness — but only, of course, if you see these things the same way as I do.

I'm neither clever nor experienced — and I don't mind a bit, because I'm certain that it's not as the result of any shrewdness or scheming on my part that you have become the loveliest thing in my whole life — that's why I should hate to be rich and knowing.

I wish you'd tell me — really tell me — what you think about *us*. It seems to me now quite impossible that I shouldn't belong to you, that I shouldn't have you making love to me for whole nights together (perhaps I'm writing the most awful things, but that's how I feel, and it's my fault, and because I love you it all seems perfectly normal. Don't, please, be shocked. As I've told you already, nothing else matters to me, not even what I think of myself).

50

You may be able to give me some advice, to say to me —
'This is what you ought to do.' My trust in you is absolute. It's
of *myself* that I'm frightened.

Good night, my dearly beloved — you hug me, oh, so tightly!
and you bite my lips. When I'm with you I'm all flame.

Your little girl

LISOU

Tuesday, 7th December

My head is stuffed full of cruel words and a relentless
seriousness — heaps of 'nevers' and 'always' and silent questions. It is very exhausting and depressing, and I want to tell
you about it. It's plain stupid ... At times, when I think of
myself without you, there seems to be a whole world between
us. But that is how I've got to think, and I've been doing so
much thinking along those lines since yesterday, that when I
find you beside me, I am overcome with amazement. I can't
believe that just because you're there I've still got everything.
I may have pondered over all these matters, but I've never
actually realized that they could happen. I've been saying to
myself — 'that's what's going to come' — as a child might say —
'I'm going to be an officer in the army', or, 'I shall have six
sons' — without for a moment considering the fact that I am
not alone in the world — and that what comes won't depend
only on me. It's odd that I should have this feeling that you're
never going to be able to forget me. I tell you — and it's true —
that there will be moments in the years ahead, when you will
turn to me. All I hope is that you won't regret anything, because nothing is worse than regret. But no human being can
give utter and wholehearted love to another without that
other carrying it about with him, whether he wants to or not.
If it were otherwise, it would be unjust. I have an idea that
you're frightened lest I may have misunderstood something
you said. .. It is difficult for me to convince you that that is
not so. I may not have understood it with my heart (my heart

51

obstinately refuses to understand, or to believe in, anything that hurts it — you must forgive it for that, as I do), but I do understand it with such little reason as I have. I know perfectly well that I have stumbled into a blind alley — and I accept that. All I want is that everything good and lovely between us should come from you. I am young, and all the rest can be mine. Whatever happens, I long for it with every fibre in my body, because it will be *your* doing, my best beloved. If my love for you can't make me brave it must be a poor thing.

There have been moments when I wanted to go away — but now I find it hard to believe that I should ever have had any such wish. It is cowardly to the last extreme, and I don't want to be a coward. You have only to touch me with your hand, and I feel that the whole wealth of the world is mine. Later on, I shall remember the moments when you touched me, and I shall have another kind of wealth, but it will be wealth, all the same.

What is hard to bear is the thought of all the things I shall know without you, and not because of you, all that I shall learn about life and love and bad moments and good. There will be times when I shall feel terribly lost, when I shall look for somebody to talk to, somebody I can tell how much I love the way in which a leaf turns in the sun, in which a branch sways — and thousands of little things like that which all add up to an intense happiness. And, oh, how I shall remember you, Yves! — nothing about you will ever be forgotten — that I swear — and I shall keep it all buried deep inside me, like those fabulous treasures which lie hidden in the depths of the sea — for ever.

Your face lit from below when you strike a match — the way in which you crush your lips with your fingers when the stub of your cigarette has got too small — your way of clenching your jaw — certain words of yours, and the way you speak them — your manner of breathing when your head is pressed to my body — and many, many other things which you don't know yourself, though they are so entirely *you* — things which no one, I am sure, will ever love as I do.

I should like to talk to you endlessly about myself while there is still time, so that you may have a true picture of me.

It is odd that the violent passions I have inspired have never aged me nor brought me any hurt. I am not proud of that, and I hate boasting. But because of them I am afraid of going back to Paris. I feel that they will be waiting for me at the gare de Lyon, like a lot of leeches, all on the look out. I am more weary than you can imagine of fighting against them. I can see the end of it all, so far as I am concerned. It seems funny to be young and yet resigned. That is a quite new experience. But I shall have learned how to be happy. It is you who have taught me that — how to be happy, and how to forget that one might have been a hundred times happier still. That is what it all amounts to. Whatever happens, you mustn't let your whole existence be poisoned by the thought that you have done me harm — you have done me so much more good than harm, darling. Nothing that you can do now will ever be able to wipe out that good. I understand so well that there are things a man doesn't do with young girls. You really are rather marvellous — and if for that only, I love you now ten times more than I did. It's almost comic how everything you say adds several inches to your halo!

I have just re-read what I have written. It truly is as though they were my last words, as though I were never going to see you again. What I have just been telling you is all terribly sad. It has spelt death to my cigarettes. There are seven stubs in the ash-tray, and so much smoke in the room that I can barely see my hand when I hold it in front of my face. I keep on thinking that quite soon now you will be going on leave, and that an evening will come when I shall have to say goodbye to you for a long time. That will be a prelude, because another goodbye will come — which will be final . . . You needn't be afraid that I shall cry, or have hysteria. I can cry only when I am alone, and I do it very discreetly, very silently, with my eyes wide open, as men do — and no one knows that anything at all is happening.

I am going to be with you exactly as I was before, because, at bottom, nothing is changed — except that my dreams have become certainties (in rather an opposite way to the one I had hoped — but that is something we can do nothing about), and certainty is, I am sure, better than dreams. My morbid evening broodings are now a thing of the past. The only risk for me is that I shall sink a little deeper — not that there is much further for me to go! . . . All I want is to give you tranquillity (I am never tranquil), and a little happiness. I have never been so happy as I am now. Obviously, for the last two days that particular feeling has been a bit obscured, but it will shine out brightly again because I mean it to, and because it does depend largely on me.

You're here, I love you, and it won't last. I shall keep your letters and a bit of candle-end. I am thinking of you. What are you doing at this moment? I lay my head on your shoulder, and your fingers are touching my neck, oh, so lightly, just where I can feel the life-blood pulsing. It won't last, Lisou. But, after all, the things that don't last are the loveliest.

I'd love to go to sleep and not wake up until tomorrow. But these damned nights are so endless.

I should like to think you noticed that never once did I ask 'Why?' It's because of that, I suppose, that I give you a feeling of tranquillity. You say what you want to say — and there's an end.

I am a little vexed with you for having said those wonderful words to me — on two occasions — not at all because they might have woken a hope in me of something fixed and solid, but simply because they weren't quite true.

Good night, Yves. Sleep well. I bite your lips, just enough to hurt you the tiniest bit. My arms are cold.

Tomorrow is a long way off. I am not unhappy — I promise you that.

LISOU

54

I'm a bit flown with wine. Not enough to weep for myself and the destiny of the human race, but enough to say outrageous things. Beloved, I adore the feel of your hands on me. They are hard, and strong, and their grip is wonderful. If I struggle a little, you must forgive me — it doesn't mean that I don't long to have them always on my body, or that I'm not abysmally unhappy when they're not there at night, and during all those long periods when I am away from you.

And I love lying pressed against you, touching your body at every point, from my lips to my knees, and seeing the sky over your ear. I know already the full worth of all those moments. Sometimes, when I am in your arms I look at your eyes, and I think: 'There are things, Elizabeth, that you must never forget — his mouth, and the warmth of his hands against your back — a warmth that penetrates through layers of clothes — and everything that contributes to the scene — the beauty, the staggering perfection of it all. You must never forget.' And when that happens, you think I am looking sad. Whether it is sadness I do not know, but this I do know that all you give me is only momentary, that there is not a moment I spend with you of which I don't take my fill, that, little girl though I am — a 'girl-who-doesn't-know-what-it-is-like', I am eaten up with the desire to be lying naked in your arms, to twine my legs with yours, to drive my nails into your shoulders. I can no longer be sure whether I am gentle or bestial, simple or complicated, young or old — the only thing I am certain of is that I want to feel the weight of your body, to hear what you would say to me if I were naked, and to find out just how far ecstasy can go. May I think all that, even though I am well aware that it is impossible? I love thinking of it. Please say I may.

My only love, there's a great wind blowing, and you, surely, must be hearing it, too. In five days' time you will no longer be listening to the wind in this place, and I shall hear it in solitude — which will be hard to bear. Will you think about me sometimes, at night? I should like you to discover that in

55

Paris the women do not have firm thighs and high breasts, that they are stupid and boring, that their hats are idiotic and their feet absurdly small, and that they are wholly without sincerity. I am the only person in the world who is 'real', Yves. You must believe that. I am all compact of reality and love. I know with certainty that this gift of myself which I offer is beautiful, sublime, unique. Whatever else you may think, you must at least admit *that*. Kiss the inside of my hand now, at once. I am terribly proud to be the 'little-girl-who-doesn't-know-what-it-is-like' — wholly and utterly her. It has not always been easy for me to resist temptation — or, shall we say, the prickings of curiosity — but 'it' is something I just can't imagine unless love goes with it. Afterwards, I was so happy because I had said 'no'. That feeling was no small reward. At heart I am a completely moral being — which is what I set out to prove, and that makes it all the more incredible that *this* should have happened to me . . . I want to tell you, too, while I am on the subject, about certain firm resolutions which I took not long ago. They are serious and important because they concern my future.

I have made up my mind to get married when I leave here. You may not understand that. It will be, I think, in May or June. If I don't do it then, I never shall. I know exactly what my state of mind will be when I land up in Paris. I shall have left you, and I shall need an antidote. That will be the only thing which will be of any use (movement, change, a new life, and, I hope, children at the earliest possible moment). If I let that chance go by without seizing it, I might not have the courage to take the fatal step later, and that terrifies me. The thought of myself as a childless old maid is horrible. I can see myself living alone and having squalid adventures in a sordid studio . . . I know I shall come to a bad end if I don't get my feet fixed firmly, and soon, in the right road.

All this is very difficult to explain, especially just now. If I have chosen this solution it is because I know that it will satisfy my overwhelming need to be loved — if not of loving. The latter I expend on you, because I love you terribly, and shall go on loving you for a long, long time, and because you will always be my only love.

I feel sleep upon my eyes, Yves, my beloved, so I am going to bed, and I shall think of tomorrow — but not beyond.

I stretch myself against you, and I stop breathing, so as to hear the throbbing of your life. Good night.

LISOU

Wednesday, 22nd December

I don't know whether it is humanly possible to forget such moments — the moments, I mean, which I spend with you.

Now, at this precise and actual moment, I want you to take my face in your hands and to look into my eyes. I love you so much, Yves, so very much. I am quite alone, so I can press this paper to my cheek and dream of you. Crush me tightly in your arms, as tightly as though you meant to force me right through your body and out on the other side. I am keeping my eyes so firmly shut that my eyebrows hurt. The sky might fall upon my head, but all would still be ideally perfect — and yet, and yet — you're off to Paris.

I know how uneasily I shall look at you when you come back (for come back you will) — like a little boy who is tortured by the thought that his sister has been eating cake out walking, while he has been indoors, and sees, yes, sees the mark of chocolate on her lips, and a few crumbs caught on the front of her frock.

If you love me — and you do, don't you? — *because* you love me, you will never go to sleep without sending a thought to watch over me. It will cling above my bed — that wretched contrivance, all white and clean, which reminds me a hundred times a day that I am in a sanatorium and not on holiday. It will perch upon my pillow, as close to me as possible, singing all night through the most strange, delicious songs, such as babies

57

make for themselves, and lunatics, and Nordic princes whom one meets in folk-tales.

Don't forget to send me a few every night so that I may sleep well.

Thursday morning. You have left a terrible emptiness here, but I am not sad. I am proud — without quite knowing why — proud because I have the harder part of staying here and waiting. I am proud of myself, of you, and of all that exists between us. I thought, this morning, that the car would never get up the hill, and the idea of you nervously pacing the hall made me want to laugh. When I heard it beneath my window I did a little pillow-biting, and then, I opened my eyes. It was a murky day, and there was something thrilling about the stillness, the immobility of everything. And now, I am lying stretched at full length, and you are in the valley which I can see away to my right. The mountain has an impassive, an impersonal, look with its cropped and curled pelt of pines. There is something leprous about it — today, it is almost ugly.

I am sitting on the radiator, writing on my knee. I am smoking the first cigarette of the day. When I went downstairs I saw men cutting firs. One of them will be for me. I am going to have a delicious little Christmas tree. What a pity that you won't be here to see it. I am sure you would have kissed my hands out of sheer gratitude for my having made something so lovely. While I am dressing it I shall think about what you must have been like as a little boy.

I can look at nothing pretty without longing to have you beside me. I should like to have had a little too much to drink, and to be resting my head on your shoulder, with my nose pressed against your neck, conscious only of your presence, and reducing all that stands between us to nothing. Is it possible that one can forget everything except one person? That happens to me when I am with you, though never completely. I am always trembling at the thought that I might discover something in you that is fated not to be mine. I should like to feel your lips travelling upwards from my feet to my mouth without once leaving my body — there, I've said it again! — and, from the depths of my heart, I pity all those who have never spoken just those words. They give one such a lovely feeling, and, besides, no one says them quite as I do. Don't they sound new-minted in your ears? Goodbye, beloved and perfect man. Think of me. I need your thoughts.

Your

LISOU

Friday, 24th December

It is a glorious day and you are in Paris. You have lost a lot, really you have, by not being here. You would have laughed to see me going down the road sandwiched between D. on my right, and Et. on my left — rather too much of a good thing, as you would say. Apart from that, all was sheer enchantment — sky, snow, and sun. I am a fool to follow all your comings and goings in imagination. As night-time approaches, I bite my lips. I am sure you're going to have a high old time celebrating the birth of the Messiah. How I envy all the people who are going to see you, talk to you, listen to you . . . I am jealous of the very beggars you pass in the street — of the gloves on your hands — I love your hands — I love your eyebrows — they're quite delicious. My second day without you. I can consider with perfect tranquillity the nine that remain. It is so good to love you.

Saturday, 2.10 a.m. I have had a terrible fit of the blues. Et. said: 'I expect Yves is in a night-club at this very moment, surrounded by women.' They told a lot of dirty stories which I didn't understand. But the Mass was lovely. There were two great fir trees with spreading branches against the white walls, and they smelt so strongly of resin that I almost dropped off. Everything was sad. I was low-spirited and thought of you. I went into Et.'s room and conjured up a vision of you living in this naked-looking place. I ate an apple and looked at the ceiling. At one moment I felt so strong a desire to escape, and to run and run until I found you, that I had to bite my lips. Well, so Christmas is over, and I realize all that you mean to me. My little fairy-lamp is just going out. I shan't sleep. I am filled with too much pain and too many desires. Sleep well, my love. I hope you are a great deal happier than I am at this moment. . . .

9 a.m. I always knew that the day after would be the worst. Luckily, there was some lovely Beethoven. What a hellish thing memory is! My body is what most brings you back to me, and I can't get rid of that. I wish I was a tiny baby, really a baby, three years old. Yesterday evening the Abbé P. wore a beautiful vestment, you know the one I mean, white, with a cross embroidered in red, and over it, a lovely white bird. Each time he raised his arm I could see the lining, which was exquisite. Lord! how sleepy I felt! The smell of pines was delicious, the candied fruit adorably sickly, and the milk in the little pots very white and slightly frothy as though fresh from the cow. The waiter's name was Gaston — and oh, how it suited him! I was terribly thirsty and he brought me a jug of water. I drank it from a very thick cup which felt smooth to my lips. For all I know, *you* may once have drunk from it!

Saturday night. People like N. make me want to cut them open just to see what they are made of inside. He is completely impenetrable. There is a fixed look in his eyes that can some-times be rather upsetting. He was terribly sad today. I think he hates Christmas, because it is a feast, and because his heart is no longer responsive to happiness outside himself. I suppose one does come to hate certain forms of rejoicing when one can no longer share in them and remains a spectator. I think I felt a little like that this year. I wouldn't have believed it possible. True, I'm in love, which I wasn't a year ago, in spite of the ring on my finger, the flowers I had been sent, and the congratulations raining down on my head. My hand is bare now, and my heart is swollen to bursting with love. I have just been reading Gide's *Corydon* — there certainly are things in human nature that I can't make head or tail of. How can a man be in love with another man? But Gide is extraordinarily stimulating. He stabs the brain awake, in spite of his sentimental belly-aches and the maudlin passages which mar his style. One wants to argue about almost everything he says — but that, at least, is something. There are so many books which have the effect only of making one want to hurry on to the next.

I am lying in bed, so tired that I feel part and parcel of the mattress.

I should like to unhook my back and hang it on the window-catch until tomorrow morning. I think I shall sleep the sleep of the just. The Abbé won't see me at Mass tomorrow, and I shan't go to the cinema. I feel completely done up.

I've just got the beginnings of a shiver down my spine. Never have I had such a complete sense of lassitude — but I love you with all my being, and if only you could kiss my eyes, this mood would vanish. Stroke me with your hands.

LISOU

Monday, 27th December

I long to have a letter from you, just to know what you are thinking about me. I know only too well that there are millions of reasons why you should not be thinking of me as I want you to think. The Sanatorium, the walks in the forest, the bells that summon one to treatment, the half-frozen mangold-wurzels — how far away and slightly trivial it must all seem to you. I envy your plunge back into normal life. I simply must break away and have something of the same sort, myself, soon. I've had about enough of this place, especially now that you are no longer here.

Tuesday morning. The sun is not up, and everything is a sort of tangerine yellow. I am smoking old stubs and thoroughly enjoying my after-the-bath laze. My hair is still wet. It is going to be a lovely day. I thought of you all the time I was naked, and could feel your hands and your lips on my damp

61

flesh. I sang all the while I was in the bath. The water was blue and clear, and the steam had covered the walls with millions of little glittering drops. It's heavenly to be naked and to squeeze spongefuls of piping hot water over one's neck — so that it trickles over one's back and shoulders, and pours between one's knees — and to go on doing it until one begins to feel cold.

Perhaps you're going for a stroll along the Seine this morning? How I should love to do that! If it's as fine with you as it is here, you must be feeling very happy — I want you to be happy — always. That is much more important than my own happiness. So, you see, you've got to be happy — it's an order!

I have to go upstairs for two hours. I am more than usually well this morning — full of vitality and youth. If I were at home I should lie on the ground in the sun, and listen to my mother coming and going in the house, talking to the cat, shutting a window, sneezing. I remember how, on fine days, I used to love to hear her starting off to do her marketing. I shall never forget the clink of Yogourt bottles all crammed together in a bag — nor the slender branches of the plum tree in front of my window — nor the goldfish going through their solemn evolutions, like priests at the altar. In the evening I adored the smooth and shining surface of the copper vase with tulips in it — my favourite flowers. The evenings were long, but one of those things I have been telling you of, or, sometimes all of them together, would fill the time. Perhaps I was happy then.

The fields in front of the Sanatorium look exactly as though they had just come back from the laundry — 'blued' like a sheet which has been left to dry in the light of the moon. I didn't sleep much last night. There were a few samples of superb stars — all twinkling away like mad: they gave a lot of light, but of rather an odd kind. I love waking up round about 4 or 5. The air is fresh and clean, and my mind feels marvellously nimble. I tackle all my problems one after the other, with unusual lucidity. My intelligence, at such times, is a well-tempered blade which bends without breaking. But that all changes as soon as full day is come.

9.10 p.m. I asked myself a question last night, and the memory of it is with me still. Perhaps you'll find it terribly indiscreet. Well, that can't be helped, so here goes. Try to imagine that it's being put by one of your men friends, and not by me, who am in love. You mustn't, of course, reply unless you feel you want to. This is the question. Are you planning to get married some time or other? If you are, I'd rather know at once, so as to get used to the idea. Good night, you-whom-I-love. Don't keep me waiting too long for a letter. I snuggle down beside you while you sleep, and nibble your ear and your neck — not bite, just nibble very gently with the tips of my teeth — I love you.

LISOU

Heavens! I almost forgot! — A Happy New Year, and may everything you want be yours — I'm wishing so many of your wishes for you. I counted nine stars just now, and I said — 'let him be happy' . . .

P.S. I shan't come down to meet you when you return from Paris. I've gone into the whole matter and decided that it might produce a lot of awkwardness for us. Still, it *would* have been marvellous to have had a whole day with you, instead of an occasional fifteen minutes. But there's nothing I can do about it. Kiss my hands. That will cheer me up.

Wednesday, 29th December

It comes over me with a feeling of horror that this is almost certainly the last letter I shall send. I haven't had a single one from you. You went away, and complete silence descended. It doesn't matter to you whether those who are left behind just rub along on the makeshift of your imagined presence, whether they plague themselves with questions, whether they write or don't write — you just wash your hands of them. It's bad and ungrateful of you. I feel a hateful longing to storm and rage. But you don't deserve that I should demean myself in that way, and give you a chance to mock. One letter is no different to you than another. These letters of mine remain unanswered. I feel that I just write them and drop them into the sea. I don't know where they go, nor to whom, nor why they exist. I take a sheet of paper, and I cover it with words for no better reason than that I feel the need to, that I love somebody and must tell him so. If the water soaks them and smudges the ink, well, that's just too bad. Anyhow, *I* shan't see them again. If, some day or other, you get them — I'm talking to you, Yves — try to make out the writing and to understand what it says. The best of myself has gone into these letters. It may not be any great shakes to receive, but it is no easy matter to give. I've done the giving, so I know. And what I have given I shall never be able to take back.

Evening. I've been asked to paint something to look like shelves with little jars on them — a chemist's shop scene for a play they're producing here. I went to a rehearsal, and found it amusing. You've no idea how happy I felt to be wearing my old paint-stained smock again. It reminded me of my one glorious year at the Beaux-Arts. You may, for all I know, have seen me in one like it, on the Boulevard Saint-Germain (mine was so stiff with modelling clay that it could have stood up on its own), pushing a baby's pram (period Louis-Philippe) filled with painting materials. The policemen used to stop the traffic to let me get across the road, and then, when I was under their noses, and they could see what my baby consisted of, they would start shouting at me.

I've been listening to some terrifically good singing from one of the English stations — the Andrews Sisters. I love that kind of song — it goes to my head like alcohol, and God knows what a mess *that* makes of me! I'm a good deal too fond of drink, and feel sure that my feet are on a slippery slope. But my father was not a drunkard, said she with an angelic expression on her face which deceived nobody. I sometimes wonder where I get these disastrous tastes *from*. My mother often says, raising her eyes to heaven — I can't imagine what I was thinking of when I conceived you . . . Won't you ever be able to see my room? I wish you could see it at this moment. You would stand as though enchanted, and you would say: 'What an adorable place you've made, with next to nothing.' Often, when I happen in on a girl-friend, I feel exactly as though I were in a servant's bedroom — that awful unwashed smell — the air that's been breathed over and over again by people who don't look after their teeth — the very sign and symbol of Purgatory (Hell's much the same, only with the addition of dirty feet and, perhaps, lice and pimples). Do you know a song called, 'On l'appelait fleur de misè-è-re'? People who perpetrate things like that ought to be strung up!

I want to talk to you of serious matters, but haven't the pluck — I don't think I should like the look in your face when you read this. First of all, kiss me all over, and say those intoxicating things of which you are a past master. This evening, I want to hear your wonderful voice and to feel your hands on my body — everywhere at once. If we were lying before a window wide open on a lovely summer sky, heavy with heat — if I had your head upon my shoulder — if we were naked and simple as two children — if your hand were on the warm hollow of my thighs where the life-blood pulses — if your moist mouth were touching my neck — if you had just said, 'I am happy' — if all we could hear was the faint swish of a fountain falling on grass— if the air smelled of pinewoods and sea-salt — if I were holding my breath so as not to disturb you — if you murmured my name in your sleep — if I were not afraid of the morrow — if, for one brief moment, you were sated with my body, and I with yours — if you loved me as I love you — then, oh then, all would be accomplished and death might come when it chose.

Look at me, Yves — look at me until your eyes ache, and then draw near. I close my eyes and do not know what part of me your lips will touch. Don't make me wait too long.

I am on the point of going to bed, like a quiet, sensible girl.

In a moment I shall be naked. It's odd how close I feel to you —
so close that I am faintly embarrassed. . . .

Thursday morning. It is abominably cold and dreary. But
every little blade of grass is covered with hoar frost, and the
sight of it sets me dreaming. If there is nothing from you in
this morning's post, I shall do something desperate. I shan't
kill myself because, after all, one never knows. There might
be a letter for me tomorrow — and that would be a pity. The
thought that my firm thighs and pretty hands might be rotting,
gives me a cold shudder down the spine.

11.30. None of the letters I was hoping for have come — from
you, nothing. I know that you have a lot to do, but all the
same, I feel sad — terribly so, and disappointed — but chiefly
sad. You're not behaving at all well, that's the long and the
short of it. I suppose that when you got back to Paris you
found an accumulation of things waiting for you, and realized
how little I mattered in your life. But if that is what you feel,
you might at least tell me. You know, or you ought to, for I
have told it you a hundred times — that the moment you want
me to fade away, I will. But I can't be expected to guess when
that will be. Your silence is not a sufficient message (besides, I
refuse, or partly refuse, to take its meaning). I believe that
you are honest enough, frank enough, to say it, if it must be
said, and your silence hurts me worse than anything. If it were
I who was in Paris I should have so many things to tell you —
but perhaps you don't like talking of yourself and your doings.

It would be some consolation if I could go to the post office
myself. I like to imagine the scene. I should hold my letter in
my hand. I should be wearing a white dress and very flimsy
sandals, and living somewhere above Vence. To reach the
village I should have to take a stony path drenched in sunlight.
I should twirl the letter between my fingers, and feel very
sorry for you away in Paris, having to wear a collar and tie.
On the way down I should meet a small boy in blue breeches,
sucking an orange. We would sit together in the shade of a
cypress, and eat warm, sticky figs, and he would tell me all

66

about spearing fishes. He might even be my son. 'Who are you writing to?' he would ask. 'To a gentleman,' I would reply, 'whom I knew once upon a time, when I was twenty. He used to say the most unforgettable things, but he was not for me. He had the same name as you.' The envelope would gleam very white in the sun. 'And you haven't seen him for a long time?' 'Not for ages, darling: I don't even know where he is, but I have written him a long, long letter, and I shall slip it into the pillar box just as though I were throwing it into the sea. He will never get it, but that doesn't matter. You see, it is very important that I should tell him all about my life.' And the little boy would say 'Yes', but he wouldn't understand a word. And now I'm going to lunch. I loathe and detest you.

Will you kiss the hollow of my hand, just once? — not for your sake, but for mine — please.

LISOU

1944

Letters

I should like to bite your ears from sheer joy, because I
am going out tomorrow, and shall have precisely until Wednesday to get used to the idea of being once again bedridden. I
must have looked pretty wretched this evening, as, indeed, I
was.

I don't want this letter to be full of groans and moans, so I
won't say another word about all that — you have enough
troubles of your own without having to put up with mine into
the bargain. I only want you to know that the first person I
thought of when I heard this crushing piece of news, was you.
I clung for all I was worth to the affection which it is just possible
you may feel for me, and that sent my courage up with a bang.
Two hours ago, I was on the point of begging you to be very,
very kind, and to write me a letter; but now all I want is that
you should be exactly as you want to be — and nothing else.

I spent all last night, Yves, chewing over that odd question
of yours, and I do at last think that I really understand what
you meant. The only thing I still find strange is the 'why?' —
which seems to me almost funny. Why? — well, because that's
how it is. There's no other possible answer. You can't know
very much about me to ask that. (If you'd said 'how?' I could
have told you at once.)

I find myself wondering whether you'll make me sorry that
I didn't indulge in a little leg-pulling. The fact that I refrained
makes me very proud. I know, without being told, that I am
a pretty rare specimen. But that is because it's in my nature
to be rare (no false modesty, you see!). I remember how, as
recently as last year, I could feel shocked and scandalized at
the idea of two engaged persons . . . anticipating the ceremony.
I felt nothing but contempt for people like that, for their lack
of conscience, for their lack of self-control, for their lack of any
sort of respect for tradition. It may have been ridiculous of

71

me to feel like that, but at least the feeling was sincere. And now along you come with your 'why?' I have given a good deal of thought to the question, and the conclusion I have reached is this — that it's because I've never wanted to. I've never wanted to for the very good reason that before you arrived on the scene, I had never been in love. I just can't separate 'that' in my mind from the idea of love-as-an-emotion. It may be a curious aberration on my part, but there it is. I find it difficult even to think of the one apart from the other. This is purely personal. I suppose the trouble is that I have got an absurdly overgrown respect for the whole business. I should like to tell you all about my thoughts and experiences, but I don't want to bore you . . . I'll wait till another time.

I'm so tired that I can't see straight. Good night. I'm going to dream that I am happy and well, and that nobody asks me questions as baffling as yours.

For all my common sense and sweet innocence, I shall also dream of the weight of your body on mine.

I love you, Yves.

I know what a burden I am to you. Forgive me.

Sunday evening. I have just been listening to Beethoven's Concerto in D. If you ever hear it in the years to come, when I'm no longer there, do, please, think of me — and of you. The whole of my love for you is in that Concerto — it is, I think, the best description of it you will ever have. The music expresses all the purity of which I am capable, all the joy, all the strength — and then, you see, it has no end, no conclusion.

9 p.m. You really are a mass of contradictions. First, you seem almost to blame me for being 'untouched', and then if I so much as hint that I was once seen naked, you behave as though I were a loose woman, and threaten to box my ears!!!

But I forgive you (laughter).

I have sweet confessions for your ear.

I love you — I am happy only when we are together. I miss everything about you — even the feel of your coat against my cheek. You can't possibly know how many times a day I want

72

you so violently that I could scream. I feel as though I could say terrible things to you this evening — for instance, that my longing for you is almost more than I can bear (am I allowed to say that?).

You don't understand why it is that I shrink from your touch — it's not me that resists, but only the bad side, the silly, self-conscious side, of me — everything in me that is simple and animal needs the feel of your hands, and cries out for them.

Monday morning. This wonderful weather fills me with every kind of illusion. I feel that it can never end. The blind of my window bellies gently inwards, and I am at peace. This morning, at six o'clock, the light of the moon and the stars was upon me — and the coolness of the air. I passed my hand over my warm, smooth body, and wished that it had been your hand. I thought of all sorts of wonderful things that I can't tell you about. I should have to be in your arms for two or three hours before I could begin to speak of them. If I were, I think I could tell you things which would set your head swimming.

I am hungry for you. I want us to be together in the dark so that I could tell you things. I can't do it in daylight: you make me feel too shy. I love the night.

One of these days I shall try to say, in the full light of the sun, that I love you.

If I seem preoccupied, that will be the reason. Don't laugh. I am, to quote Gide, in a state of mind which is at so equal a distance from both pain and joy, that it must be happiness.

I'm never bored when I am with you.

But those moments are rare, aren't they?

LISOU

Friday, 21st January: 6 p.m.

The thought of you confined to your bed all day long, and again this evening, fills me with pity. I'd give a lot if I could get out for a stroll just now, even if I had to take it alone. This

73

morning I went down to the village, and thought I should have died of cold. If I didn't catch my death, that's only because I am fated to make old bones. Apart from that, everything was marvellous. I met a very old brown dog carrying a little brass trumpet in his mouth. He seemed in such a hurry that he must have been off to some sort of meeting — and then a cow, so spotlessly white, so clean, so pretty and gentle, that she didn't look real at all, but as though she belonged to a Nativity group of toys. She nearly fell on her face in the snow, but it didn't detract from her dignity and self-possession by so much as a millimetre — she scarcely so much as raised an eyebrow. Further on, I came across a little black cat. He shot through a clutter of completely bewildered chickens, just so as to come up to me and show me that his eyes were greener than the sleeves of my jersey. He had such an adorable way of looking at me that I fell in love with him at once, and am terribly sorry that he isn't with me now. It would have been such fun to have him on my bed, as trustful as a baby, squatting on his paws, beautifully neat, and with no loose ends.

I went into a little café. The door opened on to a sort of a farmyard. There was a pump in the middle with a great tank full of very clear, very blue water, and a man with a wooden leg was carting grass. How curious it is in the country to see members of the same family constantly meeting each other without exchanging a word, though they all seem able to talk to the animals.

By the way, can you tell me how one knows when a cow or a mare is with young? It seems to me that they are permanently in that condition. They always look so swollen, so resigned — and so disillusioned.

My branch of mimosa is drooping, but it still gives off a strong, sweet smell. What I'd love this evening would be to put on a really smart dress, go somewhere, dance a little, drink, come back at some unheard-of hour, and let myself be undressed by a man. I've got all the feelings, tonight, of a pretty woman — and I'm as hungry as a cannibal. I want to eat crumby sandwiches cut in triangles, and to feel my teeth meeting through a layer of foie gras. . . .

Saturday morning. Would it be too cruel — since you're confined to bed for the next few months — to tell you all that a morning like this can mean? It was perfect in every detail. It was complete. I don't think I have ever felt so deliciously alive, so sensitive to impressions. And yet, I know a woman who at this very moment is at the point of death. I am sure that she can never have dreamed that anything like that would happen to her so soon. The idea that I might be in her place tears at my heart. What terrible regrets one must have when one looks round and *knows* that one is leaving it all for ever.

I wish I could make you hear the sound of my curtains gently brushing against the window panes. The blue of the sky is soft and faintly moist. I feel the same kind of limpid quality in myself. The smoke from my cigarette hangs in the air with a momentary hesitation, before slipping away under the blind like a snake. If only I had a lovely tree to look at — a young poplar or a birch — your absence would seem a simpler thing. You see, doing without you for more than a few hours, is a very complicated affair. In order to face it, I have to rifle the treasures of my imagination. Reason doesn't help much. I haven't got a great deal, and, where you are concerned, it is no use at all. I had the most wonderful dreams last night. I am sleeping so well now that there seems no more than the passage of a breath between the evening and the morning.

3 o'clock. Thank you for the books — but thank you is enough. Their arrival meant no more than 'here are the books. Good night'. I flipped through the pages, but found nothing. What a strange creature you are — I hope with all my heart that I shall grow tired of all this one day.

I started on the Colette volume at once. I read three pages, but found so little of her in them, that I'm not at all sure whether I am going to like it. Anyhow, reading is difficult just now — I'm thinking too much about myself, and I'm tired to the very marrow of my bones (they've found a certain amount

75

of liquid, and that makes me a bit frightened). The lines have a funny way of dancing before my eyes, and it's a real relief to shut the book and gaze away into the distance (all the same, I'll get through the *Journal à rebours* quickly, so as to let you have it back as soon as possible). You can't know how much I lose by not seeing you. If only you would write as I do!

What I most want at this moment is that you should sometimes feel the need to run for shelter into Port-Lisou. It's calm there, and comfortable. That's a matter of general knowledge— so, don't forget.

Goodbye for the present — you horrible man.

Lisou

Sunday evening, 30th January

You're certainly no match for me! That wretched letter of yours, which you started at five, ended with the clatter of your approaching dinner — and I can feel what a labour it must have been to you.

You dote on mine, you say — but get quite annoyed because the pages aren't numbered!!!

Monday morning. I expect you thought I was in a bad mood yesterday evening, didn't you? Whether I was or not, I've decided to think and write rather less in future — that'll be much wiser.

I feel that I should like to wind up this page in your style (cold enough to freeze Lake Chad):

'Weather fine — tidied room and spent some time sewing. Read Giraudoux's *Eglantine*. Looked out of the window at a sea of cloud — bought some Gauloises (blue), listened to the noise in the ventilator — so long.

Much love'
Lisou

P.S. I rather missed you between 6.35 and 7.

Wednesday morning, 2nd February

Oddly enough, the fact that I have been three days without writing to you, really worries me quite a lot. I've suddenly become shy — besides, the less one writes, the less there seems to say. You mustn't let me be so foolish again. You like getting my letters (yes, you do!) and I feel a need to write them. It would be silly to fight against that double motive.

I'm glad you wrote as you did, because one of my peculiar foibles is that I can't pass abruptly from one situation to another without a sense of pain. You must realize how simple and confiding I was with you, and I can't sweep the memory away at twenty-four hours' notice. People, I suppose, who are older or more callous, can manage to keep things like that going for longer, or else can do without them. I can't, and I'm fool enough to say so. That is why getting a cold letter from you (it wouldn't seem cold to anybody else, but when I think how much of myself I give, it seems so to me) was sheer misery. Yours of yesterday wiped all that out. I feel that I am *with* you again (this confession will probably bring me a whole bundle of telegraphese — but I can't help that).

5 o'clock. I had just settled myself down when I remembered that I had got an appointment with N., who's going to pump some air into my pneumo-thorax. I wish I hadn't got to go.

The 'Cure' is a wonderful observation post — I can hear the girls talking. Just now, one of them said in thoughtful tones — 'What, haven't you read *Jalna*? it's rather the same sort of book as *Sparkenbroke*' — !!! Up I go. The light is very harsh this evening. In the morning it was so soft, as though God had driven past during the night in a coach, and the dust of the wheels had not subsided.

Evening. Why do I look like a pleasant sort of looney tonight? The sight of myself quite worries me. My eyes are so bright that people must think I've been crying. I do so long to see you, my best beloved, and I wish very much that I could explain why it is that I love you so terribly. But I am afraid that no words could ever do that, and even if they could, and

77

I could find them, they would only give you an opportunity to laugh at me. The truly remarkable thing about you is your balance — I mean, the way in which nothing ever seems to shake you out of your way of living — your way of walking, talking, laughing, and so on, and so on. It's a sort of off-handedness which completely hypnotizes me, and turns me into a much younger person than I really am. I'm in a constant state of dread of what you're going to say, of what you do say, of what you don't say, with the result that I, who have adopted the bad habit of letting other people go to hell, of not caring, I mean, two hoots about their reactions, when I'm with you, am just 'she-who-has-found-her-master'. Don't smile so mockingly — it's all too horribly true.

So many people have hoped and prayed that this would happen to me that, sooner or later, it was bound to. I was always so conceited — you can't possibly imagine *how* conceited — and I still have a tendency that way — 'when your eyes hold me no more in thrall'. What a mess you have made of my pride!

Wouldn't you enjoy a good laugh with me this evening? — I should so love to hear you laughing. Why do you write: 'shrined in a golden memory, those evening hours with you beside me'? I do so hate the way you make a joke of lovely things! I know so well what I should have written: 'If only you had been there, with your arm round my shoulder weighing me down and making me feel small, if only I could have bent my head and touched your hand with my cheek, if only you had said how wonderful all that pale green sky and spread of flame looked — then, I should have thought that it was near perfection and could never be forgotten.' The knowledge that you can find it slightly comic freezes my blood.

I laughed a lot this evening when I was telling a friend of mine that when I was a small girl I used to clean my navel with match-stalks — her way of chortling and flapping her hands as though begging me to stop, makes me choke with sheer delight.

78

I found a passage in Byron which is so beautiful that I make you a present of it: 'The earth does not contain your like, and if it did, 'twould be in vain. Not for the world would I wish to see a woman who looked like you if she were not you indeed.' Don't you find that delightful? Both matter and manner seem to me quite perfect — I wish *I* could have written it. And there was something else, too, which I found scribbled on the corner of an envelope: 'Architecture makes me think of frozen music'. I do indeed believe that a building like the Parthenon must have the effect of a petrified symphony.

I have got all the necessary permits for my trip to C...I rather think it will be on Wednesday or Thursday. I'm only waiting for a 'spot of the ready'.

Thursday morning. What a night! I got to sleep round about twenty to five after ringing and ringing for that old blob of a Z. — who took forty minutes to answer the bell — time enough for me to die ten times over. I had a terrible pain — worse than any you've ever had — in one arm. I couldn't lift it. I noticed that a star took a whole hour to move across the space of my window — pretty quick going on the whole. When Z. did turn up, I was sitting in my nightgown, sponging my legs. I'd just had a frightful attack, and really thought my heart was going to peg out — my lump of a neighbour was sleeping as though there was nothing in the world to worry about. Do you think the performance of the *Captives* is going to be good? — I want it to be, *very* good. That's what I need.

11 o'clock. I have to do a lot of stretching in the mornings — otherwise I'm in a foul temper for the rest of the day. It's close on eleven, and I've not finished my exercises yet. It's pure joy to have a body, to extend it in every possible direction, and then let it resume its natural shape like a snail. My arm is still stupidly painful. I feel as though I had been holding up a house over my head all night.

There are such strange-looking clouds clinging to the peaks opposite, all fleecy and ravelled. I am quite sure that if I only tried hard enough I could hear them sliding over the great snowfields and bumping against the rocks — they'd sound sort of silky — like material being pulled across a table.

I must stop now: I'm simply dropping with sleepiness.

LISOU

Saturday evening, 5th February

Oh, Yves! how I long for sleep! What can I do about it? — if only you could come, and not leave me to face another night like last night, alone. It was so long, and sad, and chilly. If I could feel your hands on my body, I promise that I would not push them away — I'd hollow my back, so's you could get your arms right round me — I would share your warmth — and the night would not be nearly long enough. I would be the gentlest, sweetest, smoothest, quietest, wisest, nakedest, warmest, rarest, tremblingest and happiest of little girls. And you, the most beloved of all men.

I can't, it's obvious, go on writing to you this evening.

Goodbye for a while — I lay my head on your knees, and sleep, oh! so soundly. . . .

Sunday evening. Don't, my beloved, whatever you do, believe the fools who tell you that the *Lumière d'été* film is stupid. I found it quite remarkable, and I am sure you'd have loved it as I did — it's so true, so sincere. Sincerity's a wonderful thing, isn't it? I shall never forget the woman's face. They are sitting on the stone rim of an ornamental lake, with fountains playing. He says — 'I love you', and then, 'Kiss me.' She fixes her eyes on his, she lets them travel over his face as far as his mouth, very slowly, as though to realize to the full what is going to happen. She brings her mouth close to his mouth, while he sits there quite motionless . . . I loved that — it is all very simple — but the way in which she looks at his mouth is marvellous.

How beautiful the moon is tonight. If you were here, I could see your eyes by it. I adore looking at your eyes for minutes on end, and, as it were, losing myself in them — and then, the snow, the great and silent spread of snow, and the listening trees, and my hand so warm inside your coat — in some ways I'm like your child, aren't I?

I wonder whether you ever try to envisage the day when you'll be seeing me for the last time? — I don't think you indulge in that sort of imagining, but I do. I am obsessed by the thought of being without you, and by the idea of death.

Monday. It has begun to snow again, very quietly. It makes me feel sad to watch it. Oh God! how far away my home seems today — and how lonely I feel all of a sudden. No, I've not got a fit of the blues, and I'm not really depressed: it's only that I am afraid of things, of bitter-sweet things. I know only too well that if I stood at the window looking at the falling snow, I should stay there for hours and hours, my hands stuffed in my pockets, and not even bothering to change from one foot to the other — rather like an ostrich — and it would make me feel awful, because I should be having that sensation of going up ... up — and then, someone would come in — someone always does come in — and would say 'Oh, I'm sorry' — but that wouldn't stop them from sitting down, from fingering my belt, from remarking on my looks, the weather, the button missing from my blouse — and then opening my music portfolio.

There's that bell again! — the darkness has a hard, blue look, because it still isn't complete. Later on, it will be black — the trees are thin, with frozen drops on their branches, like birds.

Wouldn't you like to run away from all this? — to roam the streets and feel the snow in your open mouth, to walk with one foot on the pavement, and the other in the gutter, to stick your tongue out at policemen and bearded colonels and great ladies with their trailing trains — and then to get a few axe-blows in the stomach, just to see how lovely the blood looks on the snow — and not to die, never to die, to be completely invisible and invulnerable and without love — to penetrate everywhere, to make yourself familiar with everyone, to know everything. I know nothing of life, nothing at all. And here I sit looking at this letter which you will read, perhaps not understanding, not knowing what it is all about. I love you — you know that — all the rest is dust and ashes, but the rest is precisely what I have got. I should love to run about the streets of an old town in old clothes. But, most of all, I don't want to meet any children. They have a way of looking that I find quite shattering. I saw one this morning. He said 'bon jour, madame' in so adorable a voice that I went all weak at the knees — it's silly to feel like that — and it's all because of the snow. It tears my nerves to shreds.

If only I could sleep. It's not being able to sleep that frightens me.

I've just been to the window. There are four lights in the valley — very far away — and others quite close. How pretty the red glow of a window looks under a roof heaped with snow. It reminds me of those frosted cards with a branch of holly, and 'Happy Christmas' in gold letters that are rough and gritty under the finger.

No, indeed. I am without any certainty about what you think of me in general, and of my letters in particular. Wouldn't you hate it if I wasn't? That's the one thing, I think, which keeps me from being quite intolerable. Anyone as young as I am who was sure of herself would be a catastrophe. I'm still in a state of doubt where everything that has to do with me is concerned — and this evening more than usual. But I feel the possibilities bubbling up inside me. Young though I am, I have reached that stage. I have never believed that anyone is capable of loving me as I love (how idiotic to want to be unlike everyone else — that's what you think, and perhaps you're right...).

9.15. I'm so afraid you will take everything I have written seriously — and find it boring. Somehow, I can't feel humorous today, and I should hate to hear you laughing at me — at the things I say, at my 'grande dame' airs — a grande dame who'd like you to take her a bit seriously, in spite of the hot-water-bottle on her tummy, in spite of her nun's nightdress (with long sleeves buttoned to the wrist, a great pleat down the back, and all so long), in spite of her baby mouth, her tip-tilted nose, and the tiny breasts that take in nobody.

You don't really know me. We've never had two hours alone together. It would need all of that before I could begin to be myself.

Till tomorrow: good night.

LISOU

Tuesday, 15th February: 5 o'clock
I'm feeling a bit wrought-up, because I'm waiting to get my last-but-one ration of chocolate. You might think that takes a few years off my life, but it doesn't. Being over twenty-one has its disadvantages. . . .

I have just swallowed every scrap of my chocolate — after tossing three bars across to Na. The other seven I ate all at a go (I may be selfish, but, honestly, it would have been sheer torture to have given her one bar more and to have had one less for myself — I'm too fond of it).

Wednesday morning. I'm so cold that I'd like nothing better than to live inside a hot-water-bottle — not next to it, but *inside* it. O. really is too comic for words. I expect you know that song of his about the little hand and the entrecô-ô-ô-te. If the people who say that one can die of laughing are serious, then I ought to have made my debut in the next world four days ago — I'm told that a fit of really uncontrollable laughter is equal in food-value to a fair-sized beef-steak. If that is so, then I must have eaten close on a whole ox, if not more, during our bridge game yesterday evening. It doesn't take much to send me off. How fortunate, isn't it, that I wasn't born solemn?

I turned up the enclosed photographs this morning. I'm pretty sure you won't like the big one of me. It was taken last February when I was feeling fagged out. I remember exactly what the photographer looked like. He wanted me to set off my neck and throat — which meant opening my dress almost

83

down to the navel — and he touched up my lips, too, and studied the result of his labours in a looking-glass. I had the greatest difficulty to keep him from spoiling their natural shape. But you'll notice that he got his own back on my eyebrows. They don't look a bit like mine. What I do like, though, is the effect of light on the ear, and the hairs of my moustache, each one of which can be counted separately. The shiny-faced child teasing the dog is me, too — but that is a rather older picture. My own opinion is that I look a perfect pet — I adore children with damp faces, especially when they've caught the sun. The other one's also me. It was a very hot day, and I was feeling happy. The last of them is of Saint-Georges, taken from my favourite spot — the cliff-top at the far end of the beach. The smell of resin there is enough to make your head swim. At night one can see all the lights strung out along the shore, and the headlamps of cars — it's deliciously lonely, if one is by one-self, and even if one isn't — and the sea is phosphorescent. The whole place is like fairyland. You just mustn't grow old without seeing it for yourself — don't you agree? If I'm there, when that happens, and if we're still on speaking-terms, I'll take you to the exact corner shown in the photograph. Perhaps we shall be able to laugh. If so, I shall be as completely happy as I was when we laughed together three weeks ago. How about it? (What if you forgot me, Oh God!)

I am quite sure you'd like the winter mornings at Saint-Georges. Shall I describe one to you? You've no idea how vividly I remember every detail. Our house was always packed full of children, and this is what used to happen. We would all meet round the dining-table (seventeen or eighteen of us) — a long, narrow table, with places set in a row ... One would take one's empty bowl, and go along, three steps up, to the kitchen (passing on the way through a small ante-room with a white china tap and basin, where one washed one's hands before meals — the tinies had to climb on a chair). Then one put one's bowl on the red-brick, wood-burning stove, and Marie would raise her ladle — 'One of milk, one of coffee?' Then,

84

with infinite precautions, one would go back down the three steps, being careful not to stumble. In the dining-room, the chandelier would be lit — a great wooden contraption, very low hung, with swags of Toile de Jouy, and a circlet of yellow candles. It gave a wonderful light, but left the faces of those at the far end of the table in shadow. The whole room was a clutter of copper candlesticks, finger-bowls, vases, trays, fire-dogs and jug-stands — all of them glowing with a reddish colour . . . Bread would be toasting in front of the blaze in the hearth which was as tall as I am, and lined with green tiles. There was always a child sitting on the fender with a book open on its knees, dressed in a nightgown, sucking away at a piece of bread and butter, and following what it was reading with a sticky finger. I was always careful to sit down with the fire behind me, and to tilt my chair as far back as possible. Every-one would be talking at once — their eyes shining with sleep and firelight. The youngest of the company would be dragging his toy cart about under the table to an accompaniment of yawns, while the eldest, with a look of worried preoccupation, would be listening to atmospherics (on the wireless). My grandfather hearing the news was an unforgettable sight. He would sit as close as possible to the radio, and woe to anybody who so much as rustled a piece of paper, or set a marble rolling across the floor! It always ended in the same way — with a dressing down for the speaker — 'why can't the fool talk more slowly!'

All through breakfast we would watch the rain pattering down on the garden seats — which were so old that they were neither green nor brown. Across the privet-hedge we could see the street, pedestrians in rain-coats stepping over the puddles on the sidewalk, and hear the soft swish of bicycle tyres in the road. One great problem hung in the air above the heads of all of us — one urgent question which each of those present would be considering — 'What am I going to do today?' Then Agnes would get up, stretch, and say 'Right' — just that and no more, but the word held an infinity of meaning. She would go upstairs, and almost at once, from the room over-head, would come the sound of running water. 'Me first!' — 'No, me! — I spoke before you!' 'Oo, what a whopper!' etc. But Agnes would tap on the floor with a slipper — 'Antoine and Sophie — bath-time' — and, since she was the very spirit of authority, Antoine would pull up his breeches (they were always hanging about his heels), grumble out something or other, pitch his book into the fireplace, the tongs into the great cauldron, send a fine shower of water over everything, and make a dash for the stairs, leaving all the doors open behind him. For Sophie it wasn't quite so easy — *'Pease* take me up, *pease'* — and she would cling round my neck, mopping and mowing like an old half-witted dame. I would catch hold of her under the arms, and up the stairs we'd go, four steps at a time. Then, I'd throw her on to the bed — she being by this time quite red in the face from laughing so much — whisk off her nightdress, send her slippers flying, and carry her stark naked to the tub where we would find Antoine looking very dignified, and splashing away to his heart's content. It was always deliciously warm in the bathroom, and the air smelled of Eau-de-Cologne . . . The children would be all shiny and dripping, and the bath-robe would be warming on the back of a very old, very low chair in front of the fire. It would be sheer delight to wrap their bodies, all red from towelling, in the hot folds, and carry them over to the fire where their wet feet made little dark patches on the floor. Their mother, with her mouth full of pins, would be fastening the bundle which contained the most recent arrival. Through the window one could see the great leaves of the fig-tree bowing their faces beneath the lashing rain. Everything was lovely, everything was as it should be . . . There were several stunted geraniums on the balcony which no one ever remembered to bring in, and one felt that they would be in exactly the same place ten years from then. She would look up and say — 'Oh, those geraniums! — Toinon, remind me to bring them in — here's the postman!' Then I would go downstairs, and, as the room I had left dropped

86

further and further behind, I would hear the diminished sound of a voice raised in supplication — *'Pease* put my clo's on — *pease*. . . .'

That is where I stop. I am sitting thinking of what I have just written — it was all precisely as I have described — and oh, how I loved it!

I think it's going to be fine — I wish I could lay my hand on your arm so as to make you look at me. If I call to you in the night, you must come, and you must take my hand in the darkness, and console me — for what, I don't know, but that is what I want you to do. I want to hear sweet and gentle things . . . I love it when you talk to me with your mouth quite close to mine, so that I can feel your lips in the pause between your words.

Oh, Yves, I'm afraid I'm talking a lot of nonsense — but it is so long since we have spoken together of all that — of that side of life, and perhaps you have forgotten my love for you — which would be quite frightful.

And now I must say goodbye.

I part my lips just a fraction, because I want you to give me a kiss.

LISOU

Friday, 18th February

If Oscar Wilde is to be believed, I must be a highly gifted and superior young woman (he says one must be if one has learned the art of doing nothing — and I've done nothing for the last three hours but draw). . . By the by, there's something I simply must tell you, it's too good to be lost, and I think you'll agree, when you've heard it, that I must have pretty good guts if I can go on feeling for you as I do! Z. came along yesterday. 'Have you seen Y. R. since he's been kept in bed?' she asked: — 'you haven't?' — then you've missed something! He's a perfect sight! — he never was one for looks, but now it really is the limit! — he's grown a beard! — and *what* a beard! I know

87

some fellows sport fringes or little chin-tufts, but he's just smothered in hair — it really is quite frightful!' — with which she hurried away, shaking her veil, which is always proof positive that she has been convulsed to the depths of her being! As for me, I was just doubled up with laughter. She must have thought me positively callous. Oh, *please* don't shave it off until I've seen you — just once — with your appendage! I should so hate not to have had a good look at it!

I've just been seeing Dr. V. He was so encouraging that that little ghostly word 'recovery' really began to take on form and substance. I'm going to ask him for a bit of 'Paris leave' — which is about the sum-total of my desires at present. He made such a sweet little speech this morning. He certainly is quite *adorable*. The way he calls me 'child' makes me want to lick his boots. Do you like him as much as I do?

I take your left hand and lay it against my cheek. Do you still miss me sometimes? — or have you grown used to being without me? — don't answer if the answer would make me miserable — I feel frightened this evening — so naked, so vulnerable when I think that . . .

10.45. During my silent hour today I swallowed Montherlant's *Pitié pour les femmes* at a gulp — I think it's the best of his books about women. There are wonderful things in it — it made me feel very 'small-girlish'. But, Lord, how abominable the Hacquebaut creature is! — do women like that really exist? — not that she isn't intelligent — but I just can't understand — it's as though she were — I don't know how to put it — slightly decayed, rotten — do you agree? That sort of book leaves me with a curious impression — *Le Cheval blanc* — and the rest. All the women have lovers, all the men change their women every week. They speak about them in so detached a way . . . The women find men to keep them here, there and everywhere, and no one seems to think it at all out of the ordinary. Is that what really goes on? I have a horrible feeling that if I made it generally known that I'd never slept with a man — I should be a laughing-stock — it's enough to make one tear one's hair out by the handful, in a mood of sheer, miserable frustration. If that is how things are, then what am I making all this fuss about? — I might just as well tumble into bed with Monsieur Antonin, or Bo. — and that would be that . . . All the same, I feel slightly sick, and find myself wondering whether I haven't been deceiving myself all this time, whether it isn't 'they' who've been right. But if that is so, then most of my fine notions come tumbling down, my easy, pleasant illusions. It's a queer world, and I feel depressed.

I won't bore you any longer tonight — all I wanted to tell you was that I feel adrift — I don't know where the truth lies — and everything is hideously difficult.

When I stand back and take a good look at the attitude I've been adopting towards you, it seems to me that I have been behaving like a child. You have been marvellous all along, because you've never let me feel humiliated (I think that if you *had*, I could have found it in my heart to hate you — so, if that's what you want me to do, you know how to set about making me — it would be the only possible way). But, you see, a child doesn't know anything about humility — that's one of the reasons I am fond of children — they're so proud.

Dear heart, it is very late — almost midnight, and your little girl is beginning to feel sleepy all over. She would like to put her head under the bedclothes for warmth — she would like you to want to kiss her hot little tummy, and then move your lips upwards towards her mouth. She would like your body to be pressed to hers, and to fall asleep with your lips against her open palm — she wishes you a good night.

Lisou

Saturday, 26th February: 6 o'clock

The little girl has had just about enough of your rough treatment, and that is why she hasn't written. Yesterday evening I set myself a small task — namely to review all the beastly things you've said to me — and I can assure you that I found quite a good many. You're twice as proud as I am — I should so like to be beastly to *you*, but the trouble is I don't know how to set about it. So far as I can make out nothing that concerns me seems to have the slightest effect on you. You really are the oddest creature — I've quite given up trying to understand you, so I shall say no more. Should the day ever come when you decide to be rather kinder, and less mocking, when you condescend to come down a step or two, instead of forcing me up to the level of your own high horse — well, you know how happy that would make me.

It's all the nastier of you because you know so well how my mind works. Your attitude has shown me what an extraordinary diplomatic game you have been playing. I am *not* a child who has got to be handled with kid gloves — I hate being handled with kid gloves.

I may stamp and fume, but the fact is you have hurt me — and that is no light matter. I only wish I could let myself go to the devil, and turn into somebody quite different.

Do you like that book of S. Lewis's? Don't you think there's a good deal of bitter truth in it? There must be so many lives like that — full of possibilities but never amounting to anything. I think there is a good deal in what he says about there being a moment in the lives of all of us when we are offered the choice between two possible roads — or three, and how one chooses, only, later on, to realize what an appalling mistake one has made. In *L'Affair Mauritzius* Jakob Wassermann says that when one is old one can always spot the exact moment when one took the wrong turning. Don't you think that's rather awful? The very idea makes me tremble all over.

Yves, would you really mind if you didn't hear from me for a long time?

Do you know that I shall be able to make my trip to Paris in March? The prospect brings me even greater happiness than I thought it would. If only I could forget all about you for ten days — and let myself go a bit. I'm expecting a lot from this 'leave' of mine — probably too much — I always do expect too much from everything and everyone.

Why is it so long since you last wrote to me? If *I* were thirty I don't think I should be capable of so much refined cruelty. It is pretty obvious that I can't put myself in your place. I have a feeling that when you read this you won't even feel amused — or not much — but just look at your nails in that detached way which is enough to set me swearing and grinding my teeth for fifteen minutes on end — Well, you can go hang — so there!

You can go hang

LISOU

P.S. I saw a little cloud this morning, such a whorled and complicated little fellow, as pink as a bird of the East — the whole effect quite Japanese-y . . . The sole purpose of his being there was, I am sure, that we might get a deeper sense of the purity of everything — and then there were a whole lot more wanting to play copycat. The sky was full of them — more than I could count — but only for a moment — and then everything became overcast (if you try hard enough, I am sure you'll find a moral in my tale).

I gargled this evening for, I think, probably the first time in my life — it sounded exactly like the Rimsky-Korsakov running-bass — you'd have loved it, especially the end, where the bass stops — it all came back down my nose!

Sunday evening, 27th February

Please, please don't send that letter you've written, I just couldn't bear to read it. I am not suffering, really I am not.

You needn't have any fears on that score.

But why are all the people round me buzzing like flies? They are hinting at something. It is obvious they know things that I don't. They keep on talking of you and of me — as though I were a little goose who doesn't know her own mind.

91

Haven't you noticed it? I feel exactly as though I were in a room with a lot of elderly relations who are in the know, and are doing their best to make the child of the family (rather a little silly) understand something she has made up her mind not to see. Have you roped them all in for the specific purpose of getting them to help you put through your squalid little plan? If so they are doing marvellously. No doubt it was about time that I opened my ears. I am not angry. What I am feeling is something quite different from anger — and much more personal.

But since I am making my last appearance, let me confess humbly — simple-mindedly — idiotically — that I really did think you loved me. People of my age, and with my sort of temperament, do get the most impossible ideas — fortunately, you knew that!

Please forgive me for everything — I was on the wrong tack altogether. I can't have shown much intelligence — just a silly, uncomplicated little goose — and I must have bored you terribly. Be honest, and admit that I gave you a good laugh — didn't I, now?

Would you like me to return your letters? I'm not being dramatic — it's only that I want you to feel that you are quite free.

Good night — keep a high heart — and good luck for the future.

LISOU

Tuesday evening, 29th February

I just can't understand how it was that I didn't explain everything in my last letter. If there is anyone who has the right to expect the whole truth from me, surely it is you — even if telling the truth makes me suffer abominably.

In the first place, I hated the feeling that you were so far away — so little with me — though that is inevitable. Then, all around me, I heard people quoting horrible things that you had said. Honestly, I felt, each time one of the men made a remark, that it came straight from you (they were too apt to have been made by anybody who didn't know me pretty well) — and it hurt. But the worst of all, Yves, was when I found out that all these horrible things had a definite purpose — which was to detach me from you. When I was told that, I thought, well, I can't tell you all I thought and felt. I was completely bowled over. I went back in my own mind over the whole story — my sincerities, your detachment — and everything so carefully wrapped up in a few marvellous moments so that I should swallow the bitter pill more easily. I suddenly realized the full extent of my idiocy — there's no other word for it. The only thing I still don't understand is the way you went to work — it must have given you some bad moments, and it was such a long-range method (do you really think you can stall somebody off merely by saying bitter and spiteful things to her at regular intervals? I may be only twenty, but I know it's not possible). The only result has been that I am horrified at the spectacle of myself. *You* have come out of the whole affair as white as ermine — whereas I have been simply appalling — it's really almost funny. I find it odd, too, that you should seem so surprised. After all, you must know what you have said, and it's no part of my job to tell you. Do you understand what I mean? Were you really afraid that I might get my claws in you, or drag you off to the Registry Office by sheer force? (I can't write that without laughing: the whole scene is so vivid to me.) I want to be absolutely frank with you — this may be my last chance. Your friend, Et., grabbed hold of Na. one day when I wasn't there, and asked whether I was using you as an excuse for 'externalizing' a lot of high-flown sentiments — whether I was imagining things . . . 'because', he said, 'it looks as though Elizabeth has set her heart on him — whereas he, you know, is a pretty hard-crusted old bachelor' (I can't help laughing again — please forgive me) 'and all those little snubs of his are quite intentional.' Then they went on to enumerate all my house-wifely qualities (that really makes me laugh, doesn't it you?)

93

and seemed to be upset at the idea of all you were losing by not being willing to take me as your better half — that's the one thing in the whole business that genuinely amused me — and I only hope you'll find it a little diverting, too.

The trouble, of course, is that they've none of them got anything to occupy their minds — with the result that they start match-making between people to whom no such idea had ever occurred. You may think that I have forgotten certain observations you made on the subject one evening. If that is so, then, all I can say is that it makes me very sad to think that I shouldn't have managed to drop a few hints now and again which would have shown you that I had been giving a lot of thought to what you said. But, Gosh! you must have had some pretty bad moments of panic! At the same time, I can't help but feel that I didn't really understand what it was all about, and that this second-hand tittle-tattle has been of use to me in more ways than one. I see now exactly what I have meant to you. If I thought it was more than it has turned out to be, that wasn't deliberate scheming on my part, but just that I couldn't help myself.

It was the knowledge I came by of the odd, cruel means you had employed to get rid of me that induced me to write the letter which you say you hated so. The whole thing seemed to me then, and seems to me still, nothing short of vile. I thought I deserved better than to be treated in so shabby a fashion. I realize that you found me a not altogether unattractive person to study, to talk with, to look at. I'll go further and say that, in your heart, I think you have a genuine feeling of tenderness for me, though why, I don't know. But that is as far as it went. There were too many inconveniences for you in the relationship.

I am now quite convinced that you prevailed on the doctors to keep you in bed for the simple reason that you were afraid I might get you tangled up in the intricate web of my emotions. It is because I gave you occasion to think such a thing that I blame myself. I try hard to put myself in your shoes, giving you credit for a certain goodness of heart and clear-headedness, and when I do that, I feel that I, too, in similar circumstances, might well have been frightened. Still, I did do my best to tell you, more than once, that I fully intended to get married as soon as I had been discharged as cured — and that ought to have laid your fears to rest. Perhaps I expressed myself badly — or perhaps you were thinking of something else, and didn't take it in. I am just as determined as I ever was to get married as soon as possible — the day I have a child I shall leave off loving you.

I am amazed to find that I have written the whole of this long letter in an almost . . . frivolous . . . vein. I don't know what has come over me today. I'm probably suffering from reaction. However that may be, I hope you understand now that things can never again be with us as they once were. That, I should like to think, will make everything easier for you. I want you to feel that we can still be friends, 'pals'. I am more than ready to try to make a go of it on those lines. In spite of all that has been thrown in my teeth, I still think that I possess the rare qualities necessary in friendship. I could be a good friend — the kind you could slap on the back, and address as 'dear old thing'. It'd at least spare me the necessity of putting up with all your carefully planned and calculated digs. That was an abominable system, and I am only thankful that my eyes have been opened. I see you now, and think of everything that has happened, in a totally different light — an extremely melancholy one, as you must very well know. But I am trying to keep my flag flying.

LISOU

I meant to say that no doubt you share my indignation at all the gossip that has been going round. It has been very unpleasant for both of us. All I would point out is that it is you who have been responsible — not I. Speaking for myself, I would very much rather that nobody should have had any part in our affairs, and it is pretty depressing to find that the majority of mankind has the kitchen-maid outlook. Na. kept

95

it all to herself for ten days — and when, at last, she did speak it was only because she saw that I was being made miserable by your failure to write, and by your generosity in the matter of pleasantries at second-hand. She was quite right to do so. Et. irritates me beyond measure — do you really like him? — he is so utterly without subtlety — I've got hold of some modelling clay — lovely stuff to play about with. I started yesterday, and my bed's full of it — and every door-knob within range is sticky. It's all very grubby and delicious.

Quite the little Bohemian, aren't I?

L. . . .

LETTER TO JACQUES G. . . .

Tuesday, 29th February

You will never know just *how* welcome your letter was. It came just when I most needed it. It is marvellous coincidences like that which make one believe in some sort of a God . . . Someone came into my room, someone put the envelope down between my ink-pot and my glass of water — and, instead of spending the rest of the morning biting my nails, I had your budget of news to read. What do I think of it all? I think that my mood is still too much one of revolt to make it possible for me to deliver a sound, sensible judgment. I read what you wrote with pleasure, because I let myself forget who had written it. But no sooner had I folded the page than I conjured up a complete picture of you in my mind, and was at once overwhelmed by a wave of anger and prejudice. It will be a good ten days before the ebb sets in. In any case, I prefer your other literary manner — it seems to sit more easily on you. I feel that the story of Petrus might have been by anybody with a bit of talent, whereas the other is much more personal — frighteningly so. I like the way you describe the bird contracting its claw in the hollow of its hand — one can feel it — and I am at once reminded of the little kitten I left behind at home when I came here — he was only eight days old, and I went to say goodbye to him in the linen-cupboard where he had made his home. On his stomach there was a little bit of rough cord which rasped my hand — I shall never forget it. One gets such a vivid picture of you — I do, at least, because I can visualize you very clearly — in the way you speak of the man who was always messing about with girls — the rather crude, but direct and healthy, words you use (I'm talking now, of course, only of your literary self). I do so understand your admiration of Céline — in spite of myself, I'm always confusing the two of you. If Céline isn't a thin man in a bright-coloured jumper, with a high forehead and a damnably mocking crease at the corner of his mouth — then, he's no true brother of yours. Do you think it absolutely essential that we should go on for ever girding at one another? It seems to me, in all modesty, that I have had my full share. You have had a good spring-cleaning, and now that I have been wiped, washed, husked, turned over, filleted, flattened, cooled off and cut into little bits by you, I think I deserve the olive branch. It would be nice of you to bury the hatchet and to forget where you had hidden it — I have had more than enough of being perpetually on the defensive — it gets on one's nerves in the long run. You have no idea how hard you rapped me over the knuckles. I swallowed my tears, just like a small boy, full of juvenile pride, who's been hauled up in front of the headmaster. Heavens! how mortified I should have been if you had noticed it! — I blush even now at the mere thought of such a possibility. Please don't think that this handwriting is common form with me — I'm lying in bed. I can do a great deal better, really — but the general effect is very young — don't you think? — a sort of round, childish hand which brings to the eye a picture of rosy cheeks and pouting lips bending over the paper?

I won't conceal the fact that my having retained your interest is a matter of some pride to me, even though all you really care about are my blunders. I am sure that a friendship built on such complete frankness cannot but be very true and very pure. I sometimes wonder whether I am not wholly lacking in the critical sense. I make such a poor showing when it comes to saying nasty things to people. I'd love to get my own back on you, but somehow I don't seem able to. I am terribly vulnerable, whereas you aren't at all. Is it that you are always, in the long run, disappointed in people, whether friends or strangers? I certainly am — I have just experienced a massive disappointment, and I don't think I shall ever quite get over what it has done to me — I had built for myself such a wonderful treasure-house, and, pouf! over it goes in ruins. So, you see, I am feeling a bit shaken, and everything tastes of dust and ashes. It wasn't an ordinary disappointment — a gesture, a word, one had been expecting which didn't come — but the revelation of what some-one else was thinking, a calculated brutality which just killed everything in a twinkling — an entirely unexpected blow which came down bang on my head.

I expect I'm boring you. The best way of judging one's own troubles, I think, is to make a little pile of them, and then to stand back and try to see them with another person's eyes — like a connoisseur of pictures. If one can do that, one can probably laugh. But so high a degree of detachment is beyond me — for the time being, at least. It's probably the fault of the weather — there's something ominous about it ... Am I completely lacking in feeling? D'you know, the thought of the young girl lying dead in the next room wholly fails to move me. Last night, before going to sleep, I tried to make myself wretched by thinking of her — but it was no use. I imagined her lying there, fully conscious, aware of all that she was about to leave — then dead — with the little procession moving round her bed — her hands, her hair (it seems so odd that a corpse should have hair like everyone else, vigorous with life, smelling of human warmth, not rigid at all) — and my heart didn't so much as miss a beat ... But if I think about myself ... I make a mountain out of a molehill which I shall probably have forgotten in next to no time ... doesn't all that show what a perfectly horrible person I am?

I love life so intensely — how intensely you will never know. Others can die all round me — it doesn't matter to me so long as *I'm* alive, and if, one of these days, you hear that I am dead, you can say to yourself that you have never known anyone who would so have hated having to throw up the sponge.

Good luck with the treatment.

Your affectionate little bourgeoise

ELIZABETH

Thursday, 2nd March: 11.30

Oh, I wish so much, Yves, that I could believe you — but something in me has been killed, and I have a horrible fear that it may be for ever. I shall never forget how awful it is to hear people talking of what they know nothing about. Personally, I have never mixed myself up in things that didn't concern me — and that, I think, is a good rule.

Why are you being so sweet, Yves? You know that a few words would bring me back — every scrap of me — but please, please, don't take advantage of that knowledge. Where you are concerned I have no more will-power than a log of wood. I have given you a wonderful excuse for getting rid of me, and you don't seem to want to use it . . . I am not at all sure that you are acting wisely.

I can't see you tomorrow. I've been in bed since Monday with a wretched attack of 'flu which has flattened me out and sent my temperature up for I don't know how long. I'm afraid it may be a tedious business, because I feel so dreadfully tired — I'm not used to it, and it frightens me. I'll write you a long letter this evening — perhaps. I had to let you know about tomorrow being impossible. Et. will be terribly annoyed with me, but I don't care. You had to know.

All this doesn't alter the fact that I feel completely adrift. Wait till you get my long letter. I'm still feeling rather sad, though I couldn't tell you why if you asked me — probably because I'm missing a chance of seeing you tomorrow. I feel as though I had been hit on the head with a hammer, and am only very slowly coming back to consciousness — be patient with me.

There's a bird outside eating the crumbs I put on the window-sill. I'm feeling a tiny bit happy, a tiny bit sad — Oh, I don't know — I don't know anything. I should like to rest my head on your shoulder and forget.

LISOU

Thursday, 2nd March: 5 p.m.

I expect you've seen how sea-anemones, when they've been hurt or touched, close up completely and wait until the danger's past. That's how I'm feeling now. I'm still closed up, and I am writing to you from the deep privacies of my retreat. So, you see, you can't hurt me. Besides, I have become a terribly mistrustful anemone, always on the defensive, even with you — which is a pity — because I'd so much rather float on the water with all my antennae out — but that was a dream, and the trouble with dreams is that sooner or later one wakes up. You must know perfectly well the image I had constructed of you — something so idealized that it must have caused you consider-able embarrassment. You must realize, too, what a frightful shock it was for me to discover that you were capable of coldly calculating your actions and of watching their effect — I'm afraid it will be a long time before I get over that disillusion-ment. There's nothing you can do. Just at the moment I feel all stiff, unnatural and shy. I don't seem any longer able to believe that I am I or that you are you — that's why I am so upset at not being able to see you tomorrow.

This morning, when I had read your long letter, I played with the thought of laying my head on your shoulder, just for a minute — of shutting my eyes, and forgetting all but the moment's feeling — it's so lovely to be like that. But now I have pulled myself together. You see, I'm so terribly frightened, and feel safe only when I am alone in a corner with Nicolas and my music. At those times no one has a right to break in upon my privacy. You used to share it with me once, but not now any longer. I don't want it to be like that, but I can't change facts. Loneliness brings peace. One puts on a necessary act with persons one's got to see, and then, when that's over, sinks back into the two square yards of one's bed, draws one's knees up, and looks out of the window. Time passes. Almost before one notices it today has become tomorrow. I know the mountain opposite by heart. I have stared at it so hard that my eyes ache. I have reached the point now at which I can think of you without pain. Wouldn't you rather that we were just friends? I've been rapped so hard over the knuckles, that I am terrified of any relation that's more than friendship — with anyone.

You're quite right: some of the stories going round about us are really like comic turns! I must confess I couldn't help laughing at the picture of those two conspirators mounting us for exhibition purposes — each on a separate pin — me the Angel in the House in excelsis — the home-maker of a man's dreams (Heaven knows, the poor wretch who falls into my clutches is going to get an eye-opener!). It certainly is excruciating, the ideas people get about one. I should never have believed it possible that I could be cried up as a housewife — I, who can't even boil a potato! And what they say about you is even funnier still — but I'd better not say what I think about that, for fear you might take it badly. We may as well confess that, matters of deep seriousness apart, we should never get on together. I could put up with you for, I suppose, at most ten days, and you with me for eight — and that's straining the truth a bit. Before closing this light-comedy interlude, let us have one good laugh at ourselves — it's worth the effort.

8 p.m. I have just had a long visit from Dr. I. who's been telling me about the lying-in she had to attend last night in the village. It seems to have been quite awful. I used to think that everything to do with childbirth was lovely and miraculous — and I couldn't help feeling slightly disgusted by her description.

According to her, the baby took a long time in coming. I can just imagine the woman, the boiling water, the blazing fire, and then, the long, long wait — all in the middle of the night — and I. swaddling the child (it was a girl) — doing it up in a bundle with her mouth full of pins — and N. almost asleep where he stood — *what* a marvellous sight those two must have been at such a moment!

Friday morning. I oughtn't to be writing this letter at all except as a bare acknowledgment of yours. But I always seem to go off at a tangent — it's a positive disease with me.

You ask why, from beginning to end of my letter, I insist on attributing the blackest of intentions to you. Oh, Yves, do just try to put yourself in my place! To hear suddenly what I heard would be enough to sour a saint. When I got back that evening from my talk with O. and J. G. my nerves were all on edge. I had spent the whole afternoon trying not to cry — and then, out of the blue — that blow with a pole-axe! I flung myself on my bed sobbing like a perfect little fool. I couldn't stop. I simply had to take it out of somebody for having been such a little idiot — so I put you through a sieve — and kept only the worst parts.

If I had the necessary materials I'd make myself a fur-lined hood covering my face, and come along in the dark to frighten you. I should make a pretty comic ghost! I can just see D.'s face when I landed on your window-sill, rattling my chains and emitting mournful groans! I would twist your toes until you had a fit — and next morning you would write me a dignified letter about the noise of the rain and the moaning of the wind — and I should think it all great fun. I just can't be serious. Don't you think there's a rather mad look in my eyes? This letter rings false all through — I know that only too well.

It is just a little exercise in self-control — no more.

Why all this insistence, you ask, on seeing you clearly and seeing you whole? It was essential that I should so see you — everything depends on that: it is the basis of my whole belief. Any failure to do so, a moment's weakness, and I should have been lost irretrievably. Well, I found what I was looking for. Whether I did or did not like what I found is another story.

If you were to take my face in your hands and look into my eyes, you might perhaps find in them something rather baffling — something you have never seen in them before.

Goodbye for the present, dear, grumpy bachelor.

LISOU

LETTER TO JACQUES G....

Saturday, 4th March

A thousand thanks for your letter — it was a lovely one, though not exactly what I should call encouraging. It may be true that I see life as complicated (and, after all, isn't it?). I've never noticed that you see it as simple. We both have our own way of looking at what's in front of our noses — why should mine be the wrong one? Because it will bring me suffering? — well, I'm not afraid of that, and, as you say, I've made a beginning. What's so awful is, that instead of accepting the fact of suffering, and hugging it to my heart, I'm always trying to fight against it — somehow I can never believe that it's going to get me down, and yet. . . .

I find myself wondering whether you think as you do because you have known a great deal of suffering, or because you want to avoid it. Speaking for myself, I ran to meet life with a great load of illusions on my back — and now they have started dropping off, one after the other. But I hate going back on my tracks — so I shut my eyes, ostrich-fashion. I know it's a bit cowardly, but I do so detest having to suffer. Don't laugh — there are people, you know, who like it — like suffering, I mean, who cultivate it and make a display of it. I'm just the reverse — when I am happy I cry it aloud from the house-tops — which usually annoys others profoundly. Anyhow, I've not got the right sort of face for suffering, have I? It is very rarely that people take my troubles seriously — so I keep them to myself, which is safer, to say nothing of the fact that I dislike having them handled. I am not at all happy just now, but nobody would believe it if I said so. Oh, well, I shall get over it, shan't I? I am too superficial to be unhappy for long. . . .

But I swear I'm not really superficial. I wish I could prove that instead of just saying it, but how can I? I am the most appallingly clumsy person — for ever breaking what I most love — and then looking at the pieces with one finger stuck in my mouth — but never crying. That is why people think me insensitive. I've never learned how to cry properly, and I do think that crying makes a woman look so hideous. I don't like women. If I do cry sometimes, as I did on Sunday night, and bite my pillow, I feel so terribly ashamed of myself afterwards . . . The fact is, I suppose, that sort of thing ought to be done in secret. At the present moment I am feeling quite unbelievably alone — and that is what I love beyond anything. There's just me — and a sort of collective self which I trail about everywhere, consisting of a tea-pot, an ash-tray, a table-cloth, and so on — not only because I may want to use them, but because they provide me with safe and silent company. I love the feeling of calm which they produce when things out-side myself are going wrong. I do truly believe that if I hadn't always with me a certain number of very personal belongings, I should be the most unhappy person in all the world. Why should you blame me for contemplating my navel? It doesn't hurt anybody — and you've no idea what an attractive navel it is!!!

So, you think I'm not very 'bright'? — if the word weren't so comic, I should feel thoroughly vexed. As a matter of fact, I'm inclined to agree with you, that's to say if you call 'bright' the kind of person who can't say three words without swearing, who is never brought up short by anything or anybody, who always has the clinching argument at her tongue's tip just when she needs it. No, if that is being 'bright', then I'm not bright at all — far from it. I'm terribly awkward. Fortunately, I have got my pride to sustain me. Awkwardness and pride —

when things get difficult, they're always both of them in evidence — a proper pair of Siamese twins.

Monday morning. I awoke to the sound of wings, and saw some birds busy with the crumbs I had put on my window-sill (you see, 'beastifying' is another of my habits — really my mother's milk is scarcely dry on my lips!) — it was delicious. Oh, Grandpa, you really are a sport — that's the only word for it! — though I do owe being deprived of the cinema 'until I'm up and about again' to you. Punishments of that kind help enormously to make me feel like a child. Don't you think it comic that I should have to wait until I'm twenty to be forbidden something? Apart from that, there's nothing I can say — you see, I'm out of practice. Z. came in sniffing — but I looked the picture of innocence. She crossed the room and took up a position at the end of the bed, flapping her veil — a very bad sign — but why *shouldn't* people be allowed to smoke in bed? — I told her I wanted to — that was all I could find by way of excuse — she bores me and makes me thoroughly depressed. Do you know, she actually lectured me about my habit of going out into the corridor in my nightgown — because there are men who might see me! You should hear the way she says 'men'! — I really do hate her. I was well on the way to being sweet and charming this morning — and now she's spoiled it all.

There's something I want to say to you — but I'm going to get it over very quickly, because it is something I don't like talking about. I don't want you to think that I hold you responsible for all the things people are saying about me and him. I should be terribly upset to know that your dirty cracks came in part from him. All the same, I quite sincerely think that you did right to pass them on. Well, that's that, and I don't want ever to talk about it again. I've had more than enough of the subject.

My hand is positively frozen. As soon as it is capable of performing its functions, I'll write to you about Gide — it gives me the greatest pleasure to tell you that I spit in his face!

— Oh, Heavens! if only my hand would get going again — I shall work myself into a fever if I have to leave the subject like that, high and dry!

5 o'clock. Gide? . . . he's just foul, that's the long and the short of it: a writer of genius, but foul. There's not one of his books that I can read without feeling as though the pages were sticking to my fingers. Everything he writes has something slimy about it, something dubious, unpleasant, morbid — and the wonderful way in which he handles the French language makes it all the worse. The smoothness with which he talks about horrors really makes my hair stand on end! — and that trick he has of mixing them up with a sort of religiosity. He's unhealthy through and through. I just can't like anybody who shocks something in me which is beyond definition — instinct, I suppose. I have a feeling when I'm reading him that he is writing about, and describing, emotions and actions that are disgusting — even when I don't understand what it's all about. Take *L'Immoraliste,* for instance. He picks up spittle with a twig and revels in describing it . . . If the book had been my own property I would have flung it out of the window . . . And then, too — he uses his style like a bait — makes you swallow everything with a few fine phrases which satisfy one aesthetically. I am quite sure that he knows he's foul. Now, don't start tearing my eyes out for saying that — I'm perfectly willing to listen to anything you may have to say in his defence, but you'll never alter the fact that he makes me feel sick in a way I just can't explain. It's quite beyond my understanding that anyone should like Gide and Céline at one and the same time. If I had to mention somebody at the very opposite pole to Céline — it would be Gide (or Bernardin de Saint-Pierre). The one is as healthy and balanced all through as the other is disgusting. Personally, I wouldn't touch Gide with a barge-pole. I can't really explain — it's a matter of feeling. I've not read *Les Nourritures Terrestres* — I should be glad if you would lend it to me. As to Nietzsche, I've never read a word he wrote, but should like to. . . .

Have you read any Aldous Huxley? I am sure that if you have, you like him, and that if you haven't, you would. Do you honestly think it's a bad thing to read a lot? I don't know what would become of me without books. I've got heaps of ideas, you see, about these matters, but they're blown about by all the winds of heaven, and I don't seem able to shape them into a neat and harmonious whole. That I can't do so is sheer agony. It's the same thing when I try to write — I long to write — I *need* to — but I don't know what to say nor how to say it. It's like banging one's head against the walls of a room until one wants to scream. Do *you* know that feeling of impotence which leaves one completely helpless? When it comes over me I'm just like a bundle of rags. I'm frightened — terribly frightened — of achieving nothing beautiful or worth while; of dying before I can produce — like so many others — of being forgotten, as so many others have been — and I don't, oh, I don't, want that to happen. I know only too well that most of what I write is a desperate effort to express my obsessions. I spend hours, like the little girl I really am, staring at the window and churning the most fantastic ideas over and over . . . I am haunted by the thought of all that is irrevocable in any life. I want so much to *make* my life, and not just accept it ready-made — but I'm afraid of taking the wrong turning. One sees so many people who might have been happy but for one single mistake. I love life too much not to be afraid of smashing it to pieces. I do so want to be happy. The trouble is, I think, that I want it too much. Not so long ago I realized just how happy one *could* be. It all hung on so little — and so much. Now I feel stripped and bare and very poor, but not in any way an object of pity. I loathe being pitied. I am going to get married as soon as I possibly can. Then, and only then, shall I feel safe. I had never loved before all this happened — do you realize that? — and I suppose I richly deserved what eventually came about. I behaved far worse than you can possibly imagine — and it was necessary that I should suffer in order to be washed clean. I don't really know exactly where I am at the moment, but I do know exactly what I shan't have, and that knowledge is hard. I have done what you told me to do — I have looked with cold detachment — and I have seen. The wound is terribly raw and bleeding. What a true prophet you were! No one has ever spoken to me as you have done. I don't want to let things slide, as I had been doing — indeed I don't — but circumstances were too strong for me. It's so lovely to have somebody to cling to occasionally. What makes me sad is the knowledge that I gave him, in perfect sincerity, all the loveliness that one human being can give another. Oh, Grandpa! I did give every scrap of sincerity that it's in me to give. You must believe that — and now it has been returned to me, all neatly packed, with a word to the effect that I'd have done much better to keep it. What am I to do with it? — put it in a drawer, I suppose. But it's all over now. I shan't begin again. Yes, I must get married soon, before I have time to realize that everything has gone wrong. I know you laugh at me, but I'm *not* dramatizing myself, truly I'm not. Just at the moment I am utterly alone, and I find some relief in talking — that's all there is to it. I love him to distraction, and shall do, all my life. I know that now — and I don't hold it against him that he treated the whole thing lightly, and could be so detached. He's lucky . . . very lucky. Whether he realizes how serious the whole thing is I don't know.

Thank you for having listened to me so attentively and with so much kindness. I felt that you would treat what I said to you in complete confidence — was I wrong? — no, of course I wasn't. Terrible you may be, but you are not cruel when you are dealing with unhappy children. It wouldn't have been worth your while to be so nasty to me, if you weren't going to listen to my moans and groans afterwards — that's in the logic of things, isn't it?

I have got a hyacinth bulb in a jam jar, and I keep on looking to see whether the roots have sprouted. They have struck down deep into the water, and the fleshy leaves are beginning to open. Oh, how I'd love to be running barefoot in a big garden filled with a riot of flowers, my mind as empty of care as a small baby's (can't you feel the grass under your feet, and the breeze lifting the hair on your temples: can't you see the little lambs on their shaky legs with knobbly knees, and the bees buzzing under your nose — so intent on their affairs? — I'm biting my wrist in a passion of longing!). I can hear Z.'s steps in the corridor — they approach, they pass, they die away. What sort of dreams can one have with people like that near one? — people who stand with raised finger, and say 'that's forbidden!' — 'you'll be punished!' — 'you have no right!' — 'it's shocking!' Luckily, the nights are clear and almost pure. There is much consolation in a fine night — it helps one to keep one's mouth shut when one feels like complaining. I'm afraid I haven't told you how much pleasure your cigarettes gave me — all the same, I don't forgive you for calling me a little bourgeoise *de luxe*.

The gentleman on the radio has just said — 'After Bamboulla you will hear *Frisson de Vénus*' ... I had to put my fountain-pen between my teeth, and push away anything likely to be knocked over, so that I could laugh in perfect safety ... and his voice, Grandpa ... the way in which he said it! ...

Did you know there is a species of rose called *Cuisse de Nymphe émue*? — isn't that delicious? I imagine it as being faint salmon-pink veined with red, and so smooth that one could go on one's knees to it ... Ah, there's the news ... 500 killed in an Italian railway accident — in a tunnel — what a shindy there must have been! How do you react to things like that? — 'Young people today have no sense of pity' — sighs Na., raising eyes and elbows. I don't much care for Italians — except when they're at their coo-ing — men with women's voices and women with angels' — all in a very high register — singing Rossini and pelting each other with flowers — that's how *I* think of Italians ... Just off to have a smoke in the smoking room, because it's forbidden, isn't it? I wish I could pay tribute to your virtues in a string of rare words — but, having none, I raise my baby's bottle, and drink to your prosperity.

No one there — so I sat with my head on my knees, and

chewed on misery — like the sort of person who is in love with suffering. Come on, give me a good rap over the knuckles with a stick, like one of those vicious types you've told me of. I don't any longer know *where* I am — this letter is like a closed circle — if I go on with it I shall never break out — and it'll just get tighter and tighter.

If my eyes were blindfolded, and *he* was in a crowd, I could recognize his face by feel — each feature of it. That's how it is, you see. I should like to pass my long, cold fingers over his mouth and trace the exact shape of his lips — slowly — and then, afterwards, just stay there. So many things have not been done, have not been said. It's frightful what a hold all this has got on me.

I long for a forest — a brooding, mysterious forest of tall trees — where I could lose myself and read Baudelaire. There would be squirrels on the lower branches, watching me, and nibbling the nails of their tiny paws — and I should pursue my way — sovereign and indifferent — the book open in my hands. No unfinished memories like that Symphony which lacks the last movement — the allegro. I am the Fairy Sincerity come down to earth to see for herself how little respected she is . . . I have no love now for anyone but children, dear little children with their sacred medals, and their boring questions, and their pitiless frankness. Have you never seen me pass at dawn in my voluminous sky-blue gown? If you haven't, that's because you don't know how to look. Who *has* seen me, if it comes to that? — nobody, absolutely nobody. But here I am wandering off again, so good night.

ELIZABETH

How is he?

P.S. I enjoyed Gide's *Caves du Vatican* very much. It is screamingly funny, but not at all typical of Gide. Far from it.

Diary

There are so many things, needless to say, which can't, or oughtn't to, be put into words. I am reduced to wondering what conceivable purpose my letters can serve — those hours and hours spent in fruitless efforts to translate my feelings into speech.

What's the use? — there is no sadder question than that, none so idiotically sad — and yet, I often ask it — terribly often.

I won't, I won't, I mustn't.

Lisou, Lisou, my sweet, my foolish child, my darling — Lisou, look at me. It's not *true*, can't you understand that? — it's not *true*. Everybody has been lying — I have been lying, and so have you. Only look at me — what is it, my pet? . . . I bury my face deep, deep in the familiar smell of his shoulder. Everyone has been lying — I most of all, who said nothing.

Friday, 17th March

I saw him yesterday, in the evening. I felt as though I were drowning in a nightmare. Probably because I have been trying so hard to hide my feelings.

How is it possible that everything between us should be so impersonal? I strive desperately to remember — to analyse — all I felt — the way he shook hands — the way he looked at me — and I can't. Already, everything has just drifted away like smoke. I long for some memory of that moment to cling to, but it is as useless as clutching at the empty air. He seemed to be thinking of nothing at all.

I, too, want just one tiny miracle — only one. I am terrified when I think of what I am losing.

9 o'clock. So many wonderful things in *Les Nourritures Terrestres* — I am thoroughly soaked in it. In a vague sort of way I am frightened of Gide, and of what I shall find myself thinking when I shut the book.

Only the truth seems to me to be pure — and today it is so painful for me to speak it — odd.

J. G. frightens me a bit — he's a kind of a devil — I want to protect myself from him, but I am weaponless. It's enough to make one dance with rage. All the same, there are moments when he is almost kind to me.

Na. saying — 'Just at the moment life's not worth a brass farthing . . . ' I feel like that, too, this evening: it certainly isn't worth much.

I'm sorry I went yesterday evening — terribly sorry — I am so afraid he won't understand why I did. It was simply because I love him, to prove to him that to be loved by me isn't so intolerable after all, and that if I said too much in the past, I have learned now how not to say anything.

Paris is looming at the end of the month. I am wondering what I shall do when I get there.

No, I'm not really wondering at all. Things have a wonderful way of just happening, of unrolling of their own accord. I only really want to let myself float with the current.

I should dearly love to know why, for what purpose, God lets creatures like me indulge in dreams — why He spreads out before their eyes all the splendours they will never enjoy, why He allows them to wait in hope, and then removes everything out of their reach.

Perhaps He doesn't know what waiting is like.

I'm dropping with sleep. I've washed my hair. It looks awful, but feels lovely — just like the hair of a very young child.

Last night my bed was drenched in moonlight. It woke me up.

I was dreaming of the sea-shore, and the beauty of all that radiance was almost beyond bearing. I *knew* that my mouth must be showing as a black patch on my white face, and I thought of the evenings when we used to look at the mountains and say nothing, and of how I lost my combs in the snow —

with the trees thin and leafless, their branches making a delicate patterning, and time slipping by unnoticed.

'The worst kind of sickness is wishing for what one has not got' (A. Gide: *Les Nourritures Terrestres*).

That is the kind of sickness I am suffering from.

Sunday, 19th March

I believe that I am on the fringe of something exquisite, that I am skirting the marvellous. I have pulled the curtain aside, and I have seen. But as yet I have not entered in. Now is the moment of waiting, as children wait when they have been led up to the Christmas tree, as animals wait in the presence of danger. I dread the moment when either I must be penetrated and filled by what is there, or must turn tail and run away.

I must not forget his voice, nor the first time that his lips met mine. I was, as it were, struck with panic: never had my mouth dared dream of so much happiness. I feel for him an ardour of despairing gratitude, an ardour that no words of mine can ever express, but with it, too, despair that I cannot explain. Now, and only now, I am afraid to suffer.

Letters

I am so really happy deep down, that I just don't know what to say — it's all so recent, all so close to me still. Oh, Yves, I love you — I hated having to part from you just now, but I hug the thought that I can tear that last letter of yours into tiny, neat pieces. You will never know how terribly it hurt me. I read it one morning, early — it wasn't yet nine, I think — and the fingers in which I held it were trembling slightly. I opened it without hesitation because I knew what it contained — it had come too quickly for me to have any illusions — but I would rather not talk about it. I think they are playing the Ninth Symphony — are you listening? — yes, it is, I can recognize the magnificent Andante — please love it. Oh, Yves, how royally I have been rewarded for my suffering — and I wasn't counting on it — honestly, I wasn't. I felt so sure that complete indifference was to be the rule between us. I think that now I can live wholly out of the world. I am so happy that I want to bite you — Yves — my best beloved.

Do you know this of Gide's? — 'In all the azure only enough of white to make a veil, of green, to cast a shadow on the water' — isn't that superb?

If you have never seen anyone in a state of complete drunkenness, look at me. All I can do is to lie quietly in your arms, not moving at all, like a little girl who has been terribly hurt and very frightened. Don't make me speak. You have known for a long while all I have to tell you. You knew, too, that the slightest gesture would suffice to bring me back. Tell me you knew it. If you could see me now, you would laugh — my cup is too full — I want to think and not to write — that is the truth, I have no wish to write to you, but never have I so wished to be pressed close to you, and to hear you say that you are happy because of me.

I am quite alone — four girls are playing bridge on the other bed. I find them a dismal-looking lot.

Do you realize how icy-cold you used to be, even in your letters? I feel that I shall snivel all night long out of sheer happiness. Good night, Yves. You are too far away. I stretch my open hand to you over all that intervenes — people, snow, trees. Everything is quite unbelievably delicious.

Monday morning. Only, I think, if one is very simple can one confess one's happiness. You were simple yesterday, which was why I did not know what to say — because I had never known you like that — it was divine. Whatever happens, don't change. All night long I heard the sound of falling water, as from fountains. The air was warm. Everything was so perfect, so pure, and I felt certain that when I woke I should find myself not here. I longed to be lying at your side, very calmly, very quietly, just listening while you talked. Oh, how exquisite it would be to feel your arm beneath my head, my cheek against your hand, and to hear you prove to me what an idiot you have been — I should be only too ready to be convinced.

I sit here biting my pencil, and remembering. I am trying to pull my thoughts together, and it is appallingly difficult. Yesterday was so full of marvels that I cannot recapture all of it — I remember that I nibbled your burned thumb, that I spilled ashes down your sleeve, that at one moment we were talking with our mouths so close together that one tiny movement would have made my lips touch yours.

Don't forget how simple-minded and credulous I am with you. Why is it that where you are concerned I have almost no will of my own? Yet, I had the courage to do without you, without a single scrap of you, for a whole fortnight. I deserve more credit for that, I think, than for anything else in my life. I love you, Yves — beyond all measure.

LISOU

Tuesday, 21st March

Yves, I am frightened — everything is too marvellous to last. It is idiotic to feel like that, because it means that I can never enjoy the good moments to the full, because that thought is always at the back of my mind. I have been adding up all my present happiness — and the total is quite staggering — never have I held so many marvels in my two hands.

They brought me your letter yesterday evening, about three minutes before the lights were turned off. I just had time to swallow it down at top speed, and then had to wait for the dawn before I could read it all again.

It was probably rather silly of me not to go to that lecture — there might have been just a chance of my seeing you for a moment. But I should have been so disappointed if you hadn't been there. I wonder whether the day will ever come when we shall be able to see one another whenever we want, and for as long as we want, without anybody bothering about us. Wouldn't you like to send the whole universe to blazes? — I should, with all my heart. I really don't know what to do. Whatever we plan will be equally dangerous. I suppose we've just got to get used to the idea that nobody here is free — I never thought it would fret me so badly. Do you know that we could both of us be 'expelled' if somebody happened to find us outside the building during a film-show? Don't tell me it's ridiculous — I know that well enough. Oh God, what fools people are, and how little able to understand. You *must* manage to leave your bed. So far as I know, I shall go to Paris in two weeks' time, and come back at the end of a further two weeks — and that will mean a whole month gone.

How right you were! For the last few days, everyone has been as nice as nice to me. They look rather foolish, it's true, rather as though they had lost something, but they're all of them behaving frightfully decently. I long to tell them that one soon gets used to happiness. It took me precisely three days. There were still one or two things, yesterday, that I didn't understand and couldn't take for granted: today I feel like taking for granted everything I cannot understand, and, if the truth were told, I don't really understand anything, not anything at all, of what has been going on in your mind. I remember writing in my Diary, about four days ago, after I had been reading Henri Michaux, that I, too, asked only for one small miracle — a tiny one — and, lo and behold, it has happened! I have always been told that there are certain things that one must accept without question (the multiplication of the loaves and fishes, the resurrection of the body, the wedding-feast at Cana, etc. etc.), but that has never really made any difference. I have always wanted to stick my finger in my mouth and say: 'but I *want* to understand: I can't help it, I'm made that way.' Do you think you can love anyone so intolerably conceited? Not that it helps much to be conceited — in fact, it makes me rather frightened. I am incurably, abominably young, but I love you so much that it makes up for everything else.

I simply adored *L'Eternel Retour* — I can't explain the terrific impression that film made on me. I felt that I was living with the characters in a very intense and rather exhausting way. When I came out, I felt quite flattened. Anything that is very beautiful, or, at least, anything that I love with all my heart, always has the effect of sucking me dry. What I liked best of all was the scene by the fire (there is a marvellous shot which shows the flames flickering on the ceiling — there is nothing lovelier than to lie on the ground with one's head thrown back — and I envied them!). And then that other one, when he is going up to her room, with his face raised, moving through alternate zones of moonlight and shadow — I sat there biting my nails — and her cry when he's going out of the hut — the way she called him back made me feel bruised all over — and again, when he whistles under her window, and one *feels* oneself waiting with him — I positively ached — I wanted to scream — like the kids at a 'Western' — 'she's not there — she loves you, she loves you!'

I love *you*, Yves — I want to shout it from the window — I want quite simply to tell you, and to feel I needn't fear that you may one day regret all that makes me now the most enviable child in all the world.

The end, too, was beautiful — really beautiful — I wish that *I* could die in that rather uncanny way (I am speaking of the film). No one who has loved like that is ever wholly dead — *something* remains behind — don't you believe that?

I lay my hand on your eyes — it is very cold — and all you have to do is never to open them again. If you were completely blind I should be necessary to you, and how wonderful that would be! You would see everything with my eyes. I would describe the sky to you, and pictures, and people — and then, when you least expected it, I would kiss you — very hard. Your hands *are* rather like the hands of a blind man. Your fingers have a special way of touching me — which I love.

I wonder why you love me — will you please explain? May I write 'darling', just sometimes? — though I should find it as difficult to say, when I'm with you, as to say 'Yves'. I know it's stupid — but you always make me feel most terribly shy. When you're reading my letters you don't see my embarrassment, and I don't mind so much.

Oh, how I want to be near you! That particular want always grows more intense at nightfall. It reaches its peak just as I'm dropping off to sleep. It's no use trying to fight against sleep — I don't like having to stop thinking about you, but there's nothing I can do about it. I dream of rivers, of fish, of being buried, of falling from heights, but never of you — never!

Darling, we are a couple of unhappy children who live 300 yards apart and never see one another. We're always getting caught by the Sister on duty, and everyone peeks at us in the most indecent manner. I didn't tell you that the wretched Et. had another shot, in the entr'acte, before you turned up. It was all I could do not to burst out laughing! I felt exactly as though I were with a rather fastidious abbé. I'm quite sure that without his moustache, and dressed in a soutane, he would make an ideal curé.

The thought of going to Paris rather depresses me now. If I hadn't seen you again before leaving, I don't know what sort of condition I should have been in during my absence, nor what idiocies I mightn't have committed. But I shall be thinking so hard of you that it will be almost as if you were there. I had actually played with the thought of not coming back here at all, and I think that perhaps I might not have done. The idea that I might run into you at any moment and not be able to speak to you, was too frightful. It would have needed the kind of courage in which I am completely deficient — so it would have been better for me not to be here at all.

I've not really grown used to happiness. You will have to say millions and millions of lovely things to me before I even begin to believe in it, even partially. Perhaps one day I *shall* believe in it completely — I don't know. You have no idea what it means to me to be loved by you — an elderly gentleman with a serious outlook, a cool head, and a rather daunting manner. My mind is too small to take it all in — but I am quite sure that I smile in my sleep.

My hyacinth has come out — it's white. I love you — good night — you love me a great deal. Take me in your arms — I have deserved it, truly I have — and it is what I long for above all things.

Yves — rap me over the knuckles if I ever say again that I am frightened. . . .

Wednesday. It has occurred to me that there will be tulips in the gardens of the Louvre — how I love them! It would be so marvellous if we could be there together — I hug the idea of seeing it all again with you. I feel sure it must have rained on my face last night — everything is new and glittering.

Did you know that José Torrès might be coming back? If he turns up while I am away, I shall feel quite sick.

11.30. Kiss me — over and over again.

LISOU

Tuesday, 28th March

I love you. I am brimful of passion for you and I know that I am going to lie biting my knuckles far into the night. Why aren't you here to stop me? It's terrifying how I want everything — there's nothing I can say to you that isn't . . . highly improper. My desires are a heavy load . . . I should like to be sleeping pressed close beside you, and quite naked, not only for a few hours, not even for a whole night, but for ten days at least, and ten nights, on end, without once opening my eyes, but just feeling you were there, and that everything else could go hang. I feel that it is quite wrong, abnormal, in fact, that I am not in your arms at this moment. I was depressed yesterday evening. Perhaps that was the reason, and then, when you said Sa. had written to you I felt awful. It's quite idiotic, but all of a sudden I am terrified of suffering. The tiniest thing coming from you takes on such enormous proportions. Last night I felt quite certain that one day I should be very unhappy. I worked it out and was convinced that I was the wretchedest creature in the whole world. But I've forgotten all about it now — I swear I have, and feel only that I have never been as happy as I am at this moment, both in heart and body. Nobody is as happy as I am — nobody loves you as I do — nobody so longs as I do that everything should just stop dead at this point — that time should stand still. Do you think it possible that I should ever be happier? Oh, darling, I long for your kisses, for the sound of your voice, for the feel of your hands! So long as I've not got those, I've got nothing. How do you think I can possibly put up with all the people I'm going to see again? The thought of them fills me with anticipatory horror — I shall find them so stupid and so ugly — I know I shall loathe them. I am terrified of being for so many days without you. I am trembling with impatience because I shan't see you until tomorrow, and then only for so short a time.

Wednesday evening. I want to talk — about nothing in particular, as we did yesterday evening. I was so happy this morning with your head on my shoulder and the sun in my eyes. It was divine. Never have I known moments like those. It is so hard to be without you — and it grows harder every day. I am quite sure that very soon now I shall wake one morning full of rebellious thoughts, convinced that all this isn't enough — that one hour a day with you is ridiculously insufficient. Why do you make me so happy in *that* way — so that I could do the most idiotic things? — why, Yves? I want so much time with you. I should like to spend an eternity in your arms. I should like to feel the weight of your body on me — I should like not to be able to think that perhaps that will never happen. (Have you forgotten that all this is leading to nothing? I no longer understand what you say. If you truly believe that a day will come when I shall be lying naked in your arms, don't you think that would be the most marvellous fulfilment? Afterwards, I could face anything, because I should have had all that. For me it would be such an ending as I never dared hope for. I don't know what, precisely, you are thinking, but don't tell me you'd rather not — I love you enough to do without that — as you must know perfectly well.)

How badly everything is arranged. When I think that I live with people who mean nothing at all to me, that for the last eleven months I have been sleeping in a room with somebody whom I quite like, but no more, and that I can't spend even two days with you whom I love so much — it's pretty sickening — you must admit that. Darling, you make me slightly mad. My crying need is that you should be bending over me, and that not even the thickness of our clothes should be between us. This is not at all the sort of letter a sensible little girl ought to be writing. So much the worse, then. I am a sensible little girl no longer. Speak to me — tell me things that make me catch my breath. I know how I shall be on the day when there is no longer anything between us. I shall be exactly as you would have me be, somebody more wholly yours than you have ever had in the whole course of your life. I shall dig my nails into your back, I shall twist my head from side to side as one does in nightmares. How I should love, Yves, to experience all that with you — and with nobody else, ever. Are you still sorry that I am untouched, that I am quite, quite new? I long to write you terrible things, and to do things still more terrible.

I am quite sure that there cannot be in the whole world two men so capable of awakening a young girl's desires. You are, beyond all competition, my beloved. But there is something I want to ask you which is probably wholly idiotic. I do so hope that your love for me is not *only* physical — I don't know if you see what I mean — not that it matters. I will explain it better some other time. Just now I must sleep.

Good night — I love you. It would be heavenly if we were together now. Can you really believe that I could ever do without you? — or fall asleep without wishing that you were beside me?

I should love to feel your lips on my tummy. Yves, look at me — I love you.

Your
Lisou

Don't be shocked by what I have said — it is all utterly and completely true.

Friday, 31st March

Yves, I was terribly stupid this morning — I'd much better have said nothing and got out of my own mess in my own way. There are certain forms of frankness that have no point. But you must believe me when I say that I am incapable of doing anything so bad, so ugly, unless some very powerful reason had driven me to it. Do you understand what I am talking about? I loved you at that time less than I do now, but enough, all the same, to suffer as I have never before suffered in my life. I was almost certain that I had lost you for ever. Try to imagine what it would be like to live on, night and day, with that sort of certainty. And then, as a result of much thinking,

and of hearing other people's reflections on certain subjects, I
reached the point at which I felt that there was something
idiotic in the fact that I had turned twenty without knowing
anything about a side of life with which most girls of that age
are already familiar. I was very unhappy, and, because of all
these thoughts and emotions, I felt compelled not to say no.
But I wouldn't have done it, surely you know that? If it had
been something that had got to happen, I shouldn't have waited
and fought against it. I am not the sort of person who looks for
adventures. The worst thing that could possibly happen to me
would be to feel that I had disappointed you. But you must
know that I could never belong to any man but you. Does
my boundless love weigh nothing in the scales with you, my
darling? All I want is to be for you a source of happiness —
never something that you could find troublesome, ugly, or dis-
illusioning — and I feel I can be that. I no longer have any
fear that I might betray the confidence you have in me. I feel
so strong, so sure of myself. I shall walk, with head held high,
in the street. My hand will be in yours. I am so proud of
being loved by you — and proud, too, of *my* love — it is something beautiful, something very big, and very pure.

Yves, forgive me if what I told you this morning has, in any
way, lessened your good opinion of me. It mustn't. You were
very hard, and that, for me, was punishment enough. You said
things to me which made me feel as though you were twisting
my wrists so as to force me to my knees — and I went down on
my knees. There is a painful sort of pleasure in getting beyond
pride and self-esteem. I should like us to be walking along a
road with tall trees swaying above our heads — on a night with
something in it of melancholy — and coming to some spot where
we should be alone and freed from all constraint. You would
take my clothes off, piece by piece — and I would stretch myself
out beside you, quite simply, and would make love with you.
And when it was all over, my lips would be a little tired and
rather soft, and I should listen to the wind in the leaves, and
you would be very gentle. Then, later still, when it was full

night, and before going to sleep, I would lie upon your body, very quietly, with my mouth against your neck, my knees between yours, and my breast would be crushed by yours. I would not move at all — and there would be a great peace. I think about that at night, and in the daytime, too, when I am alone in bed, and want you with me. I shut my eyes and imagine so many exquisite things that I don't want to open them again. Yves, my love, do you think that we shall ever know such moments? If you say yes, I will believe you. I am writing by the light of your candle. The shadows are soft, the flame is straight and tall. But I cannot be wholly tranquil, so much do I wish that you were with me.

This morning must never happen again. It makes me too unhappy . . . For hours I was racked with pain, and the cruellest of the things you had said kept coming back into my mind.

Good night, Yves. Tell me that one day I shall be yours. I need to have that hope — even if it never happens. So say it.

No, it's impossible — I love you so much that never . . . My arms are round your neck. I love you — your own little girl

LISOU

12 o'clock. I send you this letter with a feeling that it will drop like a stone into a pond. I am a little fool, aren't I? It's not your fault if you are tired, but I still can't see the difference. I love you. You know that. And when one loves, one is a bit stupid.

L.

Sèvres, Tuesday evening, 4th April
My best beloved, I can think of nothing to say to you except that you are marvellous. At the station, my sister said there was a letter waiting for me at home. My heart missed a beat, but I never thought . . . and then, this evening, when they brought me a great pile of flowers, something overflowed in

me and I was quite incapable of saying a word for at least ten minutes. I love you, darling. This has been the most wonderful birthday of my life. There is something so infinitely precious in it all . . . I should like to close my fingers and clutch everything that I love, all these almost perfect moments, and I do nothing, because there is nothing to do — but Oh! how good it is! — I am very happy.

At the moment, I am lying on my bed before dinner. My room is still the same, with its three very soft-shaded lamps. I have put your flowers in a green terra-cotta vase — they are watching me as I write to you. They look so straight and fresh, and I feel that I am not alone.

There is a fire burning on the hearth — the curtains are drawn, and the air is mild. If only you were with me I should be perfectly happy. But I have had your letter and your flowers, all on the same day, so I haven't got much to complain about.

I had a wonderful journey. I was able to lie down at full length for part of the night, and the drinks in the dining-car were grand!

It is curious how quickly one gets back into the Paris life. Not for a moment have I felt strange or bewildered. It is almost as though I had never been away. Without the presence in me of an immense love I should feel as though I had been dreaming. But there's you — and again you, and always you, no matter that I am thinking about.

What have you been doing today? I indulged in some telephoning, and gave instructions that I was not to be disturbed. I had a bath — and then went back to bed. Mamma had lunch with me in my room. The family has not changed at all — and that is marvellous. My mother told me with a heartbroken expression that the rabbit-aquarium had been broken, and that the fish had had five little ones. I knew at once what she was talking about. It's all a question of habit.

I hadn't been in bed five minutes when somebody came and put one of the baby rabbits on my tum — I've never seen anything so delicious as that little animal — it sniffed at my neck, and then sneezed from sheer nervousness.

11.30. You are terribly far away, darling. I feel as though my heart had stopped beating each time I see anyone whose silhouette or whose voice reminds me of you, or if some gesture is made which is charged with millions of memories. That's real love, that is: I'm convinced of it!

Wednesday. I'd love to put my hands on your face and make you forget all your troubles. I adore you. What I feel about you is beyond all believing. How wonderful it will be to be back. It's so lovely to know that you will be there, and that you love me. My idea of absolute bliss is something like that. I hate to think that a whole week must elapse before you get anything from me. Don't forget me too completely.

I must leave you now. You have given me perfect happiness, and I think it must show in my face, because everyone says that I look radiant. There is only one black spot: my mother seems determined to come back with me — she won't hear of my making the journey alone — and I had been thinking every night of that one free day we were to have had . . . It's all so stupid. I do so wish that everything concerning me depended on you alone, and not on a lot of boring considerations.

Goodbye for the present, Yves. I long to see you and to snuggle up to you — I want you to be looking into my eyes. If you were, you would see how clear and bright they are. Kiss me all over, and let me go.

LISOU

X . . . Sanatorium: Sunday evening, 16th April

Beloved, being without you grows harder and harder. I have come back with a raging hunger for you, and I am not allowed to see you for more than an hour a day. Do you suffer as much as I do? I know how happy we could be away from all this. I feel that I should have been very sweet to you this evening — I should have smoothed your eyebrows with my finger and kept your head pressed against me, and told you all the things my mind is full of, but which can't be spoken in daylight.

Monday evening. To be without you makes me miserable. I wish I could think that there would be an end to all this some day — but it's terribly difficult. It is almost impossible to believe that the time will ever come when you and I will be able to walk down a street, just like ordinary people — free. The fact that I have just had a taste of liberty makes the prospect seem all the more wonderful — but without you the loveliest things lose all their charm. Tell me, Yves, that some day we shall be together and not have to keep our eyes on the clock. Just to hear that will give me the courage to face everything. Speak to me of happy things. Even if, this evening, you should be a deplorable lover, I should be the sweetest of little girls with my cheek pressed to yours — and I should know from the touch of your lids that your eyes were shut, and that all was well with you. I can give you so much happiness if only you will take it. I want to breathe through a whole night at your side. The longer time goes on, the more do I love you, and the more impossible it is to find the words in which to tell you so. If you knew, darling, how much I have missed you! — I behaved like a complete imbecile. I would go upstairs murmuring your name over and over — I would lie on my bed with my head hanging over the end of it, worn out with longing for you. There were nights when not to feel near you was torture. There wasn't a single moment of that Paris time that I wasn't thinking of you. I would shut my eyes for a little, and you were there. 'What are you thinking of?' they would ask, and I reply — 'nothing'. Oh, your kisses, darling, your hands and your words — I was without all of them. I would rather be here and see you for a few moments than so utterly parted from you. That is almost unbearable — and all because I love you so madly. . . .

Is not my skin soft and warm? I love to rub my face against you. There are times when your lips are close to mine but you do not take them. It is then that you have a look in your eyes which I adore. I long to be lost completely in all that sweetness. It is curious how your manner of looking at me can sometimes be terribly hard — and sometimes terribly sweet. There is something marvellous in a look — I love it when you give me yours.

Yves, darling, my mother knows that I love you. I talked to her about you almost the whole time. I couldn't not tell her. You see, I had to talk about you to someone. I'm afraid it may annoy you, but please forgive me. Her knowing won't spoil anything — that I promise. Besides, I didn't say that you love me — I was too shy. I felt that it would be too much like boasting about something tremendous. I can scarcely believe it myself. I love you with all my strength and with all my tenderness. I wish I could dream of you until tomorrow comes.

LISOU

Wednesday, 19th April: 5 p.m.

Don't be in pain, darling: I am very close to you. I suppose a phrenic evulsion *is* pretty beastly, isn't it? I should like to tell you that you are a gloomy beast, but your neck is so sore that I can't.

Here am I left high and dry again for a whole week. All the same, I'd rather be in my shoes than yours. Darling, I do wish I could see you. Masses of people will be paying you the most utterly boring visits — and I can't make it up to you with a single delicious one.

Thursday evening. I think I forgot to tell you not to write to me if you're feeling even the tiniest bit stiff and tired — and I am glad I did — because you *have* written — which makes me very happy. How are you?

6 p.m. I long as I never longed before to get well, to be cured, and all I can do is to wait.

I have just been reading the 'Journal' of that sensitive creature Drieu La Rochelle — it is horrible — but why didn't that woman run away and have the child if she wanted it? Can you think of a reason? *He* is a perfect monster — that's all there is to it. There is something in characters like his that completely escapes me — I just don't understand.

Oh, yes, darling — *do* turn me into a very sensual little girl — I'm well on the way to being one already. I no longer recognize myself — I am filled to overflowing, and wholly unsatisfied. What's so worrying is that all my desires are strictly concentrated on you. I don't, as I once did, find in fifty different men fifty different reasons for happiness — I discovered that when I was in Paris. I carry you about inside me as a woman must carry a child . . . I am turned in on myself, withdrawn from everything that is not you. Is that a serious complaint? It is, I think, typically feminine, and that annoys me a bit. But be that as it may I love you in a manner which seems to me quite marvellous.

Not seeing you brings back hateful times and hateful memories. Oh, we *were* idiots, you and I! Hurry up and have a neck like everybody else! Do you really think I may be able to see you on Sunday — that would be so lovely.

In one of Vicki Baum's books there is a woman who meets a man again whom she once knew in Paris. He becomes her lover, and then is horrified to discover that she wants a child by him. He says that all women tell him that. Is it true? Has any woman ever told *you* so? I am a bit disillusioned because I had always believed one could want that only once in one's life, and only with one particular man. It is such a terribly serious thing. I always find that books treat of certain matters with a quite terrifying frivolity, as though having a child were something that didn't much affect people's lives. It is not always very easy to stick to one's own ideas when books tell you the contrary — when everyone tells you the contrary. I wonder whether the day will ever come when I shall be blasé and cynical — do you think it likely? — I can't see myself as that sort of person, but I shall have to be very thoroughly protected.

I think the light's just going to go out and separate us. God knows, I don't want it to.

Yves, my darling, I must go to sleep. I should so love to be divinely beautiful for you. You are perfectly right — when I am with you I cease to be anyone at all, to have a personality of my own — and it doesn't worry me one little bit. I find it a delicious state to be in. I want to give you every scrap of *me*, and I shall never be able to take any of it back again. If you leave off loving me, there quite honestly won't be anything left — except a mass of defects. I belong wholly to you, and to you alone. I kiss your tired eyes — I touch them with my tongue, and all of a sudden you feel better. Hold me tight.

LISOU

Saturday, 22nd April: 11 p.m.

Thank you, darling, for your letter, but you mustn't write if you feel tired, or if your head aches. I am happy, Yves, terribly happy — happier than human beings are permitted to be — happy in a way that seems bottomless. Don't you think there is something arrogant in happiness? I am happy because of you. I read your letter kneeling on the floor, and I was seized by a violent desire to be with you in some way other than the physical — to know you entirely. You have become for me a stranger, and strangeness is in itself attractive, captivating. I think you will remain a stranger for a very long while — until the day comes when I belong to you. In that ultimate union does one cease really to be alone? Some such marvellous moment must exist — I believe it does — but, then, I believe in so many things. Darling, if in the time to come, I *do* ever belong to you, it will be so completely that you will be able to do with me what you will. The mere thought of such a moment fills me with rapture, and it has in it something savage and primitive. I have no fear that I shall disappoint you — I love you too much for that. I am not sure that even now you realize what a miraculous thing your loving me is. It is something that occurs so rarely. As a rule that sort of relation between two people is such a terrible bungle. Until now I have never been loved except by men whom I could never love in return. When I first got to know you, and afterwards, I kept on telling myself that there must be something abnormal about me because I had chosen to fall in love with somebody to whom I meant precisely nothing. Good night, beloved: you have never kissed my shoulders. I am sorry for your sake that you will not see me today — Why I don't know, but I am, *as you say*[1] — in terrific form.

The housemaid slapped my behind this morning — what do you think of that! — I thought it very vulgar. It's odd, but ever since I was in short frocks, people have always been slapping my behind, and telling me that I don't look at all ill — and when I try, in outraged modesty, to put some clothes on, they say: 'Oh, come off it! — as if I didn't know what a woman's made like!' — I simply hate that sort of remark!

Katherine Mansfield says somewhere, though I can't remember where, that a bird sharpens a note till it is thinned to a point . . . I find that quite perfect.

Dr. M. told me yesterday that I have got to rest a lot because I have reached what he calls a 'landing' — a point where progress temporarily stops. But I can't rest more than I do.

How much longer do you think you'll have here? — Six months? I dread the thought of having to go through another winter like the last. Can you imagine me here without you? I think that if you go, I shall go, too — it doesn't matter where. I couldn't stay on alone — that would be too frightful.

I love your wonderful lips — I want never to have them out of my sight, except when they are touching mine. Your kisses make me realize that I exist, and that I have a magnificent young body. I am sure that I am just ripe for love. I want to hear you saying things to me — it doesn't matter what, because

[1] These words are in English.

I love it when you talk, when you say — 'this is how you will be — this is what you will do — this is what I shall say to you'. Such words set me day-dreaming for hours on end when I am alone. They make me feel that I am with you still — knowing nothing, but imagining everything.

Oh, I hope it'll come soon, Yves! If only we could get right away for a week or two, and forget everything. I want you to know me utterly — all I've done, all I've thought and wanted in the days before I knew you. I am frightened of the un-explored crannies about which, maybe, you'll never know anything. There are so many of them even in the life of a little girl who's as young as I am.

I am going to read, because I have such a vivid memory of you leaning over me, and that makes me sad with longing for you.

I expect from you something as nearly like paradise as possible — only more amusing — I hope you see what I mean!

I love you — and at sight of that love there is nothing for other people to do but draw aside respectfully and let me pass — let *us* pass.

Lisou

Monday evening, 24th April: 5.20

Just when the longing to write was becoming unbearable, I saw you at a window, and shut my book . . . It is strange how different the you whom I see occasionally at a distance is from the you who talks to me and holds me in your arms. I can't establish any contact between the two. I even try to think of you dispassionately, while all the time my mind is full of the other you whom I miss so terribly. What I get from it all is a beastly feeling of distance and isolation. I feel that I shall be powerless to keep hold of you. You shut the window and go back to a life of which I know nothing. You may be in the pro-cess of writing a letter, but to whom, and about what, I have no idea. Oh, darling, it's all just pure and simple jealousy on

132

my part, but that doesn't alter the fact that I am rather miserable this evening, and have a great, huge, longing to see you.

I want somebody to whom I can grouse and grumble about your not being here. So, I shall come and pay you a visit. You are probably the only person capable of understanding what it is all about. I should like to be your mother, because then I could talk about you in a proprietary manner.

The Abbé is pacing the terrace. His head is bent over a book, and part of his sash is blowing out behind him. He passes from sunlight to shadow as regularly as clockwork. Sometimes he comes to a halt, drops his arms, and stands quite still, looking in front of him. I'd like to wave my hand to him, but I rather think his eyes are closed in ecstasy. He must be waiting for somebody or something. His to-ings and fro-ings are very calming — it is as though he were a celestial guardian.

This morning I went into those big meadows beyond the forest — it was enchanting. The road in the sunlight smelled strongly of resin, just as it does in high summer. Further on there were patches of cool shadow — like in *Alice in Wonderland*. I didn't see a doe with her fawn — nor yet a dragon — though I fully expected to. Those meadows are marvellous. I feel that I should like to be of immense size so as to cover every inch of them. There were millions of primrose tufts looking very pale in the sunlight, and all with their faces turned towards me. They were like a group of Communicants chatting together on their way from Mass. I lay down on them under a tall pine which stirred its branches: very gently as though saying 'All's well like this, go on.' And the other pines repeated: 'All's well like this, go on.' Flies were droning about just above the ground, bumble-bees were banging into everything within reach, and white butterflies were nimbly fluttering between the trunks. I was profoundly conscious of how nice the red of my dress must be looking against all that green. Just as I was stretching myself out, it came over me how much I wanted you to be there. I lay at full length, extending my body to the full, with my hips projecting slightly, and my head trying to find a comfortable hollow. For a moment I was dazzled by the great sweep of the sky, and conscious of a sort of despairing misery because I was alone. I think I talked to you. I shut my eyes and imagined that your mouth was approaching closer and closer to the twig I was holding in my teeth — Oh, why weren't you there, beloved!

The shadows of the trees, this evening, are feather-soft. I am holding your hand very tightly just to help me see how beautiful everything is.

LISOU

LETTER TO MADAME C.

Thursday, 27th April

Mummy darling, I want to talk seriously to you about serious matters. You don't seem at all to realize that there is much more than just friendship between me and Yves. I didn't say anything about it before, because I think you have good reasons for doubting the things I say and the decisions I make where my feelings are involved. But now I want you to know. I love Yves as I have never loved anybody — nobody else matters to me at all, and I would willingly go to the stake for him. If I confess that, it must be true. I know you'll be worried, because Na. has told me of the talks you have had with her, and how you dislike the idea of his being a sick man. What do you want me to do? Whether I marry him or whether I don't won't alter anything, because I could never marry anybody else. You must admit that I have never said such things about another man. Yves hasn't once mentioned marriage, but I know him, and he loves me. He talks about our children and about our life together as though it were a foregone conclusion. I should be the happiest of women if it really did happen, and that, I suppose, is the chief thing. Of course you

134

don't know him, and I realize that you must be rather frightened about it all. But if you could realize how completely happy I am, I feel sure that you would get used to the idea. Na. told me that you didn't want me to spend the day I got back with him at C. I don't really see why you should have had any objection. You let me behave exactly as I liked in Paris — on several occasions I was out all night — and I never took advantage of that freedom to do anything foolish. Do you think it likely that I should start now — and with him? I wish you knew what a wonderful person he is! You are the loser, and I can't help being sorry for you. You ought to have as much trust in him, Mummy, as you have in me — I think you forget that he's not a boy. I am quite convinced now that if I don't become his wife, something in my life will be broken beyond repair. I shall never again know feeling to this degree of perfection — and that is terribly important. I have never felt so certain about anybody before — I realize what has happened to me — and how wrong I was about myself on previous occasions. That is probably why I was never genuinely carried away — there was always something lacking. Never before have I had this longing to give all of myself, to tread my pride underfoot, and the fact of feeling like that is, I think, the best proof that any woman can have. To bear him children is what I wish, more than anything in the world. Mummy darling, you know me, and you know that I wouldn't want to shout my love from the house-tops if it weren't most awfully genuine and real. You can't have forgotten what agony it always was for me to tell you that I was in love, and how you always had to ask me before I would say a word, and how self-esteem and pride always came first with me . . . I see now how abominably I treated all those other young men. The reason, of course, was that I wasn't seriously in love at all. To love was what I needed. I am eaten up by happiness, Mummy, and I feel superbly alive. I know that we have plenty of time before us, but I've told you all this now so that you shouldn't get wrong ideas. I know how fond you are of

L. . . . and I'm terribly sorry if all this causes you pain — but you'll forget it very quickly. It's not my fault that the men who wanted to marry me were never the ones I wanted to marry. How thankful I am that I *didn't* get married — it would have been catastrophic — you must admit that. Well, that's how things are, Mummy. Send me an answer soon, and tell the whole world that I am in love with the most wonderful of men.

Don't have any doubts. I send you a great big hug. The weather's lovely and life is beautiful.

L.

Tuesday, 2nd May

You must know perfectly well, Yves, that if I didn't love you, I shouldn't mind behaving in a sensible manner and staying on here patiently, like everybody else, until I was well. But I do love you, and I have an extraordinary appetite for life which I can't describe otherwise than by saying that I long to get away from this place. When you ask whether I should like you to be with me, the question seems so pointless that I can't answer it. Can you imagine me wanting anything in which you were not the first consideration? — is it possible you can know me so little! Nothing, Yves, nothing in the whole world has the slightest charm for me if you are not part of it. Don't you know that? The person who was with me just now wasn't you at all — the way you said that you felt old, that you envied me for never being bored . . . You have a perfect genius for setting a great distance between us. I suddenly felt that I was too young for you — and terribly tiresome. Just for a moment after you'd spoken like that, it came over me that I wanted to go away quite by myself — not for my sake but for yours — and to leave you sitting on the bench. You were no more *with* me then than with the tree in the corner, and you might have found somebody to amuse you, somebody who wasn't me, who would have given you a change from me . . . Don't tell me I was behaving in a thoroughly unbalanced way — though if I was, what of it? I suppose that my love for you ought to give me calmness and balance, ought to make it impossible for things like that to affect me. But that's just what doesn't happen. The more I love you, the more do I feel as though I had been skinned alive. Consequently, you will never find me tolerable for long. It must be quite awful for you, and I can see that I must be unspeakably tedious. If only you knew what I would give to have poise, to be sensible, patient, resigned and never jealous, how I long to get rid of this absurd over-sensitiveness. I don't know what I am, but I do know what I am not . . . Is it all my fault?

I think I want to say to you: 'If there is any fire in you, then it's terribly well concealed, and you'll never let me warm all of myself at it. For whom will the tight, dark wrappings of your heart be loosened? For whom will the flames leap upwards' (but that's not really me speaking).

> Ah, what a dusty answer gets the soul
> When hot for certainties in this our life!

Oh, God — how miserable I am, darling! — not so much unhappy as miserable — and it's all because I've made such a mess of things — and always will whenever I try to achieve the only thing I really want — which is to make you happy.

I wish we had met in a hospital for those who have lost their memories. You have no idea — you can't — how bitterly I hate everything that belongs to your past — memories in which I don't figure at all — incidents that belong only to you. It needs such very little things to start one remembering.

The other day at the cinema, they played some records of tunes from *Trois Valses*. I felt certain, absolutely certain that they brought back something to your mind. I'd have liked to run away to the end of the world so as not to have to go on listening to them — or, rather, not to have to watch you listening to them — and there was nothing I could do but sit there biting my nails. That is why I am sometimes overcome

137

by an intolerable longing to go away somewhere — anywhere. I feel that there must be some place where none of that matters. But because I love you, I can't find such a place — can you understand that? There'll always be your life on one side and mine on the other. My way of loving is far from perfect — I know that only too well. But I can't change it. You are everything to me, and I am such a damnably complicated person. Can't you feel how stifling this place is? I don't believe that you can love me for long in this imperfect way — and you can tell me so if you want to — I know it already. Oh, Yves! — and all this because you were so foolish as to say that you felt old!

You have thirty-six thousand reasons for feeling old — the fact of all the chaps who are dying round you is one. Only — and here I go again bringing the whole thing back to *me*! How I should get on my nerves if I were you!

Yves, my sweet, this evening is rather like you — a little uncertain, a little stormy — and terribly captivating. I should like to draw it all into my being, into my very heart.

I must leave you now, but only for a while. I am more than ever your little girl

LISOU

Please don't re-read this letter. I have just done so — and I am terrified by all the truths in it.

Sunday, 6th May

Yves, my love, how can you expect me to be calm? I shouldn't care what came to poison my life if only I were sharing it with you — but, in that case, nothing would. I realize with hideous clarity just how necessary you are to me — and it is rather disturbing. This morning, in the horrible darkness of the X-ray room, I wanted to slip my hands under the lapels of your jacket, and to press my nose to the knot of your tie, with my cheek snuggling up against you, and hear you say all sorts of sweet things to me. You would have brought me back here; you would have turned down my sheet, and you would have said: 'Well, darling, since the orders are bed, you'd better get there like a sensible girl. I've got to run away now, but I'll come back this evening. In the meantime, write to me — tell me everything you're thinking.' And then you would have held me in your arms — very tightly — and when you had gone I should have lain very quietly, and have been very sensible, until the evening. I should have written pages and pages of the most lovely things — first to you — and, then, again to you — but rather differently expressed. In that way I should have got well, and then, one morning — a beautiful summer's morning — you would have said — 'We're going out' — and we should have set off on a long, long walk to places where there was lots of grass — and we should have spent hours and hours together. But you won't come, you won't sit on my bed this evening and read what I have been writing, you won't be there to say 'That's no good, my child' — or — 'That's quite adorable, Lisou my pet, you must go on with it.' I would so much like to know what you think about what I think — and do. Your advice is the only advice that matters to me — you must know that — and the same holds true for everything.

There are all sorts of very serious things which I long to tell you, but I should babble such a lot of nonsense if I once began, that I think I'd better not try. Don't you agree with me that it's heavenly to get flowers from somebody one loves? — it's one of the nicest things I know. I adore books and I adore flowers in a way you can't possibly understand — no man could, I'm sure of that. One can't keep flowers (it's bitterly disappointing, that — there was a sprig of lily of the valley which you'd held close to yourself — Yves), but one can open books a hundred times a day, and re-read them endlessly. So many things there are to remind me of you when you won't be here — or no longer here. I know it's rather idiotic to look at everything from that angle, but I just can't help myself. There are certain words which I always associate with you. But what I'm saying is true for you, too, darling — there'll always be millions of things to remind you of my existence. I love to think that, though, at the same time, it makes me rather frightened. Does it ever occur to you? Did you think of me yesterday when you were strolling down the streets of C.? — Heavens, how long the day seemed! — forty hours without a glimpse of you — and then, this morning, bang! another blow on the head! How can you expect me to be cool and collected? You talk of wisdom and the sweets of philosophy — but I *am* wise, as wise as it is possible to be when one is young and overflowing with life, and when one adores somebody as much as I adore you. I haven't much in the way of philosophy, I know. It always seems to me that philosophical persons are a bit thin-blooded. Besides, what do you mean by being philosophical? Oh, yes, I *know* that I'm probably the least to be pitied person in the whole place — I oughtn't to be impatient, and, especially, I oughtn't to say so at the top of my voice. That's what you were thinking the other day, wasn't it? — you were a bit shocked, weren't you? That same day you had said something to me that I shan't forget — I won't remind you of it, because it had to do with one of the subjects on which I don't want to touch. You see, nothing you say is ever lost on me. I suppose that to the world at large I shall always be what J. G. calls a 'little bourgeoise de luxe'. Well, I can't help it if I am — all I want is that you shall love me — and today I feel that I must hear you say so in plain terms. Would it be any use, d'you think, for me to pretend to myself that you have? — I need your tenderness this evening — terribly. I want to surround you with my love. Will the day ever come when I shall be able to give you twenty-four hours at a go of true and simple happiness? — from the moment of waking, when I would force you to be in a good humour — until we were ready for sleep again?

8.30. I have just seen you — though for a few moments only, and I feel completely happy. I am miserable at not having all of you, and I've only got to listen to you talking for a minute or so to feel almost fulfilled — what a parcel of contradictions. . . .

There's a lovely splash of pale sunlight — probably the last — on the mountains.

I found an old notebook of mine just now — It might amuse you to read it. I'll bring it tomorrow. It contains a lot of old things, and others more recent — the first story I ever wrote — scraps of a diary — some frightful little drawings.

11 p.m. This is just to say good night. I slip my hand under your shirt — after an hour or two of trying to find the buttons. It's marvellous, darling — and I would love to feel all your bare body against mine. I want you to give me a long kiss — a very long one — one that would last until tomorrow morning — it was so good just to lay my hand upon you.

LISOU

Monday, 15th May

It is misty, and there is a smell of chloroform. The little tree is fluttering its leaves because of the cold. It is looking at me enviously because I am snug in bed with a hot-water-bottle on my middle. I love seeing it shake its leaves in the sun as though it were trembling for joy — but in this pea-souper it seems almost out of place. I'm so glad the weather's like this today. There's no reason why I should feel happy in just this way — except your letter. If it had been fine I should have had so many reasons for rejoicing — and I don't want to.

Perhaps I *was* rather strange yesterday. You see, I realize so clearly that you will never be able to love me as I want to be loved — not that I really know how that is! I need so many more proofs than most people, and then, I'm so frightfully intuitive about things — including your thoughts — they sometimes pass from you to me in the most extraordinary way. I feel, and know, just when I might as well be in Honolulu for all the difference it would make to you. I know there are moments when you hesitate to say that you love me, because you have a qualm of conscience about that being not absolutely true. But that is as it should be. I want you to be frank about it — so few people ever are.

Of course I believe you when you tell me that I sometimes make you very happy — but all that is so terribly ephemeral, darling.

I long for the most impossible things. I long to be terribly loved by you — always with the same intensity, and I know that there never has been love like that. Oh, Yves, I know I'm a bit half-witted to torment myself like this. Please tell me so, but first of all you must give me a kiss that goes deep inside me, and you must crush me so tightly in your arms that my bones crack. When you do that I simply cease to exist! I really must change, mustn't I? I must build up some sort of refuge, open some sort of way of escape, so as to protect myself from you, mustn't I? This power you have over me is really rather ridiculous — though I have never before felt that I wanted to be rid of it. Isn't it strange to think that it has existed from the very first moment I saw you, as though I had been born to submit to it — what use did you make of it before?

Help me to free myself from it a little. Are you never afraid that you might lose me? Are you so absolutely sure of me? One day — ten years from now — I shall write a book — and then everyone will be able to feel this sense of anxiety — this mingling of love and fear — in which I am at present floundering.

9.30. I left you in order to indulge in a bit of day-dreaming — it has become a vital necessity to me, do you realize that? Just to think of you isn't always enough. I stroked the lapels of your coat, and put my hand in the sleeve. This man's coat at the end of my bed is a real presence — it's odd, the terrific impression that things which belong to you make on me.

I almost fainted during dinner — can you imagine! — I, who always thought that kind of thing happened only in servants' novelettes. . . .

I am saying good night to you by the light of a candle. When I blow it out I am left with the rather depressing smell of a parish hall. It hangs about for quite a while and reminds me of

142

my churchified childhood, all cluttered up with christenings, communions, confirmations, etc.

I always think of religion as something very much simpler — what a lot of fuss and bother they make of it.

Well, good night, and happy dreams.

Tuesday, 6 p.m. I think, my dear darling, that you would be pleased with me today. I am being very calm, with plenty of poise, and I can think about life as a whole without feelings of either fear or impatience. Perhaps I am on the way to becoming a thoroughly good person — someone quite perfect, in fact. What will you do with me if I turn out to be perfect? You seem to think that your saying in a letter that you love me ought to content me and put the coping-stone on my happiness. All I can say is that you are much to be envied if you can convince yourself of that! My God, Yves, such small comfort will never satisfy me! It is just as well that you should know here and now that I shall always be tyrannical and venomous where all that's concerned, always eager to strike nearer to the quick in you, and always anxious to give you a little more of myself. Don't, whatever you do, harbour any illusions on that score! In novels, and in real life, the character of the jealous woman has always given me the horrors. My dearest wish has always been to achieve an attitude of superior detachment — though nobody can say that I have had much success!

It may well be that you don't much care for these letters of mine in which I'm for ever talking about myself — let's be frank. I don't mind admitting that I have a great many more interesting uses for my literary gifts. I am really, I suppose, a very privileged person to have such resources of literature and art to fall back on, but I know only too well that there are circumstances in which literature and art might go to blazes for all I care.

I am sorry — but I feel quite incapable, just now, of writing you an amusing letter. I can see only too clearly what lies behind people's faces and clothes — a woman has just come into the room: she's all restless and wrought up in spite of her wrinkles — I can see something of what is going on in her mind, and it is rather embarrassing. I am terrified to think that others may be able to read me in the same way. So long as it is only you, it doesn't matter — I actually like to think that you have only got to look at me to know what is going on in my mind. There is nothing I want more, Yves.

Did you know that Katherine Mansfield died in January 1923? I was born three months later, as though I were meant to take her place. She first, then me. I am proud of that idiotic thought. Her birthday falls on 14th October. That fact is constantly present to my mind. Don't you agree that she must have been an exquisite creature? She had a way of always seeing the beautiful and poetic side of everything round her. I, too, hate what is ugly. At this moment I am listening to one of Beethoven's Symphonies — all on edge to know which it is — the Sixth? What supreme beauty! I only wish you were here with me, listening to it.

I just could not stomach *Guignol's band*[1] — found it utterly impossible to read more than three pages — it was like something sticking in my throat. I couldn't go on. I find it unspeakably filthy, unreadable, and completely lacking in interest. All the same, *Voyage au bout de la nuit* was a fine book.

Yes, it *was* the Sixth — how could I have hesitated for a moment!

If you're to leave here in September, we must devise something pleasant for me to look forward to. Even if it never happens (I am quite calm, and am taking advantage of that fact to see things as they are) it is your duty to talk to me about it because it would be so incredibly marvellous for me to have the right to think about it. Do you understand that? Provided I can have something of that kind to hope for, I can go on living. Unless I can see it in front of my nose, like a piece of sugar dangling in front of a donkey, I'm no good.

Wednesday morning. At this moment I believe in God. I wonder how people who dislike writing — who don't write —

[1] By Céline. — Translator.

144

you, for instance, can resist the temptation to take a sheet of blank paper and scribble on it. This morning I do believe in God. There really is a whole world of difference between you and me. What is your first thought when you wake up in the morning, your first impression? The first thing I do is to look at the window. Then I stretch luxuriously, and my first impression is a mix-up of you and the weather. Sometimes — this morning, for instance — it is exquisite (the weather counts for a lot, you for comparatively little — I have a feeling that you are letting something sleep between us — something that I used to love — a sort of an interest that you had for me — it's all very difficult to explain, because it is only a feeling, and that's all there is to say about it). Sometimes, on the other hand, it is disastrous — and the whole day is coloured by it, no matter what happens.

My whole body feels deliciously rested and relaxed, as though I were lying on water. I only wish it would go on for a long time.

Perhaps at the medical examination this evening they'll say to me — 'What the deuce are you doing in bed? It would be a great deal better for you to run about in the woods — in any case, we don't want to see any more of you after September.'

I have the sensation of being almost in a dream. I am going to hang up your coat in the sun. Seeing it there gives me a sort of vague feeling that you are really somewhere quite close — brushing your teeth in the bathroom — and that at any moment you may appear. The very thought makes my heart beat fit to burst. Kiss my hand and look long into my eyes before I take myself off. They have so many lovely things to say to you.

LISOU

P.S. I am listening to Beethoven's famous Concerto in D — I love it more than anything in the world. I can't hear it without the feeling that it is something that has forced its way out of me, and that it is saying things that I shall never be able to say.

Yves, my adored, my darling, do you love me — and, if so, why haven't you said so? You can't know the immense need I feel to hear it in so many words. When I let myself doubt it, I am the most miserable creature alive, but there are times when you have the most curious way of putting miles and miles between us. Do you ever sit for hours, staring straight in front of you, with a feeling that you have been completely abandoned? I don't think men ever do have that feeling. When I am with you, I want to talk to you — about myself — but we have so short a time together that I always tell myself it's not worth while beginning. I do so want you to know certain things at the precise moment that I am having feelings about them. It is very hard to have to keep them to oneself . . . When I come back here in the evening after seeing you I am filled with regret for all the things I haven't said. A hundred times today I have longed to tell you that I love you more than you can possibly imagine . . . I am writing to you by the window, because the lights have been turned off, and there is still a little of the day left. I can't see very well. Perhaps you, too, can smell this rather tormenting scent? I should so love to feel that you were just a tiny bit with me — you make me so terribly afraid. That is the chief impression left by the day on me — not a word you said but stirred in me whole worlds of terror and anguish — what a child I am!

I can't see a thing — what a pity . . . I feel a need to be simple this evening — please let me be — perhaps you could even help me, just a little, will you? I want to sit with my hand touching you, and then to talk and talk, not noticing times or persons. At the moment, I want that more than anything in the world — to be with you in some place away from here — for many hours — for a whole day.

Good night — I don't feel at all sleepy — how about you?

Thursday morning. Little Father M. can really be quite nice when he takes the trouble. He has just had his hair cut and doesn't look a day more than fourteen and a half! He said:

'So long as they have not definitely made up their minds about you . . .' It made me shudder! Do you think you could love me if I were a rib short?

Think of me tomorrow when you're at C. I shall spend the whole day thinking of you — as always. It'll be swelteringly hot, and you may, perhaps, find it rather pleasant to be back here again on the heights. I do wish you loved me so much that you couldn't think a thought or do a thing which might hurt me if I knew about it. That is precisely how I love you now. For instance, I don't let on to you that I have a weakness for the Scandinavian type of man — all fair hair, green eyes and sentiment (and how!). I haven't got the same weapons as you have in my armoury — in fact I haven't any weapons at all which I can use against you. I'll never forgive you the idiotic things you told me yesterday evening . . . on a sofa. A bit catty, weren't they??? Why do you go out of your way to hurt me? and, what's more important, what do you ever do to show your love for me? — I really began to wonder yesterday what in the world I was doing lying there beside you — which only goes to show how low I had sunk. What you ought to do is grip me tightly by the arm and tell me that I am without the faintest glimmer of intelligence.

No, I quite definitely did *not* like yesterday's film — *Monsieur des Lourdines* — I wish you'd taken me out. There was nothing big about it; one felt all the time that it had been designed as a catchpenny show for the great public. Do you remember the way the book ends? — how the father and son, reconciled at last, go for a walk with the greyhound and the setter prancing along side by side in front of them? — There is something rather grand about that, don't you think? Have you read *La Meute*? — I like the way he talks about animals.

There are some children who pass under my window every day at the same time. I adore listening to what they say. One of the little girls has a very sedate voice: 'Mummy, I've just trodden on a beetle — you shall tread on the next one . . .' There's generosity for you!

You, you know, are so terribly full of poise and self-confidence. What can I do about it? It's all very fine my reading, and re-reading, Tagore. For a quarter of an hour or so after I've finished, I feel calm, but that is about all I can manage. There is always some sort of desire rampaging about inside me. It isn't my fault, I can't help it. I expect that in ten years' time my temperament will have cooled off a bit. Probably the real reason for the difference between us is that you've got ten years of real living behind you, and I haven't. Would you mind taking off your spectacles for a moment and letting me see your eyes? I love looking at them when you kiss me — and then not looking at them. As Tagore says: 'What is important when we shut our eyes is the moment when we open them again' — there's a good deal in that — but I haven't got the phrase quite right.

Z. is being so nice that I could almost believe I'd saved her life on some occasion and then been the only person to forget all about it — I find it embarrassing. Oh, dear, how I do love these clouds — they are beautiful to look at, but they can't be bothered about producing a well-behaved little storm.

I have made up my mind to write a novel. It will take a long time, but I shall persevere to the end. I can't help laughing to myself when I think how surprised you'll be when it is finished and published. Will you please think up a pen-name for me suited to my particular kind of talent? And don't try being funny — I am quite serious.

For the first time for ages I have a feeling that I am going to be bored tomorrow — I don't know why. I have no more reason for being bored when you're in C. than I have when you're in the building over there to my right. The day will be long. Oh, darling, don't look at the pretty ladies too much — they're bound to be quite awful, because they'll know they're pretty. My hand is in yours, and you'll have to struggle with each finger separately before you can break away.

LISOU

I wish you could watch the little tree growing, as I've been doing for the last few days. At this precise moment it is uncurling its leaves because it believes there is a bit of sun — though actually there is no sun at all but only a sort of brightness which comes from the clouds being so white — but I daren't tell it so, it looks so certain that it is right — better let it go on believing. If I was it, I'd so much rather be allowed to go on believing and uncurling my leaves in peace.

Sunday, 4th June

If only you knew what a storm of adoration your little letter roused in me you'd be thoroughly pleased with yourself. Thank you, darling, for not taking all my protests this morning too seriously. I couldn't give you a complete catalogue of my miseries through the window, and, if I had, you might have concluded that I do nothing but whine . . . I just don't have any luck, that's the long and the short of it. This damned illness is going to go on for ever, and it's getting me down. I'm to have another X-ray on Monday. It's that nice, kind, N. who finds out all my rotten bits of no-good. They're back again, talking of an extra-pleural — and that's the sum-total of my week's budget of news. Tell me that I'm a wretched little girl, and let's leave it at that — the subject's only too familiar here, and it really interests no one but myself. I don't like complaining about it — not even to you. I'm so glad to have had further proof of how awfully sweet Dr. I. is to me. She was really marvellous this evening — just exactly what I needed — seeing as how you weren't there to give me what I really want. Luckily we were alone together, and I felt much less constrained. She is going to lend me some Art books, and Villon and Rabelais with the Dubout illustrations. I'm smoking her cigarettes. Don't you think she's a darling?

I rather believe — in fact, I'm sure — that if I hadn't had

your little letter this evening I shouldn't have written to you. I just shouldn't have said a thing for fear of being a bore. It was brought to me while we were at dinner. I laid it open on my lap, and read it like that. When I'd finished, my hands were trembling a little from sheer joy. Oh, I do love you so much, Yves — do you think you'll ever grow tired of hearing me say that? Yes, indeed, you ought to have taken me in your arms when I saw you. I couldn't have wished for anything lovelier. I was hard at work writing — and my pen was just flying over the paper. I shall become a real writer — you just see if I don't. I won't disappoint you, not ever.

What I adore in foreign writing is its precision — the precision of the visual impression — so that the *way* things are seen is enough in itself to give one an idea of the character of the person who's seeing. I don't know whether you catch my meaning.

French authors are for ever concerned in splitting psychological hairs when they are dealing with their heroes' thoughts. I do wish they would leave thoughts alone. I believe there's a psychology of human beings and a psychology of things which reflects it. If one concentrates on that one can produce the same result without for a moment laying hands on one's characters' secret intimacies. That's a much better way — to say nothing of the fact that it enables one to talk about *things*, which is passionately interesting.

6 o'clock. How fortunate that I saw you today — otherwise I should be tempted to go on in this strain endlessly. It is a subject I usually avoid, because once I've started on it I can't stop.

I badly need your moral support. I can't put off writing to my mother, but it'll have to be a very carefully worded letter. I don't feel brave enough to embark on it this morning — you know what a coward I am. The idea of having this operation while you are a hundred miles away, rather terrifies me. I think how lovely it would be to have you visit me after it was over, to feel that you were in the same town, to know that you were thinking of me, that I wasn't alone but could bring you to my side with a telephone call, even in the middle of the night. Oh, darling, I really do need you and your love. If you were there, the operation would be nothing at all, or almost nothing. I *am* frightened, I don't deny it — but you could come and see me on the very day it was done — it wouldn't matter if I wasn't looking my best. I should see you, and you would hold my hand between both of yours.

There is going to be a wonderful moon tonight, and I shall be thinking of you. Yves, I do wish you were here. There are so many things for me to listen to; you haven't by any means said everything there is to say. I am lying beside you now with your lips pressed to my arm, and the more you talk the more reassured and confident do I feel. Yesterday, I was terribly frightened of dying; this evening I am less so, and by tomorrow morning I shall have stopped thinking about it.

How shall we spend the day when we go into C. together? Tell me. I love to hear you talking of all the lovely and possible things to come.

It is 10.20, and I don't feel in the least sleepy. I sneaked a candle-end from the chapel store. It was heavenly just now when the moonlight was falling on my hand. Really and truly there are times when I ache all over with longing to have you with me. I am so happy that you love me — though happy is a poor word to describe what I feel. All words are poor when it's a matter of you and me.

I shall see you tomorrow — that is what I am thinking about at the moment. I shall wake up in the morning with a vague feeling of happiness, and it'll need ten minutes for me to get it into focus.

Monday morning. I couldn't bring myself to write to my mother yesterday. I shall have to get down to it now.

I do so wish that you were here to dictate what I am to say to her. I feel all tied up in knots, and shall probably sit here sucking the end of my fountain-pen, and not knowing in the least what to write.

151

I miss you a hundred times a day, and for a thousand different reasons.

I love you. I am just your own little girl, and nothing more.

LISOU

The sky is very low — like a flight of magnificent steps leading down into the valley. This summer I shall take to going out at night. It will be marvellous to be walking in the dark with nothing under my dress. The cicadas will be so thick on the ground that one'll get the impression that one is walking on them at every step. There should be some small toads, too, with reddish-brown eyes — the kind that if one picks them up one can feel their frightened breathing. Moonlight on a tree gives it a cold look, as though one had dipped it in water. I am so impatient to be free to come and go as I choose. I could bring you back mulberries on a leaf — you'd love to have them gathered by my hands. I would put them, still warm, into your mouth, and I would give you a good-night kiss that tasted of raspberries and ants.

Tuesday, 6th June

It *was* lovely, wasn't it? — but we have so little time, and it goes so quickly. It didn't frighten you, did it, to see how much I love you? I feel no wish to write to you — I'd so much rather talk, so much rather go on for ages telling you the sort of idiotic things of which I have the secret, until you were all in a daze. Only when I am with you, Yves, am I really happy, and happiest of all when I'm lying close beside you. As near as no matter you have seen me naked now — and it seems to me so simple and natural a thing that the thought of it does not make me feel in the slightest bit shy. I shall end by being quite a nice person — and about time, too, eh? It's curious to think that a man who is not a doctor has seen my breasts — it gives me some-

152

thing to brood on. I do so love the thought that you are the first, the only, and perhaps the last (I say perhaps because it all so much depends on you that I can't be sure). I am feeling rather stupid tonight, so I am going to take some gardenal to send me to sleep.

Good night, beloved — dream of me, so as not to be too far away. I love — just as though I had belonged to you for twenty-one years and two months. Do you like knowing that I am as much a part of you as your right hand?

Tuesday, 5.30. Apart from the really big thing — my love for you — quite a lot of odds and ends of happenings seem to be going on up north. I have just been listening to Pétain's quavering old voice. I long to talk to you about events, because I don't feel any too happy about the folk in Paris. I have a feeling that at any moment now postal communication may be interrupted. If you weren't here I should be horribly isolated. Still, I can't help being awfully glad about it all, in spite of the suffering that is bound to fall on everybody. The women here are perfect fools, and their chatter gets on my nerves. I've been like a bear with a sore head all day. I haven't seen a soul except at meals, and that was more than enough. I'd give a lot to have a letter — even a short one — from you. But I suppose I'll get through the day somehow without it. I'm just a tiny bit frightened because I know nobody in the Midi, and do feel so terribly cut off. I keep on imagining all sorts of frightful things, like having to have the operation at once without a soul near me. You won't abandon me, will you, if anything does happen? At the moment I am listening to some Wagner — like a vast ocean swell.

Wednesday, 5 o'clock. The weather is absolutely filthy, but I find walking in this wind rather delicious. I should have liked to tramp the road for a whole hour — even all by myself. It is so long since I've seen you, or had a word from you, that I am beginning to wonder whether you are dead or gone away. Quite two days without a sign of life. I saw Cl. perched lightly on the edge of a bench, and I think he'd have told me if you had pegged out — so I'm feeling rather comforted. Can't you find out from N. what he really thinks about my case? — you know him so well. He's such an elusive creature that I never seem able to get three minutes' talk with him. I should so like to know what's going on in his mind. Of course, if it would be a nuisance, don't bother.

The man who does the X-ray is really rather a sweetie. D'you know, he actually talked to me about my story, and in the most complimentary terms, of course. 'I like that bit about the little sausages', he said: 'nice piece of observation . . .' I couldn't think what on earth he meant. Was it possible that there is something about sausages in my story, I wondered. As a matter of fact, there is. But isn't it odd that that should have been the one thing to strike him? For a few moments I felt quite cheerful.

Oh, Yves, darling, I'm so tired. I need to see you desperately, and for hours and hours I've not had so much as a word. I suppose today will end some time, as yesterday did.

Have you ever thought about your body in glory — about the body, I mean, that you'll have at the Resurrection? I was thinking about it a moment ago, and wondering what it'd be like. It is odd to think that you and I will meet 'up there'. If you turn out to have a more glorious body than me, I shall take to my bed. How shall I ever find you in such an enormous crowd? We must arrange some way by which we shall recognize each other. I shall be holding a glorified book in my hand, or wearing a glorified shoe on my head. We'd better arrange something pretty soon — one never knows, does one?

It's time for my medical. . . .

So that's that. I can't pretend that I don't feel a bit depressed. Heavens, how it's raining! My nasturtiums are craning their necks to get a glimpse over the edge of their box. Are you fond of Renoir? — I am, tremendously. I wish I could see one now — one of the really typical, big ones. I think it would warm my heart. There is something so brilliant, so vital in the way he paints human flesh.

Oh, Yves, don't be false to me, even if I have to spend ages and ages in bed.

Which reminds me: do you think there'll be a lot of moral looseness after this war, as there was after the '14 one? The armistice may break out at any moment now — it can't be long, and I am trying to imagine what the state of people's minds will be — but somehow I can't. I suppose that's because I can look at the future only as it's likely to affect me. My mind's full of tea, and cigarettes, and being able to burn electric light in the evenings, and what'll happen to papa's job, and how things are going to work out at home.

Meanwhile, like everyone else, I'm praying that the whole business will be over soon.

I love you — but, for Heaven's sake, do give me some sort of assurance that you haven't gone away — or that you aren't dead.

LISOU

Thursday, 8th June

Our letters have crossed with perfect symmetry. I wasn't expecting yours, because I never count on hearing from you, and because I didn't want to be on tenterhooks.

Doesn't it seem centuries since we last saw each other? But I'm not making too much of a song and dance about that — I've grown to detest seeing you for an occasional three minutes in a crowd. My jealous temperament makes it impossible for me to put a gay face on — well, you know what I mean — so all is for the best.

I am feeling a bit flattened out today, as though I had been floored with a sandbag — though I don't know what has caused this particular mood. I should like to go on talking to you about my considered view on the subject of literature as seen from the point of view of the writer (the writer being me!). Perhaps there will be an opportunity after dinner. For the last few days I have given up bridge entirely, so as to go to bed early like a sensible young woman. Don't you applaud such strength of mind? I cover my bed with sheets of paper, and go floundering about in them in a mood of drunken excitement.

I've got all sorts of ideas about how I should like to write, but as soon as I try to explain them, I realize that, in fact, I write how I feel and — the essential thing — see. What I most love are details, whether in pure description or in the analysis of feelings. Nothing else, in my opinion, is of the slightest interest. Apart from details, everyone sees more or less alike. It is only in the little things that a great personality shows, only in little things that one finds a real sense of — for instance, and especially — joy. But I don't like detail of every kind. I loathe Proust's.

I, too, feel perfectly capable of writing ten pages on the taste of a bun dipped in tea (what heresy!), though I detest *his* passage on the subject. I get a lot of pleasure out of thinking — to give one example — that when Hortense puts up the luncheon menu each morning, I am probably the only person who notices the way in which she stands on tip-toe to push the drawing-pin in. I can even tell you that the soles of her slippers are cut from a piece of carpet with a pattern of red and blue flowers, and that they are almost certainly home-made. Little scraps of observation like that I find enchanting. Exactly the same holds good of the progressive change in my feelings in the course of a day. Not one of my own reactions escapes me. That is probably why you think I lack poise, but the essential structure is always the same. For instance, each time I write you a letter I am moved to do so by feelings which are never quite the same twice running, but that does not alter the fact that I love you always in the same way — a big and beautiful way which, at bottom, is perfectly simple. Oh, darling, kiss my body — wherever you like — I want to lose all sense of its separate existence, I want everything that isn't you and me to be drowned. I love you — and I want to tell you so while I look at your closed eyes near to mine — the shape of your name brings my lips closer to yours — and yet, I never speak it, except silently to myself — or when I am quite alone in my warm bed. There is madness, my love, in the way I think of you. Do you realize that?

I adore you, my dear darling. What I want to tell you to-night is completely lunatic. Don't laugh when you know — for know you must: I have quite made up my mind on that score.

I, too, should love to spend at least one hour a day with you: to be sensible of your weight, to feel your leg on mine, to slip my hand under your shirt. I love — I love your caresses — I love the feel of rain on my bare thighs — never have I so wished to be without the least scrap of clothing. I should like you to have masses and masses of drawings of me in your room, so that you might think of me all day long. It's a pity that I can't draw myself — that would be the best of all, wouldn't it? — me by me — something really out of the ordinary. One of the girls has just come to say goodbye. She is leaving tomorrow for Passy, to marry a man who was one of the patients here. Oh, I'm so jealous — so full of envy. I envy her everything — the journey, her trunks, and even the man who has come to fetch her. She does really seem to be in love with him. They're starting off together — don't you think it's all very, very beautiful?

I am afraid of hearing the result of the 'tomo'.[1] I shall be told tomorrow. Perhaps I shall never get away from this place. Oh, darling — good night.

Friday morning, 10 o'clock. Where did you go yesterday morning? I'd have loved to be walking, too. If you tell me all you saw it will be almost as though I had been with you.

Do you know this sentence from the Gospels: 'To the pure all things are pure'? — it's marvellous, I'd like to make it the corner-stone of my religion.

I am snowed under by an accumulation of letters which I ought to have written ages ago — so I must leave you. I've come on the enclosed photograph again. You liked it.

Perhaps till this afternoon — if God is kind.

12 o'clock. Thank you for your letter. Honestly, I wasn't

[1] A special form of X-ray photograph used in examining the lungs. — Translator.

157

counting on one, which makes it all the more wonderful to have it. I am glad you spoke to N. I can never get anything out of him. When he comes to see me in my room — it's only to look at the pictures on the walls — or the books — or to put polish on his nails.

Oh no, I shall never be a Holy Mother — I don't think there's any danger of that. I want to be like my own mother, and to know how to make everybody's life a thing of splendour — with very little. It's quite easy, you know — all that's necessary is a great deal of love. I know so exactly what the atmosphere round me and my children will be like — it will be precisely the same as it was at home. Everyone who comes into our house, sleeps and eats there, would gladly be chopped in tiny pieces for each one of us. People can't help but be simple when they've crossed the threshold. It's an ideal world to live in — and I've never found it anywhere else — and we owe it all to my mother, because she has always adored seeing us free and happy. By comparison with that her own happiness doesn't seem to matter to her. She is an extraordinary woman.

I'll write again if I don't see you at the lecture. It's a lovely day.

LISOU

Friday evening, 9th June

I'd quite made up my mind to write to you this afternoon — and then I couldn't. I was expecting Dr. I. and her report. I think I must have become very insensitive, because the only thing that has the slightest importance in my eyes is being able to get out from time to time to see you. I'm terrified lest they keep me in bed permanently — ouf!

Saturday. It was no good — I couldn't see a thing yesterday evening, and had to give up. Oh, Yves — there's really no reason why the Eternal Father should be so 'agin' me. I saw Dr. M. this morning — he suggested a course of 'aspiration'. That's the kind of thing one's just got to accept. What I didn't like at all was hearing him say that there was bound to be a certain amount of danger owing to the position of the lesion being close up against the wall of the chest. I had pinned all my hopes to that operation, and I am terribly upset. It really is an impossible state of affairs, isn't it? Either I've got to hang on like this for years and years, or pass out quietly during an operation for which I've been longing. It's all so perfectly idiotic. I wish I could see my mother. I'd like to have some-body who loves me within call all day long. I know it's absurd, but I'm frightened. I want to see you and nibble your fingers. I do so long to forget everything in your arms. You'll tell me that this letter is sheer lunacy. You're perfectly right — and I'd better stop writing nonsense.

I shall be seeing you tomorrow. Perhaps it will be the last time for a very long while. What a hideous prospect for me!

I am your very small and unhappy infant

LISOU

Tuesday, 13th June: 6 o'clock

'I want to be wise, to live in harmony with what is the permanent part of me' — isn't that fine? — it comes from Katherine Mansfield. Perhaps the motor-van I can hear is delivering the mail — and maybe there will be a letter from my mother: I do hope so. When she writes to me, it's as though I were back at home for ten minutes or so, stroking the kittens lying in the sun, and watching the four tomatoes and the wistaria growing (do you share my love for wistaria? — there's something so tender and romantic about it) — looking at the little rabbits rubbing noses and patiently waiting to be made into paté, remembering how furious my father always gets when the bridge game goes on till three in the morning (when he writes to me a complaining letter, it means there's been a first-class row) — and listening to my brother, only half dressed, reciting Eng-lish poetry and beating the rhythm on the radiator with a slipper — with the tea set out in cups which never match, and all the dogs of the neighbourhood sitting round in a circle — and the cats perched on the shoulders of guests who've got their hands full — Mauricette with her podgy paw in the plates, looking so graceful and so innocent that one wants her to go on doing it over and over again. Quite often all this happens in my room because it is deliciously snug, and the biggest room in the house. Oh dear, what incredible scenes it has witnessed!

Would you like me to tell you some more about my mother? — I've just heard that there won't be any post today, nor to-morrow neither — and it'll make up for her not coming to see me. I want to talk to you about her, because I want you to love her (just look at those lovely fat clouds — as white and dignified as monks). In ten or twenty years, if you haven't torn this letter up, I'd like to re-read it — I've always loved listening to stories about families — do you share that taste?

R. M. wrote a short account for one of the Reviews of the arrival of this American one from New York to sow the seed of Independence in Limoges. There was a delicious ancestral property called 'Les Montées', and six children who all adored each other. Mother's told me that she and her brother always used to walk hand in hand.

Her mother, an exquisite and extraordinarily beautiful woman, highly intelligent and very artistic, died at the age of thirty-two. Her father, twenty-three years older, was a fine type, and, from every point of view, worthy of admiration. My mother was brought up by her elder sister — who, at the moment, is under fire in her own garden. The reason we have all of us grown up in such complete freedom is, I am sure, the result of that. Mamma has always done exactly as she liked. Her father was too old to look after her, and her sister was too young. She never slapped my mother without getting as good as she gave . . . my aunts all maintain that our education has been deplorable (which doesn't prevent them from being thoroughly jealous of the happy atmosphere at home). The whole of my mother's family migrated one summer to Saint-Georges to look after a sick girl — somewhere round about

1910 — and there they stayed until the war, and during it. My father's family had been settled there for twenty years. My grandfather took the invalid under his care, and sent her flowers (an unheard-of thing for him to do, because he was a hard man) — and my mother spent whole days walking the dogs on the sea-shore — as I do — in the pouring rain, hand in hand with her sixteen-year-old brother, who went to England in 1912 with a brother of papa's. They returned to France in '14 to join the army — he was seventeen, papa nineteen — both went off to the war. My mother and her sister were nursing in a military hospital. In '18 my father was given three days' leave to get married — after which he went straight back to the front. I can imagine just what my mother's life must have been.

Neither of them was killed — and when the war was over, my parents went to the Malay States. They were terribly happy there. My father adored the open-air life, busying himself with the estate, looking after the animals, and going to bed early. Mamma was less happy — monkeys used to tweak my brother's nose when he was in bed, and snakes would frequently be found curled up in bowls of fruit. There were compensations though — pineapples for the picking just outside the front door — doesn't that make one indulge in dreams? Then my father went down with malaria, and they had to come back to France when I was due to arrive. I was resolutely awaiting them at Saint-Georges in a bed with a tester. I rather think they went through a pretty bad time for some years after my arrival. My mother's own childhood had been luxurious and she felt rather at sea. Papa suffered disappointments and had to take a job in Paris, which he hated, and still hates . . . I don't think he will ever forget the change that came over his life then. Sometimes, when I used to see him sitting by the window of an evening, smoking his pipe, I felt like crying, because I knew so well what he was thinking — though he never talked about it. His way of getting his own back was by spending whole days wandering in the woods, going out shooting at Saint-Georges, and making traps for squirrels which he set all over the place. We were always catching our feet in them. He and my mother are quite terrifyingly different and she has always held up their marriage to me as a model . . . He loves reading books about wild animals, horses (he's mad about them), and painters. He hates music, and always goes to sleep at the theatre unless the play is one of Molière's. He enjoys eating and smoking, and his meals have always got to be at precisely the same times. He would rather die than go to a cinema. He regards bridge as a game for fools (though when he does play he invariably wins in the most shameful manner). He is perfectly capable of spending a whole hour shut up in a cupboard if there's a visitor who bores him — and he's very shy and bearish — though he can be politeness itself to any woman who routs him from his hiding-place covered with embarrassed blushes. He will spend a couple of hours at a picture exhibition in front of a Monet, with his eyes all screwed up. He is so simple and so good that everybody adores him. He never scolds us, but merely says in a fierce sort of voice — 'if you don't leave off I'll tell your mother' — and that, when I was small, was the most appalling threat. But he doesn't say that now — we're too big . . . besides, mother would probably side with us. So he says nothing. The power my mother wields in the house is unbelievable — and so is mine — don't laugh! I was more or less the centre round which everything revolved. When I resumed my place there for ten days, my mother was radiant. After I left, the place was all upside down. I know so exactly what I mean to them, and what is missing when I'm not there. My mother adores young people, and has always loved the visitors whom I brought to the house. Her passion is to find out what people are really like, of what they are capable, etc., and she grows terribly attached to them, and they to her . . . It's odd to think that when there is nobody at home but her, those friends of mine will often go there for a week-end, simply in order to see *her*, to talk to *her*, and discuss everything under the sun. She has recently been ill, and I know perfectly well that *my* friends have taken her books and flowers and an occasional orange, have played bridge with her, and rolled cigarettes from that disgusting Belgian tobacco, simply and solely to please her. One of these days I must write something about her and about my father. Don't you think it sounds an odd family? — so nondescript, but so madly amusing. I'm so happy that I was born into it, and not into another. I used to think that, even when I had a weekly allowance of ten silver francs — I have never felt envious of rich people, nor of anyone at all. When mummy clutches her head and bewails her lack of education, I tell her that, and I am sure it makes up to her for everything. It must be a wonderful thing to have happy children — and you can have no idea how happy we all are together. Now that I am far away, I can realize how much it meant — to have had a happy childhood. Do you think that has made me incapable of putting up with hard knocks — or that I have never had any? The only thing that matters is to be able to share them with those one loves — and because I love you, Yves, I can put up with anything. You can't really have any doubts on the score. So long as I have your love, I shall never be frightened.

I'm not yet sufficiently trained to recognize your footstep when I hear it. I didn't get up, because it is so lovely to lie in bed and hear your voice. You said 'Elizabeth?' — and then just a few words. I've read your letter — it made me laugh to myself. I was just on the point of giving birth to a number of serious and rather confused thoughts — so, you see, I am not really in the right mood.

How right you are — the only thing that matters is that you should love me — and it is gorgeous to hear you say so. For me it is the one and only truth.

Kiss me all over. I'm no more sleepy than a pair of old braces — and it would be lovely to be with you.

Wednesday morning. Lying in bed, yesterday evening, before going to sleep, I was thinking (I do a lot of brainwork at such times) how really very far it is from being the 'thing', to tell a gentleman that one loves his caresses and his kisses, and would

163

love to be lying stark naked at his side, etc. I have never yet come across that sort of thing in any young girl's letter — and I'm a bit worried. Those things can be thought — but not said, and still less written. I can't imagine anyone else putting that sort of statement into a letter — and I feel rather self-conscious and shy about it.

I'm hot, darling — this room is stifling — and I love you terribly. Yes, indeed, we are losing minutes by the thousand — do you think we shall ever be able to make them up?

I must leave you now, my dearest dear — forgive me for being such a bore in the first part of this letter — I was feeling as solemn as a clergyman[1] — I sometimes am, you know.

LISOU

Thursday, 15th June

Write to me — I don't mind what, but write. I am feeling worried about you — you were not at all yourself just now. It makes me feel all at sea when you emerge, to however small an extent, from your habitual calmness — I'm not used to it. All the same, there were things you said which gave me great pleasure. I expect you have forgotten what they were, but that doesn't matter — I treasure them, and that is the main thing. I have an idea that you want to get away from this place, and I do so understand — especially now that you are in such good form. I should hate to think that it was the fear of leaving me alone that was keeping you back. I'm so terrified that one of these days you may regret loving me . . . I want to count for as little as possible in any decision you may make (and yet, I want you terribly to have to take me into account). The net result is that I am rather frightened. I can't help admitting that. There seem to be so many things you want which have nothing at all to do with me. What a pity it is that I am not a woman with years and years of experience behind her. I believe that I could hold you for ever if only I were cleverer.

[1] In English in the original.

164

Oh, darling, you fill me with terrors today: be good, and write to me. What *was* the matter this morning? (don't say 'nothing' — I should be bitterly disappointed at such a reply, and I shouldn't believe it).

I love you, you great brute,

your little trollop

Lisou

Friday, 16th June

I spent a lovely 'silent cure' re-reading Kipling. He really is a wonderful chap. On my way downstairs, when I was leaving home, I picked up the first book that came to hand, so as to have something to read in the train, and this was it. I didn't open it on the journey, because I spent all night talking to mummy — which was lovely. But now I'm re-reading *Plain Tales from the Hills*. I adore funny stories, don't you? There is a particular form of humour in these — all little flecks and touches — which I find quite wonderful. If ever I have to deliver a lecture, I'm sure I shall choose as subject — 'Varieties in Humour'. Kipling's is one of the best. Everything about his way of writing pleases me. I wish you'd grow a moustache — I should love it. I've just remembered something that the lady doctor said to us a little while ago. I feel like locking myself into my room with black crape on my head and several litres of narcotics. I am going to blindfold my eyes and stuff cotton-wool in my nose and ears. Everything combines to make me long to be out in the air and not stuck between four walls — in the sun and not in shadow — vertical and not horizontal — with you and not by myself.

Fortunately I do realize that there will be an end to it all some time — when I think of that, I am all het up — but it's going to be an awful long time — there's something in what you say about me being a martyr to anxiety. Have you noticed how light and delicious the air has suddenly become? There must have been rain somewhere a long way off — the little snails are pushing out their long-range eyes, and wrinkling u⌐ their noses, to find out where the wind is coming from. Ah, my friends, how pretty the grass looks — let's not hurry — let's leave a lot of slime on it before nightfall.

This complete absence of letters is weighing heavily on me at the moment. I quite enjoy it for three days. It gives me a feeling that I am a free and unattached female — and that's an intoxicating thought. But the charm wears off very quickly. This evening I want to be loved. I have not written a line in my diary for three days — I just couldn't. I open the pink notebook, look at the top of the page, and then shut the pink notebook. But the rain will revive my powers.

You won't like me to mention it, but never mind; you made me shudder with all that umbrella talk of a fortnight ago. You are quite mad. If you honestly think that I'm incapable of walking for a couple of hours in the sun, like anybody else, of taking a short cut home, etc. — well, you can call me anything you like, but nothing I could call *you* would be bad enough! I do so understand why it is you should be feeling in fine form as a result of getting out and about — it's one of the best things that can happen to one just now. But, please, Yves, don't think that I 'made' you — as you say I did — go into explanations. Surely you know me by this time, and how, when I write to you, I put down more or less everything that I've been thinking. You needn't take any notice. I find it so easy to talk about myself. All the same, I never tell you a quarter of the things I should like to.

The weather this evening is after my own heart — everything so soft, and damp, and grey. There were some delicious pink patches in the sky a while back.

They've just turned off the lights. It's neither day nor night — just a blueness.

Good night: I lick your eyelids.

Saturday evening. Naturally, just when I feel the itch to write as never before, the light is going to go out. What have you been doing today? I put the most extraordinary energy into wasting time. There are days when I have a perfect genius for it.

Isn't this weather frightful? I wish I could go for a walk in old clothes, with a pipe in my mouth. I long to take you with me this evening to Saint-Georges. I would blindfold you and not let you use your eyes until you were bang in the middle of the beach with exactly this kind of sky overhead. It would be wonderful. I feel just like walking with my head thrown back, so as to be able to feel the rain on my face. I shouldn't be a bit afraid of tripping over a fallen tree-trunk, or of disappearing into a ravine.

It's gone out — damn! The window is wide open, and looks rather wonderful.

I was just talking about being on the beach, all complete with pipe and old clothes. There would be such a wind that we shouldn't be able to talk. Quite close to the beach, about fifty yards from it, my grandmother (paternal) has a house. There is practically no furniture in it, and what there is is very old and quite awful. I love it. We used to keep our canoes there in the summer. The garden is shut away and quite delightful — it gives one a feeling of royal peace. The door can be opened only from the inside, so that one can shut the world out altogether. I spent a month there with a girl friend two years ago — it was grand. That's where I would take you. We would build a fire in the huge hearth, and perhaps drink something like what you made me drink which was so good (I still think about it when I'm feeling lazy), and you would be in great form, just like you were the other day, and I wouldn't cudgel my brains in an effort to find out why. Would you enjoy that, even if there *is* no furniture? — I don't mean that there aren't any tables, and soup tureens, and a lot of beds — though they're all of them frightful. We could have such a good time there.

I'm going to leave you now and have a good think. But it'll be a nice think. I am happier tonight than I have been for a long while.

Monday evening, 19th June

I am feeling very happy. I wonder whether you know how everything I do with you takes on a splendid significance? What you say to me is all quite extraordinarily lovely — staggering, in fact. I've been brooding all day on the most marvellous things — I can't tell you what, there were too many of them. I can't think of anything better than to belong to you for always. That's probably the reason that I have such an amazing feeling when you stride along ahead and I put my hand in yours, and hang on tight — it is something I never felt before — lovely, and quite inexplicable. Oh, I do love you, Yves.

Tuesday morning. It appears that I am not to be martyred this week — hooray!

Na. managed to wheedle my radio set out of me, and now she is at it from morning to night, trying to get an atmospheric with an Anglo-Saxon sound, it is maddening, like being inside a birdcage or a steam turbine.

The woman who goes round with the Hoover has just been in to tuck me up. She said I looked just like a baby (how I loathe that kind of remark from people who don't know what they're talking about!). How did you sleep without a companion? Splendidly, I expect — and so did I. It's really so much nicer. About four in the morning, I ate an orange — I love eating fruit in what the English call the 'small hours'. At Saint-Georges, in summer-time, I often used to get up in the course of the night, and go downstairs for some. But there were so many of us that I was almost certain to run into some member of the family intent on raiding the larder. There was always, when that happened, a good deal of humming and hawing — 'how are you feeling? — lovely night, isn't it?' — and then each of us would creep away to hang about somewhere, looking as though butter wouldn't melt in our mouths, until the other had gone. The simplest method, naturally, was to go and pick the fruit off the trees — but Marie, who was terrified of marauding tramps, had got hold of a pistol and issued a general warning. . . .

Marie's a real terror, you know — I'm sure she'd frighten you. On one occasion she pinched a mad-woman who had got into the house and hidden under a bed ... She was once ship-wrecked, and spent three days clinging to a piece of wood, off the Irish coast. She has only to raise a finger or wink an eye to have everyone doing exactly what she wants. Personally, I am always exceedingly careful about what I say to her — and so would you be.

I have just read a very interesting article on the employment of old men. There's a good deal to be done in that way, don't you think? Do you really believe that *we* shall be old some day? I have a feeling that we shan't — which is all to the good. Not that you wouldn't make a very handsome old gentleman, and I an adorable old lady — but I don't want us to be old — it is so lovely to be as we are. In ten years' time I shall still be very young — the same age as Na. — what a wonderful thought! — and very seductive ... I feel, no matter what you say, that, as a woman of thirty, I shall 'have something'.

Have you given any thought to the problem of emptying the lavatory basin? I warn you that I take up an enormous amount of space in the bathroom with my clutter — there are so many things I have to have there, and when I get soap in my eyes it's never *my* belongings that I knock over! — never!

May I bring my animals with me? — Sacha, Nicolas, my tortoise, and the rest of them? — including my dove? And shall I be allowed to sing out of tune whenever I want to? Up to the present I've always run into a very common prejudice where my singing is concerned. I am never allowed to finish a phrase — it's perfectly hateful. And you will teach me the Creed, won't you?

Yesterday, one of the nurses paid me a visit. She knocked three times and came into the room carrying a tray of instruments. She said, 'good-morning, ma'am' — I gathered that she had come to pull out my teeth. This was news to me, and I didn't know which teeth to suggest. Finally, she realized that she had come to the wrong room.

169

They have just brought me eleven letters — just think of that! — seven of them from my mother. I love you *so much*,[1] my dear darling.

5 o'clock. My mother quite agrees about having the extra-pleural done in Paris. Did you know that Di. had been operated on by Dr. R. ten days ago? It makes me sick with envy.

Tomorrow's the first day of summer. What time does it start? have you any idea? I seem to remember that you knew the exact moment of the birth of spring — God! — how happy I was that day!

Don't forget to send me any criticisms or remarks you may chance to hear about my story. I have had quite a number of compliments — in fact, they're falling as thick as rain, and I'm preening my feathers. My brother, after twenty-three lines of friendly criticism (lack of cohesion — easy subject — too little solid work, etc.), finished up with: 'All that doesn't alter the fact that I'm damned if I could have done anything half as good!' . . . Wouldn't you like to give him a kiss on the forehead for saying that? — I should. As to my mother — she sent me a little lecture (very well deserved) on the general imperviousness of her children, all of whom, she says, live in their private worlds. I, it appears, am especially guilty (now more than ever, don't you think?) — in conclusion she says that she hopes I am learning a little altruism as the result of leading what she calls the 'contemplative life' here.

My room is full of white daisies. I am particularly fond of them — they have a surprised and innocent look which I find attractive.

I meant to ask you whether I could have a cat of my own — very small and very black — also, some fish — I adore fish — and, of course, a dog, rather a big one: there is something rather silly about small dogs. What a pity that I don't like birds in cages — it might have been rather fun to have one. But perhaps you do? — what a business it would be. I knew a man once

[1] In English.

who had a lovely parrot — all the colours of the rainbow. What I should really like would be to bring up young snakes in cotton-wool. I may — mayn't I?

That's all for now

Lisou

Wednesday morning, 21st June

Late last night, I heard about A. L.'s death. I'm afraid it must have made you very sad. I didn't know him well, but the thought of death is always painful to me. It must have affected you much more nearly. I am thinking of you — I love you — and that says everything.

Don't write to me if you'd rather not — I shall understand perfectly. Oh, darling, I do so terribly want to be simple. I am going to try very, very hard, from now on.

Isn't the smell of this weather delicious? — I'm so glad I'm alive — so vividly alive.

You do love me, don't you? — I want to be with you under tall trees — I adore trees — especially when there is a high wind to set them rocking.

Lisou

Thursday evening, 22nd June

Yes, I do feel annoyed, and it would be pretty surprising if I didn't. After all, people don't change their natures in forty-eight hours. I told you not to write if you didn't want to, but I must say I don't feel particularly flattered after four days of complete silence. I needn't tell you that — you know me well enough to realize it for yourself. I'd much better not say anything.

I would have come to say good morning to you, but I was in a state of complete nudity at the time, and could find nothing in which to drape myself but a face-towel — which would have been a bit exiguous.

I *was* feeling a bit tired on Sunday evening, and I needed you badly. Na. was the soul of efficiency. She made me some tisane, filled a hot-water-bottle, shook up my pillows, and all the rest of it. The general effect was to make me feel that I was entitled to take myself seriously. But I should so much have liked to have you with me, close beside me . . . After all these attentions, I slept like a log — but last night was positively epic.

At three o'clock in the morning I rang the buzzer for nurse . . . At five I started crying from sheer exasperation, and fell asleep at last in a flood of angry tears. I am quite sure that if only they'd let me go for walks and get a bit of exercise, things wouldn't be nearly so bad. But to spend a whole long night alone with nothing to do, is really a bit too much. Always complaining, aren't I? — well, I *want* to complain, and you must just put up with me — you can, can't you?

I wish I could be with you often as I was on Sunday evening — but it's the coming back to complete loneliness that's so awful. Were you frightened of the thunder this afternoon? The first peal really terrified me — it was so loud. But when I had pulled myself together, I loved it. What a pity it didn't happen at night. Didn't you find the rain quite wonderful? — it came down so hard that it must have made holes in the leaves — almost tropical.

I've got it on my conscience to write my Paris letters, so's I can give them to the pretty girl who's leaving tomorrow morning. Leaving for Paris — it sounds like a fairy-tale. Yes, my conscience *is* giving me trouble — so, good night. I *have* put down my name for bridge. Do try to make them finish early. I hate having to see you in a crowd of people who mean absolutely nothing to me. Good night.

Friday morning. I read some of Haedens' literary criticism a few months ago. S. lent me the book — it contains a number of very good things, and others not so good. One feels rather that he is going out of his way to differ from the accepted view, and cry up a lot of things that no one has read — probably because they're not worth reading. I remember being rather shocked at the way he spoke of the Parnassian poets — whom I adore. But I haven't read the book right through — I had to send it back before I had finished. Generally speaking, I don't like reading books about books — and I dislike critics who impose their own ideas upon the reader, because one always lets oneself be influenced by them. I so much prefer to read the books they are talking about for myself. When I was at the Lycée, this mania of the professors for airing their opinions was peculiarly repellent to me. So much did I hate those years, that I should like to be able to wipe out the memory of them completely. It is really rather curious that my feelings about my time at the Lycée should be so violent. On the other hand, one thing that happened to me I shall never forget. We were told to write an essay on the subject of 'Jeanne d'Arc'. As was only to be expected, I didn't know a single date, or the names of any of the battles. The sum of my knowledge amounted to this — that she had heard voices — that she had had the King anointed and crowned at Rheims (but which King?) — and had been burned at the stake. With these three facts before me, I covered fourteen pages in my smallest handwriting. I treated her life as a sort of story, and bothered about nothing but my personal ideas on the subject. I really did feel that I had got my own back — though I must say my heart was in my boots when it came to showing up what I had done. Would you believe it, my dear, I came out top with eighteen marks, and had to go up on to the dais and read my effort out loud! After that, the professor put up with all my whims, including my preference for the last place at the far end of the back row, where I spent my time drawing, and making plans of houses. He took me to see Victor Hugo's house, and treated me to a snack at a wonderful place near the Luxembourg — but I think I must have been a disappointment to him, because the invitation was never repeated. I was as stiff and unresponsive as a broomstick.

After that plunge into my girlhood's memories, I will now proceed to give you the news from Sèvres. I must say they don't seem to be getting on too badly. My mother is still confined to bed, but I've no idea what is wrong with her. My dear sister holds the reins of government and is making a great success as mistress of the house. My brother is writing a novel — each evening he reads what he has done during the day to my mother, who comments, and criticizes, and drinks beer (she writes: 'I am completely happy when they have all gone out, and I am left to myself with good books, good music, the cats, and a supply of beer.' There was one bit in her yesterday's letter which made me almost die of laughing — 'I must really tidy my bed before I go to sleep — it's covered with newspapers, books, socks waiting to be darned — to say nothing of Mauricette and your father' — when papa's in disgrace he is always referred to as 'your father' — when he's in favour she says 'my husband' — they are two quite different persons in her mind).

I think they all spend a good deal of time every night in the cellar. But it has become a habit. Cooked meals are, I gather, distributed night and morning — and they all go along with their mess-tins in their hands. I don't feel at all easy in my mind about my brother if he has to do the queueing. He is quite capable of standing behind the first lot of people he sees, if he has been sent out for skim-milk, finding himself in a draper's shop, being offered silk stockings, and then returning home fuming and saying that things 'can't go on like this'. Mamma daren't say a word to him because whenever she used to go for the milk I had invariably to make a round of the Sèvres shops an hour later to find in which of them she had left it! . . . Oh Lord, what a family! . . . to say nothing of the times when she forgets to put her skirt on. I have a vision of myself running after her to point out the omission — though, fortunately, unlike myself, she does wear *something* underneath. Still, it's pretty comic to see a lady with hat, bag, coat buttoned up to the neck, and a preoccupied expression, running round in her combinations! I expect you'll think that all this is sadly lacking in dignity — but what can I do about it? — and anyhow, there aren't many people about in our neighbourhood, so nobody notices — and we have a good joke to keep us going for a whole week — which is what really matters.

9 o'clock. At last I can be with you again. I have just written some very delicate and disagreeable letters — I do so hate deliberately giving pain. I had just settled down at six o'clock to write to you, when Dr. I. turned up. She sat down on my bed — which immediately heeled over on the outside, so that I had to move into the opposite corner in order to redress the balance. She was, as usual, terrific.

Saturday morning. I was extremely disappointed to learn that today wasn't Sunday — it seems as though the week will never end. I would give at least sixpence to have a normal voice. For the last five days I have been as hoarse as a barmaid (in the docks district) — and the sounds it makes are not attractive. I do hope it'll be all right by tomorrow, otherwise you won't recognize me ('What has happened' — you will say — 'to her silvery tones? — her crystalline laugh, where is it?').

There was no reason at all why you should thank me for making you happy — though I can't imagine anything nicer than to know that I have — perfect bliss. But it is essential that I *should know*. I shall always be tiresome about things like that. I sometimes wonder whether everybody is the same, or whether I really am a bit cracked.

The nasturtiums are growing like . . . but I don't suppose you care two hoots about them . . . I shall tell Na. She's interested.

I am so happy at the prospect of seeing you tomorrow. It is such a long time. . . .

I've got to get dressed now . . . I do so want to be with you. I long for you to kiss my lips, very often and very hard.

LISOU

Saturday, 24th June: 6 o'clock

I would gladly have given a year of my life (provided that didn't mean I'd got to die next year) never to have got your letter. I wish it had been lost, stolen on the way here, or made illegible by the rain. I hated it, and for a quarter of an hour really thought we were going to have a serious quarrel for the first time. I was due for a medical which lasted rather a long time, with the result that the worst of my ill temper has now drained away. A little while back I would willingly have clawed your eyes out — but now I am merely amazed that you could write to me like that about Jean-Jacques. You must have known how it would hurt me.

I suppose, too, that I ought to take some of your reproaches as being aimed at me. The truth is, I simply don't know whether what I write has any meaning. There are moments when the pointlessness of it all leaves me flattened, and I feel just miserable. Isn't it true that I have sent you letters which, in so far as they might have produced any effect, have been utterly useless? — and that in spite of my putting all of myself into them? To get sincerity across means sweating blood. I have always been absolutely sincere where you are concerned, but there have been moments when I have suffered agonies simply because I realized how hopeless it was to try to make you understand. Just you try once in a while to keep a diary and to tell the strict truth — perhaps that would make you less hoity-toity in your attitude to those who have brought it off.

Anyhow, I think I'd much better chuck everything I've ever written into the wastepaper basket. I am profoundly out of love with the art of writing. It is an activity only suited to the sick and the idle — and I don't want to be either.

What are you doing at this moment? — probably playing bridge. It is late, and I must really tear myself away from you. I want to catch up a bit on my mail, and I don't know whether I am feeling sufficiently courageous. I'd so much rather sit quiet and listen to music.

Till tomorrow, my love

Your
Lisou

Oh, God, Yves — *how* I longed to be utterly yours yesterday! — it really is frightful. Tell me that it's not wicked of me to feel like that, tell me that it is one of the permitted things, tell me, above all, that I have the right to tell it you.

9 o'clock. What wonderful weather — I do so long to be out . . . When I am finally cured I shall go walking for an hour — no, for two hours, on the terrace with the wind full in my face, and there'll be nobody to stop me, unless, that is, you raise any objections.

I've just been thinking that I once wrote you a letter in which I said that I shouldn't be able to stand you for more than a week — and you me for half that time. That makes me laugh now, and the cream of the jest is that, at the time, I really thought it. My nerves were completely on edge, and I knew that you were feeling much the same, only more so. We were going through a bad period. I am so flabbergasted when I think about what has happened to me, dear love — when I think that you've known masses of women who are far more beautiful than I can ever hope to be — and that it is to me, Lisou, that you are giving your hand. It makes me feel dizzy — and very proud.

There is one thing I want to ask you, Yves — but I don't dare. I can do it now because it is dark, and because I am close beside you with my mouth against your ear. Shall you ever again see any of the women whom you . . . who . . . what I mean is the women you used to know in the old days? Shall you meet them when you get back to Paris? I hate the idea that you may — you'll probably tell me to go to the devil with my idiotic questions — but I had to ask you, because I want to be sincere and frank with you. And now, good night. I am going to smoke one more cigarette. I am like a cat — this wind makes me feel quite mad. Oh, by the way, I learned this evening that I am not going to be martyred this week — they've run short of anaesthetics. I love you, and I am quite sure that no one will be as happy as I shall on the day when I have a ring on my finger which you'll have been responsible for putting there.

Tuesday morning. Oh, why can't I be out of doors? I've got cramp all over from having been sensible for far too long. It is the sort of day that makes one rebel against everything — but that's a pretty constant condition with me!

I can't explain why it has suddenly come over me that I want to give up keeping a diary. Something you said gave me the feeling that it is a peculiarly sterile occupation. I asked myself, you see, whether it really 'corresponded to anything' inside me — and I found it didn't. It was just that it satisfied an itch in me to write something — probably the result was not very interesting. I feel pretty sure that I haven't got the stuff of a real writer in me. So, I've let it all go to blazes for the moment — though only, I expect, for the moment. Even now I'm pretty sure that I shan't be able to resist the temptation — I even feel rather annoyed with myself for tearing up ten pages of notes two days ago. I ought to be less impulsive, and to think before I act. Tell me so, and I shall believe it.

I should like to know what exactly you mean by 'correspond to something' where it's a question of writing. I want you to explain why you don't agree with me about my diary — I badly need to have things in general explained to me (small-minded, limited outlook, restricted . . . etc. etc.).

I have had a letter about my story. I had sent it to a funny old oddity who came to see me here last October. I'd like to know what you think of his comments. While reading his letter, I sort of saw him patting me on the back and shaking me like a plum tree. A lot of my very good friends have been about 44. He was responsible for my taking more marine risks than ever before in my life — both swimming and sailing. I spent my last summer of really radiant health at Saint-Georges with him, and I believe that my always looking as though nothing would ever tire me was one of the reasons why I cracked up. But it was a wonderful time, and I don't regret it for a moment. Besides, if I had never got what I have got now, I shouldn't have come here, I shouldn't have known you, and God knows what futile sort of an existence I might be leading at this moment. Oh, darling, *what* a lucky escape! It really does seem as though there were a divinity that shapes our ends — a pre-ordained something in all that has happened — don't you think so?

It is raining. I loved what you said about us bathing on the beach at night. It must be wonderful to lie beside somebody who is all wet and shining. I have a raging thirst to have moments like that with you. But when is it going to be, Yves, when?

I love looking at you when your eyes are shut. You have got lashes like a small boy's — shining and faintly red. Besides, I know that your eyes are hidden away behind them, and that I shall be the first person to see them.

I should like you to look at my mouth and to say: 'I want to kiss you' — the very thought sets my blood racing.

There are a lot of tiresome questions I'd like to ask you. Tell me if I may.

L.

Tuesday, 27th June

How stupid yesterday evening was. Apart from the sky looking lovely when we went out, and your kissing my hand, there was nothing to leave happy memories. I shall try in future not to break unnecessarily the daily monotony which you seem to enjoy. I still feel guilty about having kept you from your bridge.

The only reason why I went out at all was to see you — the cinema, and all that, left me completely cold. If you really think that fifteen minutes of freedom are not worth the risk of our absence being noticed, then I'll try to think it too. I do realize how difficult everything is here, and the sort of climate in which we live. I felt yesterday evening that you were just on the point of saying something frightful which you would have almost certainly regretted afterwards. My love for you

179

may have its high spots, but, as you know even better than I do, it has no low ones. There is something very childish and exigent in the way I love you — and an evening like yesterday can only make me wretched. You had no reason to be annoyed with me — and that's what I really wanted to say.

I'm not just making a silly fuss about nothing. I am only too well aware that there is something in the sort of life I am leading and in my love for you which produces a condition very like hysteria and isn't true to my character. I wish I could be shut right away for months and not come out again until I was cured and had recovered some sort of poise. It would be wonderful to see you again then — if you still loved me.

What do you think about it all? I haven't got much common sense, and I lack the gift of resignation. I am pretty certain that I could never be 'resigned' to anything. Don't forget that you have a terrific influence over me and over my actions, and that I always listen to what you have to say. I love you and I am perfectly odious — how silly it all is.

LISOU

It is a lovely day. I have just put on the headphones and heard the Chaplain's voice, on the Sanatorium radio, saying: 'There is no common denominator between God and the world' — so I hung them up on the rail of my bed, and had a drink of water.

Friday evening, 30th June
Bald people must have extraordinary freedom of mind. Apart from the fact that they must find it very difficult to know where to begin when they wash their faces, I sincerely envy them. Dr. I. said that we are a terribly good-looking and attractive couple. I like hearing things like that. Do you realize that it will soon be a whole year since we were introduced?

I have learned a number of extraordinary things today —

among them, that there were no such things as kisses before the time of the Romans. It was the Roman husbands who took to saluting their wives in that way in order to find out whether they had been drinking! When the husband was not available, the duty devolved upon his best friend (naturally, abuses crept in!) — isn't that odd? But how was it that kissing wasn't discovered earlier? I'm glad I didn't live in prehistoric times.

Sunday. I have washed everything in my room that is washable. Now I tell myself that it will all have to be done over again, and I find that thought discouraging. That is what's so awful about kitchen work. One spends hours plucking, husking, cooking, browning, basting, keeping an eye on things, etc. — and the food is all gobbled up in twenty minutes by people who talk all the time and leave the table looking as though they thought that they had had only their due. When *I* cook, I like my work to be audibly appreciated from one end of the meal to the other, with 'ohs' and 'ahs' and 'bravos' — and ruminative silences. So you want me, do you, to tell you the story of the little dog who lifted his leg? Well, it all happened in ancient times, long before J. C. — and it was a very small dog. One day, he wanted to go somewhere. It was his custom, whenever that happened, to go behind a wall or a tree. On this particular occasion he found a wall, but, while he was performing, the wall fell on him. So that's why his descendants all hold up the wall with their hind leg.

Monday evening. I find this storm extraordinarily satisfying. You know how much I love storms — the rather heavy tenseness in the atmosphere, and the noise of the rain on the leaves. I saw the prettiest thing in the world this afternoon — a drop suspended on the tip of a leaf and sparkling in the sun in the most amazing way. It hung there for a moment, and then fell. When it had gone, the tree seemed to lack something.

I have just noticed that you've never said to me — I love a storm — I love the rain — I love the night. I know, of course, that you love the sun, but that's all. For me these things of the external world are enormously important. I never get tired of talking about them. There is no such thing, you know, as just 'me' — but always a me surrounded by a certain number of *things* — weather, smells, colours, shapes, etc.

I have a feeling that I should like to hear some Mozart — and that is something I don't believe you will ever say to me. Is it because you never want things like that? I suppose that goes with being old — as you are. Personally, I walk through life with a whole load of wants. I know, too, that you would never know a quiet moment if we were in the Métro together — you've told me so yourself — a man's nose, an old lady's back hair, the feather in somebody's hat — and there is a certain amount of truth in what you say. Have you read *Martin Eden*? — I think it's in that book that there's a girl who stares at the back of a man's neck, and makes herself positively ill because she wants to touch it so much. In the end she does. That kind of thing happens to me a hundred times a day when I'm with you. I look at your hand, and I have to bite my lips to keep myself from touching it — it is a wonderful kind of torture. Have you ever felt like that? It is quite incredible how much I love you. I am always discovering a new aspect of my love, and I'm always amazed. I think back to those moments when I lay beside you with every part of my body touching your body. Ah, *then* the whole happiness of the world was mine! Whatever happens, I shall have had that, and it is something I have never before had with anybody. I should like to write to you endlessly on this subject which is a particular favourite with me, but the lights have been turned off, and this damned storm has blotted out what daylight there was.

I want my son to be pugnacious and rather odious. Any sweetness in his look would be reserved for me only — not even for you. I detest flabby little boys with smarmed-down hair.

Tuesday morning. A swine of a day, dear friend. Don't tell me that you didn't hear the thunder yesterday, because I shouldn't believe you.

How are you getting on with Etzel Andergast? I confess that I'm a bit stuck. I don't think I really understand the character

182

of Marie. She deceives her husband a little too readily — and then all that about the man who frightens her, whom she doesn't love but can't shake off. The truth of the matter is, she's got no will of her own. These are matters, I realize, about which I don't know much, but it does seem to me absolutely inexcusable for a woman — especially a woman with children — to behave in such a way. The fact that most people attach very little importance to *that*, rather revolts me. There's nothing drearier, I think, than these stories about deceiving and being deceived. Why can't people *think* before they decide? What a pity that I can't develop my theories on the subject to you. Of course, the fact that it'd be *you* to whom I should be talking would cause me a sort of embarrassment. You might think my views not worth much because of my being, so to speak, a prejudiced witness.

Tuesday evening. I think I shall spend all my life fighting about Bach. Are you fond of him? The first impression his music makes on me is one of serenity — and I hate serenity in music — music ought to be full of emotions, problems, violence — and a lot of other things I can't explain. Bach was a happy man, and his music was the music of a happy man. I can just imagine him knocking off work in the evening, and starting again next morning — with the prospect of a good meal in between. I can quite easily listen for a whole hour without getting anything out of what I hear except a feeling of extraordinary poise — and that ill suits my temperament. He always falls on his feet — never drives blindly ahead into his music with the sort of passion, the sheer physical energy, that one gets in Beethoven and Wagner. He knows exactly where he's going. There is never that marvellous unrolling of emotional texture which is what I love in those other two. It's probably an awful thing to say — but Bach bores me except the Concerto for two violins, which I am sure you know. That is lovely — and quiet — and simple — and very pure . . . but nothing else. . . .

Wednesday morning. I have been listening to one of Haydn's trios, which I adore. Its overflowing joyousness is infectious.

It makes me feel that I, too, am brimming with health and vigour. But that can be no more than an impression, seeing that I am in bed.

Hold me very tightly so that I can believe that I am only a *thing* which is unbelievably happy just to belong to you.

LISOU

Wednesday, 5th July

I think that your walks have an extraordinarily good effect on you. If they produce one letter a week like the last, I shall bless them. There was so much in it to make me happy. Besides, it made me laugh — and I adore laughing.

Do just look how lovely the moon is — she hangs suspended above the mountains, and something is drawing her very gently upwards.

I am going to read your letter again and indulge in a little dreaming before I go to sleep. You'd rather I didn't take any gardenal, wouldn't you? But if I don't you must hold my hand, and twine your fingers in mine.

Thursday, 6 o'clock. Oh, Yves, what a lot of time I have wasted today! I haven't done a thing since yesterday evening. It's perfectly shameful. True, I did mean to write to you this morning, but instead of doing so I spent three hours scribbling and thinking that, when all's said and done, life is very beautiful and terribly precious, and that the most important thing is to do nothing that might make it miscarry. Everyone thinks that, I know, when the weather's fine, but the truth of it is *always* with me. The most ordinary things, when one has stripped them to the bone, are sometimes the most moving. That's probably why one does them again and again.

Do you realize how much a tree gains by being seen from below when the sun is shining and the sky is blue? After lunch I lay on the grass and stared up. There were patches of light on the leaves, and patches of shadow, too, and one branch

184

quite on its own, as though detached, with the sun full on it, swaying with a perfect grace. Tiny little dazzling winged creatures were flying about, endlessly criss-crossing, and there were long threads, blown by the wind and glittering in the sun. It was all quite delicious. But I did so want to stretch out my hand and put it in yours, and show you everything instead of just describing it in a letter.

I hate it when you stop kissing me. I think I could spend hours without taking my lips from yours for a single moment. I don't want it ever to stop. I have been thinking that if you *should* deceive me with anybody, I should go quite wild and kill myself. Killing you wouldn't do any good, because then I should be left all alone, and killing her wouldn't alter anything. So you see it's myself I shall have to suppress — because then I shouldn't any longer know, I shouldn't be unhappy, and it would all be a dream. You would find a little letter when you got back, something very sober and well phrased. I should do the killing very neatly, all by myself in a wood. You would not be at all surprised at finding a letter from me, because I write to you so often. But afterwards, oh, afterwards, you would be awfully annoyed. You would think: 'That damned Lisou — she's been as good as her word . . . I know she warned me, but that was a long time ago . . . What on earth am I to do?'

All very sad, don't you think? You've no idea how little I want to die — especially for that sort of reason.

I love you with my lips, with my body, with my legs, with my hands — do you fully realize that?

Friday morning. I have just been thinking of all that life holds in store for me if I get well. Things of which I know nothing. It is rather an upsetting thought.

Are you taking part in the Bridge Tournament? I suppose the answer is yes. I'm sorry I can't enter for it — it would have amused me a lot.

Goodbye for now. I'd like to stretch out my arm so that you could kiss it on the inside — and go on for a long time.

LISOU

Monday, 10th July: 9 p.m.

I love you, Yves. I want a thousand things that I haven't got — yet. But I shall have them, shan't I? I shall be pressed close to you, from my mouth to my knees — in the dark — and I shall grunt with happiness. Does pleasure — physical pleasure — make one cry? Go on kissing me all over — wherever you wish — I love you so violently, so completely. Good night, my love — you belong to me and to nobody else. Will you still love me in ten — in twenty — years' time?

Tuesday evening. If I have a set-back you will come and see me, won't you? When I think that I may have to start all over again writing to you beside the same open window, looking on to the same landscape — it does rather send my heart into my boots. I only hope that I shall not have the same horrible feeling I had that time you were in Paris. It was as though I were addressing a ghost, an idea, a memory — a nothingness — that was the point. Each time I posted a letter I had the same feeling of helplessness. You were so completely beyond my reach. I remember the sort of careless air I assumed when I went through the day's post, and how miserable I was, and surprised, each time. There were moments when I didn't understand, and others when I understood only too well. I pity those who can't endure such galling wounds to their self-esteem. Some of my memories are wonderful, others frightful, but that is something that everybody has to put up with. Of one thing, though, I am sure, that you have never had any unpleasant memory of me. Nothing I can do will ever make you suffer.

I am sure that I ought not to attach any importance to the gloomy times you have caused me. But I love you too much not to be sensitive to everything that has to do with you — with us. I suppose you'd be very much relieved, wouldn't you, if I could accept once and for all the fact that you love me? Personally, I can't imagine such a situation.

On Sunday morning, after Mass, I had a feeling that my presence meant absolutely nothing to you. When that happens,

I want to go off somewhere — not because I'm angry, or anything of that sort — but because I'm in pain. That was why I did not come to see you in the afternoon. I was tired, and it was raining like anything. I didn't want to have to put up with the smell of wet dogs and a lot of people. But I should have loved you to be there, all the same. I should so much have liked to be with you, just once, when night fell: to look at the sky, and then at your eyes fixed on me with a serious, astonished expression — and to press your hand in mine just to let you know that merely to see you looking at me sets my heart beating.

I should love to be lying stark naked in a big bed, my head hanging down a little, talking to you through the bathroom door. What I should be saying I don't know — that I was feeling lonely, perhaps, or that I was cold, or that I wanted you to come quickly. I should see the faint circle of light on the ceiling, and I should be beating time to some gay tune with my foot on the pillow. Perhaps you would be singing? There would be a thick curtain in front of the window, and all the world would be blotted out. You would like all that, wouldn't you? The longing for it makes me tremble all over. And then you would open the door, and I should raise my head and watch you coming towards me. But I shouldn't have much time for that. In the twinkling of an eye you would be lying pressed close to me, your hands on my back and your lips on every part of me at once. When you kiss me I have the impression that I can feel your lips all over me. Oh, Yves, how lovely! — how wonderful love is! I am for ever telling myself stories like that, in the dark. I'm in love.

I am feeling rather miserable — can't you feel it? I need the sound of your voice. These days without the slightest sign from you are interminable. Take me in your arms, darling, and carry me far away, and then, thy will be done, not mine.

Wednesday night. You know, darling, I don't think the Good God is very fond of me. I must have put His back up without realizing. It's not enough for Him now that I am confined to bed between meals, that I never so much as stick my nose out of doors, that I can see you only for thirty minutes each week. Where I am concerned He is insatiable. Ever since last Friday I've been a bit under the weather, with a slight temperature — and now, this evening, suddenly, 100.6 — and off to bed I go. Same old food container — same old business of spilling potatoes down my neck, and upsetting everything on the floor. There is something ominous about it all. I'm a bit stupid tonight — my head feels all knobs and sharp edges . . . Oh, Yves, don't *let* me be so miserable! Do something, go on a pilgrimage — anything, but do get me out of this mood. I'm tired of fighting, but, most of all, I can't bear the thought that I don't know when I shall see you again. You made a bad bargain when you fell in love with me. I do so want to be through with all this — but what can I do about it? . . . I'm going steadily backwards, you must see that. Darling, darling, shall I ever be well? Can I draw from you the courage I need? You are the only person who can give it to me. I expect you think I lack guts — I know I do. But it's not my fault — really it isn't. I long to have courage so as not to poison your existence like this. But I haven't any. I must talk to you about it, really I must. If only you were here, I'd do it with my mouth pressed to your neck.

If I hadn't lost all sense of dignity, all pride, I wouldn't be begging you not to wait a week before writing to me. A letter from you is all I want, I swear it is. When are you going out next? I love the letters you send me when you get back from your tramps, because you talk to me about my body — and I love that — yes, sir, said she, blushing through her spread fingers — I love that — one is as one is. I am a thoroughly nasty little girl, and you have made me quite impossible in those ways. That kind of thing was never necessary to me before. It is all a terrific discovery for me — and yet the thought that any man but you should caress me in the ways you do makes me blush redder than the Russian flag. And it's all because I love you more than anything in the world. Give me

188

a kiss for my pains, and then I'll say 'more, more!' like a child.

If your going to Mass on Sunday morning depended solely on me, I'd say go and worship the Lord on the high hills. But take me with you in spirit — that is all I ask.

Thursday morning. What a lovely day it is — not at all hot; just exactly as I like it — it might have been made for me. I am waiting for Dr. M. to pay me a visit, and I've got collywobbles in the tum from sheer terror, though I really don't know why. I always get the impression that he is about to make the most frightful decisions about me — he frightens me, honestly he does. So I've come to you for a little courage, if you don't mind — I don't ask you to do more than listen.

I have just swallowed one of d'Annunzio's books at a gulp, *Forse che si, forse che no* — quite ridiculous considered as a whole, but with lovely things every ten pages or so. I adored *il Fuoco*. I have a weakness for Italian lyricism, and the sensitive way Italians have of seeing faces and imparting life and meaning to them. 'This he said to her within her mouth, under the tongue. He said it in her throat, at the tip-top of her heart, for he had taken her chin in his hand, and from her lips her deepest breath.' Don't you think that's beautiful? I can hear a child crying to its mother about something — something to do with a scooter — sounds terrible to me.

Dr. M. hasn't been. Oh, I've just heard a quite lovely poem of Valéry's, and now they are reading one of G. Apollinaire's — *Pont Mirabeau* — very sad and simple: 'Vienne la nuit, sonne l'heure, les jours passent, moi je demeure.'

I can feel my heart beating in my throat. I don't like it when it goes so fast.

Goodbye for now — till when? I am not at all serene. Think hard of me. I am all alone and rather anxious.

Your little girl
LISOU

Friday, 14th July: 6 p.m.

I have just got back from my medical, and feel thoroughly impregnated with the disgusting smell there always is up there. I wasn't allowed to remain standing for even a quarter of a second. They made me lie down, wrapped me in a blanket, and all the rest of it. But nobody said another word to me. I loathe their silences. And, Heavens, what a lot of them there were! One of them was a man called F. — tall, with the snub nose of a nice, well-behaved child. I suppose he's taken the place of N. who's just going to be married. He looks pleasant, so I don't mind.

9 p.m. Your little girl is feeling rather low this evening — I'm a bit wobbly on my legs — rather like a drunken ostrich.

Another night to be got through without you. I only hope it will pass quickly for both of us.

Saturday morning. What a heavenly day, my love! I'm lying with my head tipped well back, looking at the beautiful sky. It's washed clean, and is so restful. I can feel the restfulness on my legs and shoulders — it is as sweet as one of your kisses. I am in the mood to appreciate my bed. As soon as I get out of it all my pride goes.

2 p.m. How delicious the smell of lavender is! I love you, Yves, and I am missing your lips terribly. When shall I feel them again?

There are big flies, bees, and little puffs of air. The smell of everything is exquisite. I am sucking a lemon. How can you ever bear to stop using your eyes and feeling things?

4 p.m. I have just re-read your letter, and let me say, in passing, that your way of looking after yourself is worthy of a lunatic — of a good, nice little average lunatic like one finds everywhere! Goodness! How terrified I am in retrospect when I think of your system! It worked this time, but it might have had the most frightful results . . . luckily, you didn't tell me about it till afterwards. If I'd known at the time I should have been a great deal iller than you. You may think that one can snatch at health, that it's one's due — I don't. About happiness

I agree — I think I have certainly deserved mine — but health depends on so many things one can't do anything about. If my health depended only on me, I'd be splashing in the sea at this moment. There is no justice in this business of being well or ill, and the strongest looking people are often the ones who peg out first — that's what frightens me.

This is the worst part of the day for me. I feel cold and hot at one and the same time. I wish the evening were here. I'm going to break off this letter again.

9 p.m. I don't want to write: I want to be with you. I'm sure it will be a lovely day tomorrow, and that you'll probably go for a walk instead of coming to Mass. What chiefly occupies my mind is the thought that we might have had a quiet hour together, and I'm full of regrets — I do so love those times. . . .

It would be marvellous just to feel your arm under my head and your hand on my shoulder. I should feel so rested if I were lying beside you, telling you stories, or, rather, listening to yours.

I am rather tired, Yves — they forced another 800 c³ of air into me — and then started all over again. I could have done without that, believe me.

Kiss me — my lips are waiting for you. Yours hover close to them for the fraction of a second: my eyes are eloquent of all the things I don't put into words — and then, oh then, it is marvellous!

Your tender
LISOU

An angel has left his coral-red robe on one of the peaks, and it is hanging down almost into the valley. Small winged creatures are flying round my lamp, and keep on bumping against the shade. I love the soft sound of their powdery wings. There is scarcely a soul but me in the building. Nevertheless, somebody, in a moment or two, will slam a door and shout: 'Coming with me across the river for a swim?' — and I shall answer, 'Yes'. And I shall get up and go down to the river, with nothing on under my dress, and the icy water will grip my thighs, my stomach and my shoulders, and my hair will drift on the water, like in slow motion, and I shall reach the other bank and feel cleansed of my fever and my pain.

Wednesday, 19th July: 6 p.m.

It is difficult to talk to you about myself. My temperature won't go down. It makes me feel tired, drugged, miserable and frightened. At the medicals (I have them, roughly, every other day now) nobody says a word to me. They can't find anything new. Sometimes there's liquid in this damned hole in my chest, sometimes there isn't. The right lung's almost certainly going to start sticking once more — I bet that's where the trouble's going to flare up again — I can feel it. There are things one can't explain to anyone, though one feels them in the most horrible way — more a slight sensation of burning than any definite pain — that's all — I remember the first time — it's just rather maddening, my dear sir.

Dr. M. comes to see me quite often. He says he can't proceed with my 'aspiration' so long as I've got this fever. We've got to wait, he says . . . wait, the same old story.

I've as good as asked my mother to come — I only hope she'll be able to. In any case, she wouldn't dream of letting the summer go by without paying me a visit.

I am glad you enjoyed yesterday evening. I, too, had a pleasant time — at nine things weren't going very well — but after that, it was exquisite. I wrote until Na. came back — listening to good music almost all the while. The window was wide open, my legs were naked under the sheet, there was scarcely a sound in the building, and I felt completely alone and away from everything. But time passes with extraordinary slowness — and the general impression was strange — I shan't forget that evening.

They've taken to doing the X-rays in my own room. I don't

192

like it. . . Besides, the brutes made me lose two movements of a particularly beautiful Beethoven Quartet.

Here's my dinner — I must leave you: good night.

Lisou

9 p.m. This evening I am feeling utterly at the mercy of the happy Saint-Georges' long-ago. 'I can't give you anything but love baby — that's the only thing I am plenty of baby.'[1]

Oh, the bitter-sweet of songs to which one listened when life was different, when tomorrow counted for so little. It is not regret that one feels — it's something much worse. This savour of happy memories when things have gone wrong, this love of living when one goes in terror of losing one's life — no, not regrets, but desires — vast and not to be formulated — the desire to begin all over again, to be again what one was once — the desire to forget, to rediscover, to dive all over again into the waters of life, to feel, to open one's mouth, one's legs, one's eyes, one's fingers — oh, surely, surely I shall know once more what it is to live!

To gather flame-coloured zinnias — to drink coffee poured from a graceful pot of polished silver into fragile cups of blue china — to run when the bell sounds for dinner, with canoes balanced on our heads, bare-footed like Indians — and my perfect grandmother looking at me and saying that I am beautiful, and the children, drowsed with warmth, silently dipping fingers and lumps of sugar into all the cups!

People passing in the dark night, talking loudly, laughing: in summer one always heard voices late into the night — the distant music of a dance — the laughter of women and children chasing each other round their parents who had lost all authority because their mouths were full of barley-sugar and soft caramels.

The thirsty dogs would drag me across the flower-beds, all

---

[1] The words of this song are given by the writer in English, and I have reproduced them exactly as printed. So far as I remember, the last part of the quotation (for what it is worth) should run 'that's the only thing I have, baby'. — Translator

agog for their kennels — and I would pick fruit, sweet, sticky fruit, from the trees as I passed them. And then — my room, with a damp bathing-dress making wet stains on the wooden floor, and the little piles of white sand which had run out of the beach-shoes — and afterwards, I would sleep, oh so lightly, until the moment of the early-morning swim. . . .

Paradise lost. . . .

Saturday morning, 22nd July

What a strange creature you are, Yves — with a manner of loving that is all your own. I just don't understand you. I try to persuade myself that it is a question of temperament, of emotional timidity — but I am amazed that you can leave me like this for days together, in utter loneliness.

I ask for nothing now — it is a little late for that — and, anyhow, you have always done exactly as you wished in these matters. The fact remains, however, that I have never felt so great a need of you — but that is something you seem incapable of grasping.

Don't write to me — I should feel that you were doing it only because of my letters, and not because you really wanted to. I can get out of my troubles in my own way — but you are, really and truly you are, *odd*. I have a feeling that so many things are so much more important to you than me — which is curious, and doesn't at all fit in with my idea of what love should be. Perhaps it is because you've never had to do before with anyone so young, and therefore can't *know*.

Goodbye for the present, Yves. Do you like this weather? I do. I breathe it in through the pores of my skin.

I find courage in the thought that one of these days, in spite of everything, I shall see you again.

Your
LISOU

1 o'clock. Here is the letter I was on the point of sending when you turned up. I plan to write to you again this evening, if I can — I'm beginning to feel very low — temperature still over 100° at night. It begins to wear you down when it's gone on like that for so long.

Thank you for your long letter — I loved reading it.

While I was waiting for Ma., I bumped into my new stable-companion, a vast, shapeless creature — I think I must have given her a fright, because she gaped a lot, and appeared to be catching her feet in everything that came in her way — still she helped to take my mind off my troubles.

Till this evening. I hope you'll have a wonderful walk tomorrow — here's my hand on that.

Saturday evening, 22nd July: 11 o'clock

I'm not feeling much like scribbling at the moment — I've got a whale of a headache.

They're coming out from the film-show. I rather like the sound of footsteps and voices in the dark — it makes me feel as though I were living in a town. I have begun a story which may turn out well, if I take enough trouble — in any case, it serves as a distraction. As soon as the rough draft is finished I'll let you have it. I hope it will convey the feeling of that 'seaside happiness' which has been constantly with me while I was writing — of that very special atmosphere which I love so dearly.

I don't suppose you much liked the first part of the note I sent you this morning. You probably called me all the names under the sun — from 'stupid' to 'complicated' with 'cracked' thrown in for good measure. Not that I care — what I wrote perfectly expressed what I was thinking, though with rather less venom and virulence. I still think that there's something odd about you — and I find it frightening. It isn't easy to achieve spiritual peace without seeing you — not that producing spiritual peace is much in your line, or not, at least, where I am concerned. It's no good pretending that I'm not terribly afraid that you might weary of my absence rather less quickly than of my presence . . . There are moments when I wonder whether you were brought up very strictly or not. I rather think you were, or, in any case, that you were deprived of any constant tenderness. Consequently, you don't feel any need to expend it on others. I, on the other hand, am perpetually conscious of needing, of craving, just that — and you, I must admit, do rather throw me out of my stride. Several times I have begged you to give me rather more frequent evidence of your feeling for me. That was stupid, and I won't do it again. I'm convinced that it's all a question of character, and I respect you enormously for being true to yourself. Still, I don't see why you shouldn't know that it has made things hard for me. Now, at least, I understand you better, and accept you as you are — because there's nothing else I can do, since I happen to love you in my own way — which is not at all affected by considerations of self-esteem or the duty of respecting others. It's a nice way, mine is. It is complete, and it gives you absolute power over me. Please take me in your arms for a moment, and then lay me gently back on the pillow, so that sleep may come, in its turn, and do the same. I love you, dear, small boy (I mean that — you seemed so very young the other day — you don't mind, do you? — good). Lay your head on my breast, and speak to me as you do when we have had an hour together — simply — freely. Stop, for a while, from being the serious, impenetrable gentleman whom the rest of the world sees and hears every day. Just think that you are with me, with the Lisou whom you love (you do, you know) — and who loves you so much that she would give every drop of blood in her veins for you. That's the truth, and you well know it. Just think that your 'attitude' so far as I am concerned is entirely without importance, and that I have a right to something else. Oh, darling, darling! — why do I feel so old tonight?

I'm cold — I have forgotten the sound of your voice, and am wearing myself out in an effort to recapture it. When will you write something to me like what I write to you? In itself it is so small a thing, but it means so much. Oh God, how different — how quite incredibly different, we are.

My headache is getting worse and worse, and my tummy is positively howling for food. So good night — Lord of my life.

Sunday morning, 10.20 a.m. Another Sunday! Is it fine enough to let you go tickling the mountain-tops? I have done all I can manage in the matter of good wishes. My goodness! — but it was lovely yesterday evening when the lights went off! The sky had been washed clean by the rain and was glittering away like anything. I saw an enormous shooting-star — I'm sure it was half way to being a comet!

I've just had a visit from Dr. M. — very shilly-shallying. He talked for talking's sake, and was rather unnerving. He has written on his own to my mother asking her to come if she can possibly manage it. Oh, Heavens! — am I as ill as all that, Yves? But I've had a good think and brought myself to accept the idea — incredible though it may seem! — I really do wonder what's happening to me.

My morale is excellent, and my desire to live stronger than ever. I rely on that to get me out of every difficulty. The sky was so lovely yesterday evening, that I feel quite certain that nothing like that — you know what I mean — is possible. It would be *too* monstrous — there's no other word for it.

But that doesn't alter the fact that I am frightened. Goodbye for the moment. I do love you so much.

LISOU

Monday, 24th July: 12 o'clock

I am going to write you a proper letter. This is just a covering note with the two things I am sending back. It was lovely having something again from you to read.

I had my lunch on the table, just like a grown-up person — with the sun on my hands. I'm resurrecting all over — and feel much better.

Oh, how I'd love to see you and hear you and part my lips when you kissed me!

What a lovely day it is. Perhaps I shall be allowed out on Sunday — I hope so — it'll be three weeks, I think.

Keep me in mind — because I love you.

LISOU

Monday evening, 24th July

I blushed to the ears with joy and pleasure when I read what you say about my love completely enveloping you. That makes up for everything. There is that about you which makes me feel that I would gladly be your adoring dog — and I have an idea that you know it! I'm certainly not so much surrounded by your love as you are by mine, but that can't be helped, darling. This evening, I just don't care. I adore you as you are — rather hard, rather secretive, wrapped round with all the prestige which the things I don't know about give you in my eyes. But what always amazes me, what I don't begin to understand, is that you shouldn't feel an irresistible desire to talk to me, to shout your love for me aloud. That's what I want to do — and the impulse comes from the deepest and most sincere part of me. I couldn't resist it if I tried. But you are a man, older than me, and very, very different. I'm so glad to know that you were deprived in youth of the whole delicious atmosphere of tenderness, because I feel that perhaps, one day, I shall be able to give it to you. Once you've had it, you won't ever be able to do without it again — and you'll be miserable when I'm not there. Even now, if I stopped loving you overnight, and saying that I loved you, you would be miserable, wouldn't you?

There are moments when I reproach myself a good deal for being so utterly and wholly yours, because it is all against the traditional rules of love-making. But to pretend I wasn't would mean my playing a part, and that sort of thing seems to me mean and paltry. There are many things of which I am

198

quite incapable where you are concerned, because it is astonishing how you bring out all the best in me — whether I owe that to you or to my radiant love, I don't know. The fact is, that with you I feel cleaner and more pure and more upright than I ever do at other times. I have never been particularly perverse or false, but I have not always done the things I ought to have done — and I feel that a love like mine washes me clean of any blame I may have incurred. Don't you think so, too?

Tuesday morning. Oh, darling, *yes* — I have only too good reasons for feeling frightened. In the first place, there's something hypocritical about the very nature of this disease — and hypocrisy of any kind always frightens me.[1]

I'm going to talk a little about myself, if you don't mind. It was all to the good, for many reasons, that I should have had a total pneumo on the other side, because the extra-pleural makes for safety. A year ago I had a fine cavity on that side which has developed with startling rapidity, involving bloodspitting and the whole bag of tricks. A year's not a long time — and then the sticking began again just at the level of the lesion. It's all extremely tiresome. Even if there are no complications, it means months and months of bed — no doubt of that. One gets wearied by never seeing where it's all going to end, especially when one has had a cure almost within one's grasp, as was the case last winter. You make me so terribly anxious to be cured.

I saw Do. last evening, and she spoke to me about Switzerland. She said it would be the best possible solution from every point of view — operation, comfort, climate. Perhaps I shall go when the war's over. Whatever I do, it'll certainly be a year or two before I'm properly patched up — don't you agree? — and the idea of staying on here, after you'd gone, would, for me, be quite impossible. Courage is my middle name, I know, but I don't think I could bear it. Why, even as it is, you've only got to

---

[1] This passage is obscure. I am led to think that by 'hypocrisy' the writer means the *appearance* of health and energy which so often marks the consumptive patient. — Translator.

spend a day in C. for me to become the most wretched of mortals.

5 o'clock. The fruit-woman — or rather, the fruit-man — was here just now, and as soon as I heard his cart I was out of bed in a jiffy, and went in person to do my marketing. The weather made it especially delicious. The fruit had a strong scent, and the open air was heavenly. The fruit-merchant turned out to be a rather handsome young fellow of the Italian bricklayer type, with a face full of character, but, Oh! such black nails! . . . it was a thousand pities to see him handling so much beauty. He 'threw' in a huge peach because it was a bit bruised. But I wasn't able to stay long — my ridiculous legs refused to support me, and I had to go upstairs again, pausing on the way to sit on the steps, and now I'm reclining beneath a sheet, as worn out as though I'd been walking across the valley on my hands. I almost feel like laughing. I don't fancy the idea of exhibiting myself to you in this state — which doesn't suit me at all, but there's nothing I can do about it. My new room-mate is a constant source of amazement to me. She has a very odd shape, but, quite apart from that, is really a most extraordinary crea-ture. Lying in bed with plenty of food in her stomach is all she thinks about. She has never, she says, been so happy in her life before. It's as good as a holiday, etc. etc. She spends all her time sewing, and never writes a line — which seems to be a most abnormal state of affairs (though it wouldn't to you — you're probably thinking that some people don't know what real happiness is — you great brute! — but I love you all the same). She is as indolent as a Slav — the kind of person I want to jab with a knitting-needle. If I did, I'm sure she'd give me a sweet smile and say she'd never felt anything so delicious — adding that this place is sheer paradise . . . Still, in many ways she's rather touching. Her mother's dead — which is awful for her — and she herself doesn't care whether she lives or doesn't — which is worse (unless she's to be envied — I don't know. Personally, I'd rather hang on to life, which seems to make nonsense of any reasons for losing it).

I shall live with her as though there were a wall between our two beds. L., whom I like a lot, frequently comes to see me. I enjoy that. She is a real comic and always has heaps of screamingly funny stories to tell.

Where did you go on your last walk? — I'd love to know. You will take me with you on Sunday, won't you, if I'm allowed out? — even if we go very far, and climb very high: even if it's very tiring. Ugh! I'm having a consultation with Dr. M. on Friday afternoon, and until that's over, I'm free to worry myself sick as much as I like.

Great waves of scent are blowing in from the sweet-peas in the window of the room next door — rather sugary and sickly, like mignonette, but not unpleasant because everything all round is so beautiful . . . Why do roses fade so soon? I get the benefit, too, of D.'s pinks — but they don't seem to *want* to live. I doubt whether Ma. can get much enjoyment from them. They die almost while one's looking at them.

8 o'clock. I've been pressed into a game of bridge — it's ages since I played. My bed is going to act as table, which is always rather uncomfortable, because the cards get under the pillows and into all sorts of impossible places. Still, it adds a little variety to the game — which is why I like it. You'd hate it, I'm sure. Everyone thinks it quite mad of me to keep my lamp burning in broad daylight — there's still sunlight in the valley. I do it to bring out the magnificent red of the roses — it gives them a quite indescribable translucency.

Wednesday morning. I suppose you're out walking at this very moment — lucky Yves. But when you are tramping the hills a big bit of me is trotting behind — and I like to feel that. All the same, I *should* like to know where you are at this moment. I hope you're surrounded by shimmering trees, and tall grass, and patches of sunlight.

One of my nasturtiums is in flower. Perhaps you can see it from your window — can you? It is brilliant, and fresh and velvety. I mess it about so much that I shall probably kill it — touching it with my fingers and lifting its face, as one does with children when one wants them to look at one. The round leaves, when the sun shines through them, are a sort of golden-yellow.

From what Do. says — and the other, whom I don't remember having met — it's pretty useless for me to hope for much yet awhile. They make me more than ever anxious to be operated on by Dr. R., but I have a feeling (nothing more precise) that if my mother comes, they'll decide to pack me off to Paris there to be carved up by Dr. X. I don't think I shall have to wait much longer. It seems that there's a wonderful Italian surgeon in Switzerland, who treats adhesions by suction, without removing the rib. If it weren't for this damned war it might be all over and done with by this time. I'm coming more and more to look at world-happenings from a terribly selfish and narrow point of view — I expect everyone does, to some extent, though they won't admit it.

I had a very uncomfortable night — kept on waking up, which is rather beastly, and the heat was appalling. How I long for winter!

Coming down from the medical just now — I'd been for an injection in my arm — I was suddenly overcome by a feeling of sheer joy. Going into my room I was met by the smell of flowers and fruit, and there was a book lying open, a pile of your letters on the radio, sunlight and silence. There was a radiant look about everything. On my pillow I found a thick packet of mail — letters dated the 19th — it was all marvellous.

My mother talks a lot about that play by Albert Camus — le Malentendu — which she's going to see. Would you like to see it? — I should. A young man I knew has been shot by the Germans in a train — it's quite awful — and I'm feeling dazed at the news. Such a strange way to die — and then I think of the efforts we're all of us making here to keep alive.

Till Sunday — perhaps. How lovely it would be to put my clothes on again and look like everybody else.

And to see you.

Speak my name before you kiss me.

I love the sound of it, spoken by you.

LISOU

I get such a curious feeling when I lean out of the window.
It's because of the grasshoppers — I feel as though I were going
mad — their shrilling seems to get right inside me, so that I am
conscious of it through and through, to the tips of my hair.

What a heavy sort of day — quite terrifying. I loathe the
heat. It is extraordinary to think that there actually are people
who can move with elegance in this furnace! I am completely
prostrated though I haven't stirred an inch. For the last twelve
hours I have had two desires, and two only — to be cool and to
see you. I lump them together like that because they are
equally intense. Never have I so longed to live just for a little
with you — a day, an evening, would be enough — a few
hours. Oh, Yves, I've had enough of being without you. I
simply *must* know that you do think of me and do love me.
Yes, there I go again — *I* know, but please, darling, don't be
angry — I need you so much and see you so little. You do
understand, don't you?

I remember what it was like lying beside you, being held so
tight in your arms — and I want it to begin all over again.

My mother is really the oddest of creatures! She sits by me
winding endless balls of wool (which is her way of telling me to
do some knitting) and saying the most awful things to me —
that I'm not particularly intelligent, that I'm incompetent,
that I'll never get any better. She passes my sentimental past
in review — she calls it my 'massacre' — and doesn't really
believe a word I say — till it gets beyond all bearing. I have
spoken to her about you — about us — I hope you don't mind:
you oughtn't to, because it means no more than if I had been
talking to my own reflection in the glass. Here is a summary of
what she said. 'My poor child, so you really think, do you, that
this man who has had thirty years in which to discover the
delights of living alone and free, who is highly intelligent and
likes a peaceful existence, wants to burden himself with somebody like you? All I can say is, he must be mad. He doesn't
see the abyss into which he is deliberately proposing to plunge

— but I shall warn him. He must be made to see the danger he's running,' etc. It isn't very pleasant for me to hear all that (I've forgotten most of her arguments, which is a pity), and, besides, I don't believe it's true. I told her that you were extravagantly brave, and that, so far as I could see, you didn't give any signs of being frightened of me — but her only reply was to raise incredulous brows, and to say that in six months' time I should have forgotten the whole business. That touched me on the raw. I told her that she was no better than a wrecker — as a result of which she didn't sleep a wink and apologized to me next day for having been so sceptical. Now she says *amen* to everything I say — 'yes, dear' — 'certainly, dear' — 'of course, dear' — 'I don't doubt it, dear' — which is, if anything, worse. Oh, well, what does it matter? After all, what she thinks doesn't mean a thing. I have decided to snap my fingers at her, and I shall start this evening. Her dearest hope is that you will break my spirit. If only she knew that you've been able to do exactly as you like with me ever since the first day we met (it'll be a year ago tomorrow) . . . but she wouldn't believe it, so there's no point in my telling her. It isn't that she thinks you incapable of having a devastating effect upon anybody, but that she finds this attitude of mine out of keeping with my earlier record. It is true, all the same, that I am completely idiotic about you. I realize that only too well now that I see you so seldom and so inadequately. I spend whole hours scratching the wall with my nails in a mood of utter frustration, thinking of you, and with every scrap of my body hungering for you. There are moments of delirious happiness when I think you love me, because to love somebody who loves one is something rare and of incalculable value. But there are also moments of abysmal depression because you are not here to tell me so. It all sounds very complicated, but then I *am* a complicated person. But deep down I feel that you understand me perfectly.

There's a lovely light. My wash-basin is full of the kind of enormous flowers I detest — pale yellow dahlias. They belong to a girl who asked me to keep them for her till tomorrow.

They're horribly vulgar, but that doesn't prevent me from ecstatically burying my nose in them, just so as to feel their cool petals against my mouth. I long for one of your kisses, Yves, I think of them so much that I am quite exhausted. I can feel your lips on mine, gently at first, and then more fiercely, and your tongue touching my teeth before it plunges deep into my mouth. It is as though you were taking all of me, and I grip your wrists because the enveloping happiness is too much for me. I am afraid of dying from sheer excess of emotion. Can you feel it when I am like that? — stretched taut and tense against you? Oh, darling, how long and hard it is to wait, to love you, and to be so far away.

It is midnight, my best-beloved — and your little girl is going to sleep. Goodness! how hot it is! Caroline, the housemaid, says it's awful to have a husband in weather like this. Good night.

Assumption: 11 a.m. The sky is blue, marvellously blue. How wonderful it would be to be lying in your arms at this minute! I feel as though the whole world were just dangling in the sunlight, drunk with joy. I slept all night long like an old soak, till eight o'clock this morning — without waking up once. Not a single dream did I have. It's a curious thing, but I can't somehow feel any dividing line between yesterday and today. I'm wondering whether you are out walking while the Abbé P. is wearing himself to a shadow in Chapel. How gorgeous it must be in the shade of great tufted trees, with the sun striking between the leaves and making great splashes on the ground. I can smell in imagination the Saint-Georges' pines. The very thought of them tears at my heart and brings a lump into my throat. Pines are so tall. When one is in the forest one can hear them talking to the sky and the wind. It's so lovely — that, and the resin running into little tin mugs which twinkle in the sun. There are enormous ants drowned in them.

Don't be surprised this afternoon if I keep my eyes fixed on your mouth. I do so love loving you.

Your
Lisou

It is nice of you not to write and so distract me from giving all my time to my mother. She would be very grateful if she knew. Still, I do, in fact, spend much more time without her than with her. I'm not sure that fundamentally she mayn't be right to regard you as a bit mad. If you are both in agreement on that point, I shall end by believing it, too . . . Anyhow, I understand what you both mean, and nothing could surprise me less — whereas I should be staggered if the contrary turned out to be true. That you should sometimes want to plunge into this mad adventure constantly amazes me. I am probably the most genuinely surprised of the three of us.

I have never read anything by Cocteau. Will you lend me the book you mention? I should like to sample it.

Yesterday, a long discussion with my mother, who is now prepared to face the fact that I want to get away from here as soon as the war is over . . . I feel I simply must go somewhere else. She seems to agree with me about this, because she said — 'I'll think it over.' I find the idea of Switzerland very tempting — Leysin, for instance, which they tell me is scientifically the last word in efficiency. Alternatively, there's a private sanatorium at Avon, in the Forest of Fontainebleau — where K. Mansfield was. I think I should like that, because I've heard that the rooms are charming — and especially because friends could motor out to see me. I've had more than enough of this place, truly I have! The people get on my nerves — all of them. I want to have a room to myself, to be able to look out on beautiful trees, and to see whom I want to see. This perpetual community existence is getting me down. I've more or less reached the point of being able to ignore the others — except when they burst into the room to ask what my temperature is. When that happens, I want to send them to blazes! You must have had some taste of these delights last winter, when you were in bed for so long.

I have just been reading an excellent book about Baudelaire — excellent, probably, for no better reason than that it *is* about

Baudelaire. What a staggering creature he was — though a bit foul. It's odd that anyone should be so over-sensitive both to the beautiful and the ugly things in life. I believe that what he wanted more than anything else was to shock people — and he certainly succeeded! There's a photograph on the cover which I've seen before. The intelligence-cum-cruelty of his expression gets under my skin. I have the impression that no matter what one might have done or said in his presence, he would just have smiled. I stare at him in the hope that he will be the first to lower his eyes — but I needn't tell you that he never is . . . One corner of his mouth curls a little, and he is obviously longing to tell me all sorts of things, and to give me advice. He treats me as though I were a nit-wit, says that I've got a tidy load of illusions to shed, and that the sooner I realize it the better. To all of which I reply that I have already made considerable progress, and am still hard at it. He congratulates me, and then proceeds to treat me to a number of Oscar Wilde-ish epigrams about behaviour, against which I struggle a good deal, because not all of them are very admirable. 'My dear child, *get* something out of life, and don't take things so seriously. Nothing really matters, since the same end is waiting for all of us. Above all, keep clear of sentiment.' Then, I: 'But, my dear sir, I can't be other than I am. With me, everything is an excuse for sentiment.' — This sample will give you a good idea of our dialogues. Which of us will come out on top in the long run, I don't know. Meanwhile, I am feeling profoundly discouraged, and I've a large bone to pick with you for having taken from me even the wish to write you letters. But that's not really your fault — just the result of a wretched combination of circumstances. No, when I come to think of it, I don't want to pick a bone with you at all. I raise my hand to your lips to have the palm kissed.

Really, modern poetry is *most* extraordinary. I am still obstinate about not liking what I can't understand. I don't condemn it. I do something much more humble — I just admit that I don't like it. Nobody can blame me for that, I think, but it's not something to make a hullabaloo about. One of these days I shall probably burst as a result of suppressing all my most genuine and spontaneous impulses — after which there'll be nothing for it but to disappear down a deep hole.

I don't know at what point in this letter I passed from Saturday to Sunday morning, but I feel pretty certain that it has been Sunday morning for the last few hours. Isn't it extraordinary to think there's fighting going on close to Versailles? I can't help feeling I should like to be there, though I need hardly say that I should be terrified out of my life. Sooner or later, I suppose, I shall hear whether our English and American friends are all living or dead. I've got a horrid feeling that when we meet them again, there'll be a terribly constrained atmosphere, and that none of us will be able to find a thing to say.

I saw Na. this morning — very much excited, like everybody else. Yesterday evening I had a long visit from L. She sat down close to me with her elbows on her knees, and I told her that I badly want to get away. Then her lips began to tremble, and she suddenly turned and looked out of the window. A big tear landed on her black skirt. I didn't quite know what to say, so I took her hand which seemed very small and cold. I am afraid she is terribly unhappy.

If you go to church, I hope you'll have a very short sermon, and the kind of thoroughly sensible neighbours you like.

Goodbye for the present. When you want *La Reine Morte* she is yours for the asking.

Your servant — as they say in the theatre

LISOU

Have you seen the last number of *Confluences*? I came across a few lines about our magazine. There was a piece on the subject of my story. In spite of my pleasure at being noticed, I felt thoroughly vexed. He (the man who wrote the review) finds that my story is 'clever'. I think myself that that is the last thing it is. My mother holds the view that it is terribly clumsy. I'd so much rather that he (the above-mentioned gentleman) had said that it was 'very crude with a number of good things in it'. . . .

Saturday, 2nd September
I have spent such marvellous moments with you, times that were in a world apart, that I find it painful to start again in a less beautiful relationship. You do understand that, don't you? You have given my love a devastating wound. I suppose it can be healed, because what I got from you this morning has set me in a whirl. Everything sweet and tender that you have brought yourself to say to me during the last few months I have had to force out of you — and I think you know it. That I did force it out of you was due to the fact that I was in dire need, and because your tenderness is all that matters to me. You don't seem to have realized that for a single moment. Suddenly I find myself up against things, and I get a shock. It may quite well last, I know, for several months. This time it isn't a case of the former utterly exhausting alternatives, but of a coldness, of a complete lack of understanding, which is far worse. That is something I can't bear from you after the joys and discoveries which you and I have shared. I demand too much, I am too jealous and too egotistical in my love for you to make it possible for me to live like that. It is not altogether your fault, but insofar as it is mine, it isn't really my fault either. I can't suddenly leave off being my natural self. I know that my behaviour threatens to poison our happiness, but at least it is sincere. The sincerity and frankness of children has always rather embarrassed me, and I have a feeling that I affect you in somewhat the same way. But one can't blame children for it, can one (if you knew how good this cigarette is that I'm smoking, you'd be livid with envy — I kiss the palm of your hand, beloved)? Your letter made me very happy, of that you can be sure, but it also caused me considerable embarrassment, because I don't want to suffer again as I did before as a result of

your behaviour. It was stupid of me to do so, because you do love me. But I won't deny that it might happen, and that possibility frightens me. I believe you when you say that many things have been poisoned for you. Do you really think I shouldn't understand if you told me what they are? The idea that you not only feel no need of me at such moments, but that you can deliberately write me the kind of letters you did, thereby setting estrangement between us, is very hard to bear. I feel completely flattened, and the only thing for me to do now is to relapse into silence (but that is hard, too, because I hate not saying what I think . . .).

Well, that is the position as I see it. Don't believe that I don't know what I want. What I want is, more than anything else, you — and, in the second place, not to suffer — or at least to suffer for some reason I can understand and gauge, such as having no more to expect from you.

I know only too well that the life here throws one terribly off balance. It is the wrong thing for people like you and me. I have always tried to resist its influence, but, since this business of loving you started, I have realized just what damage it can do to *feelings*, no matter how big or how beautiful they may be. I have kept mine intact, but it seems to me that yours have had to stand up to a number of horribly violent assaults. It is no use denying that the power of mere *time* is almost beyond belief. I would gladly give several years of my precious life to have that month in Paris. The thought of us each going our own ways for an unspecified period, fills me with terror . . . I am frightened, because for the last few months I have seen scarcely anything of you, and can measure the effect of that upon myself. I feel certain that it will be much worse if I don't see you at all. I can so well imagine the situation — you in Paris, I here, or somewhere else, and getting from you the sort of letter I have been getting recently. Surely you can understand my wish that, rather than have that, I would prefer that everything should stop *now*? It seems to me that a slow and gradual ending, with everything being gradually whittled down, would not be worthy of us (if you can bring yourself to do so, re-read your letters. You can't not notice the slow emotional diminuendo — it's been enough to drive me crazy). I like to think that you, in my place, would have acted precisely as I have done. I know that I should have incurred my own contempt had I just let things slip lower and lower. I fear that we are facing an almost insoluble problem, and I wish you would tell me what you really think.

I certainly shall not be able to go out tomorrow. I am feeling completely exhausted. That damned bronchial X-ray has the most ridiculous effect on my nervous system — and, to make matters worse, my nerves weren't in any too good a condition when I went for it. It seems to me that I shall soon be a fit subject for solitary confinement. I could really have strangled you for being there, with your chest all naked . . . I wish you could have known how, when it was over, I just wanted to be in your arms — that and nothing more. But I did hate you for having come — I'm sure you could have avoided the meeting.

3 o'clock. I can't read, and I can't do anything — so here I am again. What awful weather! I'd like to go out and walk right across the plateau in the rain — with a perpetual scowl!

Ever since my mother came she has been at me to take my walks without her — it was I who said no. So, don't think too hardly of her — as a matter of fact she was very much surprised that I refused. But for some time now I have felt so odd in your company, and you have been so different from what you used to be, that I thought it far better to stick close to her. In that way I didn't feel so lost and lonely.

Erik? — an odd chap, very intelligent, whom we more or less adopted into the family, because he was living all alone, and was an interesting person. He was much too cerebral, and has now elected to fight in order to break away from all that. It's not a bad idea — but he made the decision in a mood of bitterness and hatred that's really quite awful. He used to write a lot. I gave him my story to read. When he'd finished it, he jotted down a few comments. We are extraordinarily clear-sighted about each other. In his notes, he repeated what he has often said to me — 'Less dreaming, more living.' My mother, who read them, felt precisely as you did. She thinks it quite idiotic to tell me that just now, and she is very cross with him for giving me the idea that I might do more than I do. That, I confess, did not strike me. He always levelled the same reproach at me, even when I wasn't ill, and he was perfectly right.

Saturday evening. Hip Hip Hurrah! — I'm cold! I've wound myself round my hot-water-bottle like a dog. Oh, Yves! I love you passionately, you know that — and terribly, too. You are dealing some frightful blows at this love of mine, but I think it can still stand up to a few more. It's got to. There are moments when I want to shake myself and say: 'Good heavens, Lisou! if you can't stand *that*, your love must be a poor thing!' — Is that true, Yves? Haven't I given you all of me, the good as well as the bad? Haven't I talked to you, loved you, desired you, more than anyone has ever done? — I am sure I have — and *you'll* be sure one of these days, whether I am with you or not. I've told you that the whole situation constitutes a very serious problem, a kind of a fight that has got to be waged. I have always felt that I could deal with any attack coming from the outside, but when it's a question of fighting *you*, then I'm beaten before the battle begins. All these torments are so useless. I am a little like Pucet lost in the forest, without stones in his pouch or a feather in his cap. He sees a light and goes towards it, brimming over with confidence — and the light vanishes. Then he does all sorts of deeds of prowess — climbs trees, shouts, sobs, takes decisions, and is frightened, turn and turn about, until he sees the light again. Then he forgets everything, and starts off once more, straight ahead, and the whole process begins over again. Each time his misery is a little greater, his joy a little less. He can no longer forget the darkness, the wild beasts, the storm and the ogre (but at least there is a happy ending — and that is encouraging).

I do so wish that you would talk to me about all our difficulties, and tell me how important you think they are. But I don't think I am deceiving myself when I believe that if we do come through victorious — that's to say, as close to one another as we were in the past — it'll be because that's how it was meant to end, in which case it will all have been worth while. I love you, all of you, utterly and completely, but when I suffer I lose all my weapons — and that does a little something towards killing my faith in you.

Honestly and truly I have fallen pretty low this time. You've come at the critical moment to give me a hand up, but it'll be some while before I recover entirely. The feeling that one has been let down is terrible — one doesn't forget it easily. What is so awful is the thought that probably none of this would ever have happened if we had seen one another often and under happier conditions. That is something we can't do anything about, and it may go on for a long time yet — how long? I am not being very brilliant. I am intolerable in this, as I am in every other, way. . . .

I am glad I've talked to you at such length about all the matters that affect us so nearly. I am egotistical about us both, and I feel quite certain that I have got to be.

Thank you so much, Yves, for those voluptuous smokes. It is a delight I had quite forgotten, and I don't think I deserved it. If I want a cachou may I come and take one from your tongue with my lips? With your permission, I will live a little less and hope a little more.

I don't imagine you'll be doing anything very dangerous tomorrow — with this wind you'll need good anchors and tough mooring ropes.

So long, your little girl

LISOU

P.S. I am quite sure it's because our love is so exceptionally great and beautiful that it stands up to all this so badly.

Sunday morning. Good morning. The air is so fresh and so light — it smells of the coming winter. In November we'll go to the Bois de Boulogne, and you'll hold my arm tight in yours.

Sunday evening, 24th September

I don't know why it is, but I am simply dropping with fatigue this evening. I could quite easily fall asleep with my nose on this sheet of paper, like a child over its box of bricks, if it weren't that I feel I have something of great value to say. Take my face in your two hands, and look first into my eyes and then at my lips, bending slightly towards me. Oh, how I love you, Yves! I should like more than anything that you should tell me a story — one chapter each evening — after which we would go to bed — and I should fall asleep chortling with satisfaction.

Monday morning. I love this cold. I have just seen Dr. I. I am to be allowed to go upstairs for the cure. I start tomorrow. It is wonderful to feel that I can go out whenever I want to. It's five months, you know, since I was last able to do that, and it seems wonderful. I. brought me a long letter from Vi. — full of nothing — I expected better. What a painful feeling disappointment is. She also described to me the two days she had spent in C. I just threw out a hint — in the most innocent way possible — that I should enjoy making a trip down there, and she doesn't see any reason why I shouldn't. She has had a letter from Erik (he has embarked on a long argument with her about communism). He thinks he'll be coming back, and sends me all sorts of disagreeable messages, half of which I've unfortunately forgotten, though some of them, I know, were to the effect that I don't bother about anything but style — that the only sensations I am concerned with are purely physical — that I can't talk about anything else (on that score he lumps me with Colette — Oh, how I wish it were true!). These comments amused me for a bit, but now I find him getting on my nerves. There's a whole category of persons with whom I find it difficult to put up since knowing you.

This is my last day of solitude — rather a pity: I've enjoyed it. I could walk about the room half naked, talk to myself, and see nobody. Every night I thought you might pay me a visit — but you never did. You've no idea how charming this room can be at night — it almost makes me forget where I am. Sa. dropped in the day after she got back from her adventurous trip to C. When I saw her looking so small and thin, I wanted to fill her arms with all my flowers, just to please her. But people who look as fragile as that always paralyse me: I'm afraid of making the slightest movement for fear of knocking them over, or of seeing them throw a faint in front of my eyes. When she left me, she said 'Goodbye' in a dry, sharp voice which reminded me of you. I remember how, the day after *you* got back from C., I saw the two of you together on the road that runs behind the Sanatorium — and the sight made an extraordinary impression on me. I looked at you both for quite a while, feeling quite shaky, but the agreement and understanding between you seemed to be so complete, that I just couldn't be jealous. She has her share of you, but mine is so much lovelier that I can't grudge it her. Mine *is* lovelier, isn't it? She hasn't got your arm to press hers, your hands to bring her pain, pleasure, and fear — your mouth given in kisses. She doesn't know the way in which your lashes spread on your cheek when you shut your eyes, nor the weight of your body, nor the special colour of the sky seen above your head when you say something marvellous. Such things are mine, and mine alone. How lovely *my* share in you is, Yves, and how illimitable. I could never reach the end of the catalogue!

You know, don't you, that one can write letters to anywhere in France now? I only hope that the news from Paris won't be long delayed. I want to know whether or not T. is dead — you can't imagine what a dear he is — I know you'd have appreciated him. I daren't write to his mother to ask what has happened — so there's nothing for it but to wait. But waiting is hard, especially when one feels that one has been, to some extent, responsible. The whole thing had a shattering effect on me, and it all came at a time when I hadn't got you to lean on and to make me forget it. I don't feel so badly now, but I did hurt him terribly, and the knowledge that I did so poisoned my existence. His letters were as painful for me to get as for

215

him to write. He won't accept me just as a friend, though we have so many ideas and tastes in common. What a pity it is that he isn't my brother.

I hesitated a bit before talking about him to you like this. I thought I might be being terribly indiscreet — from his point of view. But I don't think — I can't feel — that there is anything wrong in what I am doing, and, as always, I trust my feelings. Besides, I wanted you to know something about him, and what damage I'm capable of doing with my thoughtlessness and my little-girl airs. What I did to him is something that doesn't get mended — and his wasn't the only case. Oh, well, it's all over now. So long as *you* don't punish me, that is all I mind about. Don't think hardly of me. My love for you is something total, and this is the first time I have ever loved like that. It isn't my fault that I never felt in the same way before I knew you — is it? But it is terrible to cause so much pain, and there are times when I loathe myself.

LISOU

C. . . . Friday evening, 29th September

I am feeling a bit knocked up, darling, and I want to make contact with you. You are in bed at this moment, just as I am, and how much better off I'd be if I were lying beside you. There is nobody here with me in the room. My mother is gallivanting about the streets, while I'm having a good, sensible 'lay-down' before dinner. As a matter of fact, I'm not at all hungry, and I'm so longing for you to be here with me that nothing else matters. It seems strange to be once more hearing the noise of cars in the streets . . . What funny things cities are! There are so many children about that I don't know which way to turn. There was one adorable mite in front of me at the cinema. I had to keep telling him to sit down — otherwise I shouldn't have seen a thing.

C. . . . is, on the whole, pretty lively, but, all the same, I am bored to death. The men all look like toughs. I've noticed a very handsome woman in our hotel, with masses of fair hair — just your type: but Na. told me some pretty beastly things about her. After lunch, I sat in the lounge for a while, sipping a Chartreuse, and the people there made a very sinister impression on me. It seemed to me that not one of all those men and women were leading what I should call 'good' lives — by which I don't mean morally good, but aesthetically and emotionally. None of the couples I saw made me think — 'There, at any rate, are two who live for each other'. They all had the same air of wanting to be somewhere else — and that made me feel bitter — I'm just off to dine. Goodbye for the present: I am brim-full of you.

Midnight, the 2nd. It is sheer delight to be in a horizontal position. I love you. I want to be yours. I am tired, and I feel desperately lonely when you're not with me. It's quite frightful having to live without you. Up on our mountain I don't feel it so much, but down here, where existence is normal, I'm conscious all the time of being in a howling wilderness. I'm going to bed now, because I am positively dropping with exhaustion, and because I can do nothing but repeat the same words to you over and over again, endlessly.

Saturday morning. Good morning, Yves. Can you tell me why the people in this damned town sing the *Internationale* at 3 a.m.? My mother's out, having one last run-around. The *Bec Fin* is a delicious spot at night — we were at the far end close to the fire-place. It was crammed with Americans — all very gay, and the air was reeking with tobacco smoke — quite indescribable. Unfortunately, we had to leave early, because of the film. It was *Souls at Sea* — Gary Cooper. If I'm ever unfaithful to you, it will be with him. He's got such a *good* face — almost too good to be true. It was lovely walking along the streets in the dark, imagining that the footsteps at my side were yours, and that we were in Paris — lovely, and rather sad. There was a beautiful moon, and the sky was full of stars. I'm wondering whether that pneumoperitoneum is making you feel bad or not. Bells are sounding all over the place because it's just ten — I love chiming bells — and fat white pigeons are flying to and fro in front of the open window. In the distance, a street-merchant is crying his wares — but I can't hear what they are. Kiss me quickly, my dear darling. I want to burst into tears. I don't seem to know how to go on living when you're not with me. Everything here fills me with disgust, everything hurts me. Each time a man looks at me I want to spit in his face. I'm just going for a walk. Yesterday I came across a baby crying its eyes out, but it stopped suddenly when it saw me, and smiled. That was the best moment of the day.

Everything that holds me to you drags at my heart-strings abominably. All the same, I love to feel just how much. . . .

X . . . *Sanatorium, Saturday night.* Now once more I can be vividly conscious that I am not very far from you . . . As always when I return from a plunge into the outside world, I'm spending ten minutes arranging flowers in a vase, and generally tidying up.

By and large, the impression left on me by this holiday is unpleasant. My mother would be miserable if she knew that. The chief effect of my two days away is to make me realize how young I still am. So many things shock me, even now. I feel them to be quite monstrous — and sometimes wonder whether I shall ever get used to them.

After lunch, I went into an exquisite garden which goes by the name of the Town Park. There were masses of flowers of all sorts, babies on the paths, nurses on the benches, and old gentlemen sunning themselves. But what I chiefly remember, Yves, are the roses — such lovely, such perfect roses that everything seemed to be transfigured because of them. I should have liked to pick one for you, but didn't dare. I had to be satisfied with sniffing them in an off-hand manner.

Did you go climbing on Friday morning? — I expect you did, it was such a lovely day. Did you enjoy yourself, and is your shoulder still painful? I bought some Swiss papers. Mummy says they'll interest you, so I'll send them along. I am feeling awfully cold, my dearest dear, and must say good night. I should so love to see you.

LISOU

Tuesday evening, 3rd October

I am longing for a roaring fire and cups of tea laced with rum. How gorgeous it would be if we could stretch our hands to the blaze, and see the red glow through the transparent skin, me leaning with my back against your knees. Perhaps, like that, I should be able to forget all the hateful things you said to me this morning. I have a lingering hope that you were just exasperated by my snivelling, and didn't quite realize what you were saying. To be told that one's shortness of breath is just put on is pretty hard to swallow. It would never occur to me to 'put on' anything of the sort when I'm alone — unless, of course, that's what I am always doing, from morning till night, without being conscious of it . . . I said nothing this morning because it was obviously so much better that I should go away . . . It really is extraordinary how everything about you can, in a flash, become hostile and full of hatred. There was something in the way you looked at me that I shall find it hard to forget — and for *such* a reason, too . . . it really was all too amazing. Would you like me to explain why and how I am short of breath? You seemed to me to be quite incapable of understanding. Don't you realize that I have three pneumos, a sheet of tissue joining up which gives me a lot of pain, a fine big hole in the lung, and a diaphragm that's as stiff as a board? I find it hard to believe that one could have any better reason for being short of breath. I should so much have preferred never having had to explain things of this sort to you. Does it never occur to you that I would much rather think of other things? — that I might feel mortified at the subject coming up in so ridiculous a manner? *Please* never accuse me in that way again, it hurts too much. Will you promise? Still, the situation has this amount of good, that I am the only person in the place who's entitled to use the lift. Thank Heavens, *you're* not my doctor! The medical authorities do, at least, show more understanding than you.

How fantastic that it is dark now by half-past six! I keep thinking of last year. Still, however that may be, I adore being with you in the dark — one feels so much closer, don't you think? — I remember the first time you kissed me: you just took my face between your hands, I scarcely felt your lips, and asked you, with rather a scared look, why you had done it . . . That must have been a whole year ago. I am reading an excellent book translated from the Russian, called — *Without Taking Breath* (very apposite, don't you think?). It really is most awfully good — powerful and out of the ordinary. I love losing myself in that sort of existence. It is curious, too, to think what a good novel one could write round one's own life — if only one had enough faith and enough intelligence to know what to put in and what to leave out. Mere talent is a secondary matter — all that counts is the interest (I believe that with my feelings though I don't think it with my mind. For me, talent — style — are the chief considerations, but I know I am wrong about this, and shall probably change my mind as I grow older . . . One day I shall start telling the story of my life, without bothering about style. I am busy collecting material!). I wish you would read this book. It is particularly interesting just now. I, personally, have rather a weakness for the sort of writing which mixes ruggedness with sentimentality — and it seems to suit the Russians. They are capable of any number of unusual and attractive subtleties, and, by nature, they are passionate. I think *you* are rather like a Russian. Don't be annoyed: I have known several very nice ones! Now I've got to refill my hot-water-bottle. I'm so cold that it freezes when I touch it! Good night, my beloved (in spite of everything). I'm terribly glad to think that you are to stay on here till January — don't grab me by the ears — it's true!

Wednesday evening. You bring up against me what I said about

T. I wonder what momentary fit of insanity led me to tell you about it — please forgive me. It was just one of those perfectly idiotic, inexplicable and useless things one does — and afterwards regrets — at least that's how it is with people who suffer from my particular form of stupidity. You are right to reproach me. It was an absurd thing to do and, quite apart from that, utterly unlike me. I am amazed at myself. But I do want you to realize that my object in writing as I did was to share with somebody else the terrible weight which the incident laid upon me. I know that I ought to have washed my hands of it once and for all, but I can't. At the moment when Erik turned up, we had been talking about him. You were being more distant, more unapproachable than ever, and I was all at sea and very miserable. All I am doing now is what I should have liked to do then — telling you everything and asking for your help. But to do it now has no longer the same point, and I do understand why you should have felt some surprise. All the same, I am sure that you are quite wrong to speak as you do about his lack of modesty. My own idea is that when people are deeply in love, they forget all about modesty . . . That is what frightened me in you at a time when I didn't know you as well as I do now — and there are still certain facets of your character which I find it hard to accept. Is it lack of modesty on my part to tell you that you are all in the world to me, that I simply can't imagine living without you, that I want to lie stark naked in your arms, and to give myself wholly to you? If it is, then I am wholly lacking in modesty, and you are very properly annoyed. But what do you expect? — I can't not speak as I do, and, since my way of speaking is the result of my immense love, I naturally imagine that those who love me as much as I do them cannot but behave in the same way, irrespective of character or any nonsense of that sort.

I should rather like to talk about other things, but it is very late. It was lovely seeing you this evening. It would be lovelier still to think that this pneumoperitoneum business wasn't going

221

on — I'm going to hate not getting a glimpse of you for ten days. There are moments when I no longer feel quite sure which is your mouth and which is mine. I am happy, Yves, when your arms hold me tight. Then, I am the most utterly contented person in the whole world.

Thursday evening. I have just been turning over in my mind all the things I wrote to you on the subject of T. One thing is certain, that the tragic aspect of his love gives him an importance he wouldn't otherwise have had. But don't, for a single moment, run away with the idea that I have let that influence me. It is a curious fact, in general, how some people hate being happy in love — Jews, in particular. And yet, to my mind, nothing is more beautiful than to love. In this Russian book, as you'll see, the author seems to think that grandeur can come only from suffering. But that's wrong, isn't it? I think you'll like the book — I, certainly, shall never forget it — (I love the way he talks about dogs) and there's a great deal of humour in it, too.

LISOU

Friday, 13th October

Have you ever read any of Rilke's poetry? It shares, with the *Fleurs du Mal*, the honours of my bedside table. I know nothing that touches me so deeply as his poems, even in translation. I have an idea that I understand, and feel, precisely as he would have wished me to. I could have loved that man, even though he did look like a gloomy and disgusted seal. He was living at the Hotel Biron at the same time as Rodin. He must have had the most exquisite taste. When he speaks of the wind in a fig-tree, and of the tree's joy in it, I actually, for a moment, become the tree. Do you see what I mean? — it's very difficult to explain. I could read his poetry for hours without growing tired, toasting bread in front of the fire all the while. Since there are so many things I shall never be able to do again, I treasure moments like that, such sweet, peaceful moments, and I feel sure that life can still be marvellous — even without swimming and boating and sunlight and an upright stance and children. — Don't you think I am right? — always assuming, of course, that you existed for me as much as — or more than — you do now. It is curious how one can bring oneself to accept a totally different kind of world merely as the result of being ill. None of the things for which I longed so passionately two years ago will ever now be realized. But I no longer feel the least regret — or only, at times, a passing one. It would, I think, be much harder for you. Here is one of Rilke's poems. It might be something you had once written for me without noticing what you were doing:

> Could you, if one day I lost you, sleep
> Nor know that I was rustling like a tasselled lime
> Above your head?
> Nor know that I was watching you, and laying
> Words on your breasts like eyelids, on your limbs
> And lips? Nor that I would leave you
> Shut in upon your loneliness which would be
> Like to a garden peopled with star-anise
> And with balm?

Isn't that delicious? I adore every line of it. Oh, my darling! — if only I could find words to tell you of all the extraordinary things I felt during those few moments that we spent together last Sunday, among the leaves and under the rain! Never have I felt anything so strongly, so ... I don't know how to put it except to say that it was beautiful. I am not a little girl any longer — there is something I know now and never knew before. That expectant waiting — and the sweetness — and the flood of fire in my veins — quicker and quicker, higher and higher, further and further, deeper and deeper — I love you — you clasp me tightly — and I am happy — why do you say 'in an indecent manner'? My happiness could never, where you are concerned, be indecent, and nobody else knows anything

223

about it. Do I seem childish to you? Do try to understand what it all meant to me — it was so utterly new, and now, thinking of it, I look at my body with something like amazement. It was marvellous — incredible — unique. I would never have said a word to you if you had not lain there for so long.

I have been thinking of what you said to me about sculpture. I really don't think I can ever take it up again. I would rather not recapture the taste for it if it meant having to give it up later, or only doing it by halves. It is one of the things one can't start if one doesn't mean to give oneself to it body and soul. When the passion seizes me I am quite capable of working for a week on end without once going to bed. And then, there's the nervous excitement, which is more exhausting than anything else. At such moments I feel that I could bodily assault anyone who interrupted me.

No news from the medical front. I asked Dr. M. for an interview, and he came to see me yesterday, at the same time as the X-ray man. He seemed in rather more of a hurry than before to get me operated on, and he's going to write to Dr. R. He thinks it much wiser for me not to wait until R. comes here. That means I shall go to Paris. You won't be there, and I am frightened. He is strongly of the opinion that the operation ought to be done before my right pneumo has completely joined up. I don't suppose I should come back here afterwards, but everything's still extremely vague and uncertain.

LISOU

LETTER TO MADAME C.

Saturday, 28th October

There's a film-show this evening, so I've got a little time in which to write to you. This morning one of the new arrivals brought me your big envelope with all the letters in it. You can't imagine the extraordinary effect that the sight of it produced on me. I sat in front of all those letters, completely incapable of reading them — I started on one, then left it, took up another, buried my head in the pillow and had a good cry, then started to laugh — in fact, I behaved like a perfect idiot. Finally, I read the lot during the Silent Cure — and was delighted. I have learned so much since yesterday that I am in a complete daze — all your news, and then, to cap everything, Dr. I.'s return yesterday evening. I feel rather bad about you not being here because it looks as though the hour for making a final decision has struck . . . When I saw her yesterday evening, she told me that Vi. had been at home with Erik, and that she's heard nothing from Dr. R. Actually, what she said was — 'I think he must be with the troops on the Eastern front, so we shall have to think of something else.'

'What else?'

'Switzerland, if you can manage it' (it was the first time she had mentioned Switzerland to me, and it rather took my breath away) — 'Write to your mother. I'm still hoping for an answer from Dr. R. If one doesn't come in a few days, it'll mean that he has gone away, and that it's no use counting on him. But you have got to make up your mind. To delay any longer is mere waste of time. We'll wait a fortnight, perhaps rather less.' So that's that. It's all pretty clear — but I can't pretend that I'm not feeling slightly sick. It's all so on top of me now, so fixed and certain. The snag is — that it's going to cost the most awful lot . . . and you've had to pay out such enormous sums recently. It makes me feel terrible when I think of all that money being spent on things which give no pleasure to any of us! I've talked it all over with Yves (who is being quite wonderful), and he says that the exchange will probably be ruinous . . . Oh, Mummy, what a beastly mess it all is! . . . I don't know what to say . . . I am simply giving you the facts, and I don't want to bring pressure of any kind to bear on you. I know that what you most wish is to do what I want — and that's desperate enough for me in all conscience . . . All I want is to get the whole horrible business over and done with as soon as possible. And then, I think of you, how you have no sooner got home where everyone is waiting for your coming as though it were that of a Messiah, than up I jump and carry you off again, away from them, away from everything . . . Perhaps you might manage not to come, isn't that a possibility? I'm courageous enough and confident enough to face that decision, if you make it. After all, if things go well, I shall be up and about again very quickly. I'm not in the least frightened — it's only that I want to know definitely what's going to happen instead of floundering about in this state of uncertainty. I hate being the centre of so much fuss. On the whole, I think it better that you should stay in Paris, because you may have things to do there, if it *is* to be Switzerland. I. is wholeheartedly against letting any unknown chap do the operation. The opinion seems to be general that I ought to have a really good man — flattering, but rather frightening, too . . . Yves has bucked me up and doped me no end this morning, with the result that I feel now that I could go to the scaffold without a tremor. It is such a blessing that he is on the spot. He says that I've been under two thumbs, yours and his, and that now you are no longer here he's going to take your place and tell me exactly what's got to be done, what I've got to ask the doctors, and all the rest of it. There is only one thing he regrets — that he's not free to go with me and act as my guide through all the troubles. It is at moments like these that I really appreciate the difference in age between us, his calm and sensible temperament, and everything about him that is solid and serious. So don't bother about me. I am in good hands, and there's one person at least here who doesn't regard me as merely a medical *case*.

What a game! I. has changed us all round at meal-times, and broken up our group, in the hope of getting us to eat more. The food here nauseates me — same old beans, same old potatoes, same old taste. How could anyone be expected to work up an appetite? I no longer get any butter. Fortunately, my room-mate gives me a piece of chocolate now and again. She's a nice creature, but a perfect fool, and reduced to a state of dithering panic by the very thought of this disease. Her temperature has only to go up to 99 for her to see herself on the operating-table, minus a rib! It really is screamingly funny, and I get a lot of amusement out of telling her the most hair-raising things. She is just off now for her cure, and I'm dressing in a nice warm room. The snow has all melted. There was an unbelievably thick fog earlier, but the sun came through in the course of the morning, and hopes are high for tomorrow. We're having another film on Tuesday. I continue to take my cure with Li. in the most exemplary fashion.

I have simply devoured papa's 'Journal' of the Liberation of Paris — I found it completely shattering. What an experience! . . . I do so understand his regretting that he was almost alone, with no one to share his joy (to use a very inadequate word). The whole thing must have been *too* overwhelming — especially for someone who, like him, took part in the war of '14. It seems to me that though we have all been scattered during these great events, they have, somehow, drawn us even more closely together. Don't you agree? I long to see him, and to tell him that he really is quite . . . marvellous — I can think of no other expression! Personal ideas and tastes don't seem to matter: one gets above them, and sees human beings stripped to the essentials. I belong to a wonderful family, Mummy — I think you're *all* marvellous, and I'm the happiest person in the world. I see now that I haven't always realized that, and I feel ashamed . . . I long to see the lot of you together, with me in the middle — but even at a distance of 600 kilometres I feel that I am closer to you than I ever was — and that is something that no one will ever be able to take from us. I had a curiously vivid impression this morning at the sight of all your letters — the different hand-writings but all of them conveying the same message of affection. I've never felt anything quite so strongly — I wanted to tell Yves about it, but somehow I couldn't. What I feel about him, you see, is so totally different. I don't mind now if I get nothing from you for the next six months. This morning's batch was something in the nature of a miracle. I'm sure papa would have loved to have you with him during the liberation . . . I've just remembered that you were married in the middle of a war. . . .

It's all profoundly moving . . . or perhaps it is that I am just morbidly sensitive. . . .

Monday morning. Li.'s parents won't be starting for Paris until Thursday, so I'll post this. Madame E. says that it will arrive just as soon. I saw her yesterday morning. It started to snow again a few hours ago — fog — weather beastly. An American film yesterday, with Joan Crawford, Gable and Franchot Tone — not a bit funny. Perhaps I need readjusting — but the fact is I scarcely laughed at all.

Please let me have a quick answer to all my questions about the operation. I should so like everything to be settled soon. Madame E. offered me some potatoes — and brought me walnuts and two pancakes.

I send you a big hug — it's for all of you. The problem of what to wear on one's feet in this snow is terrible.

I adore Chopin — how about you?

Monday evening. The mail arrived too late this morning for me to be able to answer all the letters I got. One thing, however, seems to me to be important, and that is what papa says about Dr. R. being in Paris — it changes everything. I'll try to see I. this evening. We're waiting for Dr. E. who may bring the latest news. Your letter's dated the 26th, papa's the 27th — I have also received the one you sent me from Lyon. That seems to me extraordinary. But the great thing is that the post from Paris is pretty quick. I should be very pleased if I could get out of having to go to Switzerland. I should have to wait so horribly long for letters. Yves is pleased, too. If it turns out that I have to go to Paris, there would be no point whatever in your coming to fetch me. I'll try to reach some sort of understanding with Erik, so that I can leave with him. Besides Yves has quite made up his mind to go with me as far as C. . . . and put me on the train. He says he'll explain it all to I. With this ordeal lying ahead of me, I should so love to have a few hours with him. We could lunch together. Do you realize that we have never been together — away from this place?

I'm waiting before packing my bag, therefore, until I hear what Erik may have to say, or what news you may have to send. So far I have seen neither Vi. nor Erik. I think Vi. will be here tomorrow. This talk about a small parcel makes me very impatient to see her ... What is Jean-Jacques' verdict — and Hélène's? Simple she may be, but she's charming. I think I shall add a postscript to this letter before sending it off tomorrow.

Nine o'clock — a chance to get it off after all. I'll write again tomorrow.

L.

Saturday night, 11th November

There's a cut-glass vase on the table with three dark red roses in it. I have been looking at them for the last three hours. Twice I tried to do something else, but it was no use. Yves, darling, I love you so much that I am in grave danger of becoming completely insane — I am already — I can feel it. That particular condition began with me rather more than a year ago, and it has been growing steadily worse and more beautifully pronounced ever since. I've tried everything in the hope of lessening the fatal effects, but since you don't do a thing to help me, I've abandoned the attempt.

I am utterly without poise — I only wish you could lend me a little of yours ... You spread chaos — and *what* chaos! — in my little inside, and then you leave me to cut a way through the tangle of my feelings, desires and memories, as best I can ... You are most marvellously beloved ... If you so much as touch my hand the world has a different taste. Even while I write these words the miracle to some extent occurs. I never thought love could reach such a pitch, had never foreseen such an extravagance of feeling. But, Yves, aren't you afraid of me sometimes? It amazes me that you shouldn't be. I'm quite beside myself — not in the usual sense of 'Oh, my dear, he made me feel utterly beside myself!' — but in another, and what that is I am sure you know. When you look at me, and your eyes pause at my mouth, my feelings are too much for me — my lips part — and then I go weak all over — something red-hot seems to be melting in my breast and running down into my legs, and into still deeper profundities . . . and then you start talking of something else, and I come to the surface again. I love it when your voice fishes me up like that from far, far down, bringing me back to daylight.

I said to you, one night, when you had swept me to the heights (I love you so when I am half naked) that I was too small for all that. But now I don't think that's true — it's only that I am too small to give you back all you give me. But I do so want . . . I am always the one who receives. But I love you — my love is big, big, and all of it I give to you, and you can't but be happy because of it. I don't feel frightened at all this evening — tomorrow's far away — and soon I shan't even be able to think about tomorrow. It's to be in three months, and only then, if . . . it's terrifying. I shall be utterly lost without you — I wonder if you really know *how* utterly. But I'd rather be the one to go. I pity you having to stay on here without me.

I can feel my heart throbbing in my throat. I can smell the scent of roses. I can feel your kisses, your one particular kiss — as no one else in the world could ever do.

Tell me to be calm and sensible. Tell me not to write. Tell me that my tummy is soft. Tell me that you have nothing more to say to me, and nothing more to hear. Tell me to stop talking.

LISOU

Monday evening, 20th November
I think I've got a hundred things to say to you, and that I am in the right mood to say them. But I can give no guarantee. I am answering a letter of yours. I've answered it once already,

but, unless my memory is at fault, I didn't send what I wrote. Of course it's possible that you might deceive me, but whatever you did, you'd always love me more than I deserve — and that's not false modesty. At the moment, I deserve nothing at all — I'm worthless, capricious, touchy, spiteful, and, more than anything else, sad — yes, sad. You'd never have guessed it, would you? — that's my small triumph. But for this evening, just for this evening, I am laying down my arms. You'll find me tomorrow once again a sturdy fighter — it makes me happy to think that.

You don't know how sick at heart I feel. If you could see me just now you'd believe it. I wonder whether the day will ever come when you will give me the sort of feeling I so desperately need in our relationship. I don't know what to call it — all I do know is that I want to cling to something else, something other than you. I knew it yesterday. You were sitting beside me, and had just said that you were going to spend a week in the Midi. If I hadn't been sitting down when you said it, I should be feeling now that I hadn't a bone in my body. A horrible, and quite indefinable, feeling came over me. I longed to be able to laugh at myself, to mock. One of the things I've never been able to do is laugh at myself — I said as much to some-body — I can't remember to whom — in a letter yesterday morning, and now, like a bolt from the blue, it's just happened. I shall have learned heaps and heaps of things from being with you, and I shall emerge from the experience with the gifts of silence, reserve, secretiveness — and perhaps with a sense of humour about myself . . . I owe you much. My mother, I think, will be delighted. Devoted to me though she is, she hates my temperament. I'm saying all this quite seriously. I don't see why you should smile. Look at me. Do you know what I am really like at bottom? I'm a consummate actress, and I defy you to judge of my real state of mind on any given day.

Well, to go on. You were sitting beside me, and I suddenly felt a longing to laugh — at myself, that goes without saying. I rejoice, Yves, at your news. The thought that one of us two will be looking at the sea and feeling the sunshine, gives me great happiness. It'll be almost as though I were there, too. I am terribly childish, you know, in the sense that I think much too much in terms of *us*, instead of about you and me as separate entities, with each our own bit of road to jog along. It is the puerile product of my particular kind of passion. It is false — people like you are a living proof of that. Your view is the right one — I admit that, and from now on I shall jog along on my own road and leave you to yours.

I know perfectly well that, figuratively speaking, you are raising one fist to heaven and, with the other, giving me a good clout on the nose. I know that you're thinking — 'and all because I was fool enough to mention this little trip of mine!' — I put myself in your place, and understand so well what is going on in your mind that I might *be* you. Heavens above! — what an exasperating creature I am! Why don't you tell me so? — I should only laugh a little louder, that's all. At this present moment I no longer feel much like laughing. But in my heart of hearts I'm pleased. I have decided that you are exactly, eminently and perfectly what I need as a corrective. I don't think I shall write to you again before I leave, and afterwards, I'm afraid I may find it even more difficult to do so. I dreamed a few nights ago — it was the night when I slept so well — that I had lost sight of you for four years, and then come across you again on a station platform, somewhere abroad. I was alone — you were with a fair-haired woman rather like Madeleine Ozeray. She was looking at me with a very ill-natured smile, perhaps because I was watching what you were doing with your hands . . . You had taken off one of your gloves — the right-hand one — in order to say how-do-you-do to me, and I was hypnotized by your fingers. They had completely changed. They belonged to hands which I had known but which weren't yours. You were saying something in which the words — 'four years ago: is it really as long as that', occurred, and I was tugging at the handle of my suit-case. I said 'Oh, yes', or something equally intelligent, and all the time I was wishing that I had never been born . . . You were, both of you, perfectly calm and, so far as appearances went, pleasant and friendly. My shadow was broken by the edge of the platform in a rather ridiculous way. You looked at it, and that made me feel ill at ease. When I woke up the same rather hateful impression was still with me. Please realize that I was in a rather particularly charming mood. It was as though I had been reborn. I know perfectly well that something of the same kind might actually happen. I have odd presentiments. Seriously, though — I no longer believe that we shall ever live together. That word 'together' is, to me, marvellous, but I think it is difficult to make of it an attainable goal. I started all wrong. I don't doubt that you love me — if only you could know with what violence I long to abandon myself to that idea — the only idea, I think, that has ever meant anything to me. But, though I believe you, I can't achieve that abandonment, and, unless I do, I can't love as I should love. With you, I daren't. There is always about you something which sets me on the defensive, something that damps my ardour and my happiness. I want to cry out to you — 'Stop! for heaven's sake, stop! — don't say what you were going to say' — and then you say it. I suffer from a horrible sort of self-love which immediately makes me want to hurt you, too — to brazen things out — to seem . . . But that really is too idiotic, and time and time again I have regretted it. I won't do it again. I'm going away. I shall take a stupid journey, surrounded by frightful men. My family is going to be a disappointment. I shall find home smaller and colder than I expected — my sister dim — my father sad — my brother tired. It will rain, I expect. I shall look down into the street and see the heads of the children who live on the floor below. No one will have remembered to put flowers in my room. I shan't stay more than three days. I shall take my suit-case and catch another train, Métro, this time, and I shall be weighed down by the kind of weariness that takes the colour and taste out of everything. I can feel it all as though I were there already. Christmas? — I love Christmas because it is terribly important that there should be somebody who does — but I am never so depressed as on these festive evenings — and never so much regret that I have ceased to believe in Santa Claus. I have to force myself to be happy, to make others happy. I have always made enormous efforts to that end. Oh, I hate Christmas, and the thought of going home throws me into a panic. When I'm lying alone in my bed with the fire burning, what good will it do me? What more shall I have there than I should have had here, or anywhere else? I say to myself — I shall write. Write what, and for whom? You don't feel what I write — not even now. You don't feel anything. I don't want to lose my temper. I want to make you laugh, as you did a month ago, and, most of all, I want you to look as though you had never had this letter — all the same, I'd like you to re-read it when I've gone. You are the most terrible thing that could ever have happened to anyone of my kind: terrible and lovely, but, for me, crushing. I am too small. When I am far from you I shall recover my normal weight. I love being alone, quite alone.

My neighbour is snoring. I can see a star, one single star — my own.

Goodbye till tomorrow — man whom I love. Life is extraordinarily beautiful.

Tuesday evening. I didn't have a moment this afternoon to add a postscript, so here I am, with my electric torch under my chin. You lost a lot by not going to the lecture. It was good, and the discussion was amusing — the whole thing exquisitely intelligent — the kind of evening that reconciles one to the whole world. . . .

But what about you, Yves? I never thought it possible that I should be in such a hurry to get away. Sa. once said to me — I can't remember in what connection — that you are extremely sensitive. She must, I think, know you better than I do. You have never shown yourself sensitive in anything that has to do with me. I won't say anything definite — I've done it so often before, only to fall into your arms again each time. I'll just be content to feel — it's about the only thing I know how to do properly.

'For those who think, life is a comedy: for those who feel, a tragedy' — probably true.

I'm cold because the window is open. I'm miserable because I can't take a train tomorrow without seeing you. I hope and pray that you won't come with me to C. . . . In particular I hope and pray that I shan't change my mind between now and then . . . No, I won't, not even once. There are so many things I've got to let drain off and settle. If you're not sick of me, that's because you are solidly built. Don't be angry with me for bringing up all these disagreeables again. It was difficult for me to go further. I can see any number of stars tonight, and life seems less magnificent. You looked very happy this evening — quite radiant. That is how I should like to remember you. I love it when you're gay — especially when it's to some extent because of me.

I feel that I could be endlessly beastly to everybody. Only my mother stands firm. I can't tell you how hopelessly my friendships have played me false . . . and there am I, pretending I've got everything I want . . . I've made a desert around myself, for various reasons. There is a whole side of me, I think, about which you know nothing — the hateful side of me . . . I mean it. What sort of a future can you see for me? — I can see none.

To hear me talk you'd think I was still terribly privileged — an adorable family, friends, people who are fond of me — and a happy temperament which can adapt itself to anything . . . You don't know what agonies I have gone through in an effort to convince myself of all that. Why it has all collapsed just now, I don't know — nor why I seem not to care. You certainly don't count for nothing in the sum-total — but how, I wonder, do you count for anything?

I wish I could explain it all to you — but it is so nebulous, and so excessively difficult. If only I could think instead of feel, but I am not intelligent enough for that. I think you are being a terrible disappointment to me just now. I looked for so much more from you — in the way of morale. Never have I needed more to have some support. But I've got beyond all that. I swear to you that I am happier and calmer at this moment than I have ever been. I regard myself as a fool, and that amuses me. There was a time when it would have made me cry — but that's a thing of the past. I laughed yesterday when you told me that my eyes looked funny — complete abandonment to tears is very restful.

I'm cold. Please don't talk to me about all this. There's still time in which to stir the mud, but I haven't the courage to face it. I kiss your eyes, and your left ear.

Wednesday evening. The light's still on apparently, which spells disaster for you, because here I am again. I am certainly out of luck's way, beloved. Vi. was with me all afternoon until dinner — quite ravishing, I devoured her with my eyes — an extremely agreeable occupation. She told me all about her having gone to see them at home. She found them very cold, and in a not very good humour . . . and then, Heaven knows why, she started talking about you and O. being drunk at C. . . . You wanted to sleep with a woman. I only hope she didn't see from my face the pain she was causing me. I imagine I felt much as one feels when one has just received a revolver bullet in the stomach. I longed to curl up, with my knees to my chin, and to be deaf to everything. Don't worry, I laughed very gaily. All the same, it's odd that something which happened two months ago — and words which anyone in your place might have spoken — at least, I think so — should hurt so abominably. Coming just now, it was pure bad luck — and I had had enough of that already.

I shall show my gratitude by going down with her to C. . . . on Friday. Anything to get away from here, even for a day. I can't breathe in this place. I want to see whether it is possible to forget some of all this — just to see.

Dr. I. tells me that I can go out quite a lot when I get to

Paris. I certainly shall: I've no desire whatever to stay at home — they give me the horrors, the whole lot of them. I sincerely hope that my visit will be a short one — if it isn't, I shall burst.

Apart from all that, nothing new — the night is empty of rain and of stars.

I'm dropping with fatigue, and there's an ache in one corner of my head.

ELIZABETH

Sunday evening, 26th November

The awful thing is, Yves, that I didn't enjoy myself at C. ... not for a single moment. But I expect you realized that one can't change one's nature overnight. Do you know what gave me the most pleasure in all those twenty-four hours? In the first place, the episode, or rather episodes, of my umbrella, because, no matter what the circumstances, that kind of comic adventure always gets me — and that, I can't help thinking, is all to the good. You would have died of laughing to see the crowd that gathered, the serious look on the faces of the men — men always get excited over anything in the least mechanical ... and the tram which gradually emptied — much to our advantage. The best is the enemy of the good, as a University Professor with a heavy moustache and a carefully pressed suit sententiously remarked — and me buying aspirin at a chemist's, where I caught the damned thing in all the bottles. The same farce was repeated in every shop we entered. I did enjoy that — and also the sinister light which gave such a wonderful colour to the bunches of ripe maize hanging at the doors of the houses all along the street — and a baby at the tram-shop who slipped his hand into mine in the mistaken belief that I was his mother ... He was wearing a white mitten, and stood staring at the tyres of the cars with startled eyes. His father, a perfect idiot, had told him not to move. He was obviously dying to touch them. I closed my fingers on his, though not too tightly, so that he

237

shouldn't look up. When he discovered his mistake, he started to howl, which confused me not a little.

I was in luck's way so far as children were concerned. In the tram a small boy plucked me by the sleeve to offer me his seat. I tried to refuse, but it was difficult. He was quite exquisite to look at, very fair, with a thin, pointed face all dusted with down, and a pair of interminable eyelashes wet with rain. He stood in front of me, holding himself very upright. He was wearing a khaki forage-cap on the back of his head, with a row of revolver, or machine-gun, empty cartridges strung across the front of it. When the speed of the tram increased, he hollowed his cheeks and held his breath. From time to time he turned and smiled at me in the way I like. As, no doubt, you have noticed, there is a kind of waterfall. Quite idiotically, I told him that it was called a cascade. Every five minutes he repeated the word 'cascade' as though it held some enormous significance for him. The stupid part of the incident was that the combination of physical fatigue, general run-down-ness, regret, and such a degree of depression as I had never imagined one *could* feel, led to my seeing this boy in a rather special light. I wanted to lay my cheek against his back and doze off — to ask him his name, so that I might send him something, some marvellous toy which would make it impossible for him ever to forget me. I had the greatest difficulty in persuading myself that he had done nothing more memorable than give me his seat (but I was wrong there — it has stayed in my memory, magnificently).

And that's all, Yves. Apart from those odds and ends the impression the place made on me was poisonous — married men ogling every woman who passed, and the women quite horrible, with an obscene look in their eyes, and equivocal words on their lips — oh, I don't know — hundreds of things that made me shudder. What I am looking for probably doesn't exist. All the same, I *have* known men, two at least, who, when they were in my company, would never so much as glance at another woman — no matter how exciting she might

238

be. I felt firmly convinced that for them there was something else, with the result that I was able to be myself, and that nothing irrelevant ever came between us. The trouble was that I could never give them that one sublime thing which I'm only now beginning to appreciate at its full value.

You, Yves, will never give it me, and you know that as well as I do. I understand you so well. I had a long talk about everything yesterday with a married man. His view was that for a man not to look at a pretty woman is abnormal — and I think he meant it as a compliment . . . I suppose I must be a very special case. I have to be handled with the greatest delicacy: too many things hurt me, I am at the mercy of too much. What Vi. said played more havoc with me than either you or she will ever realize. I had a feeling that every word she spoke was tearing part of me away, that I was bleeding all over. Do you think a day will ever come when I shall be able to forget all about it, and remember only what is best in you? I sincerely hope so. These horrible, horrible things keep passing through my brain. It appears that one of the things you have against me is that I ride you on too tight a rein. I could almost bring myself to laugh at that! You could have made me endure the pains of Hell if you had wanted to. Suddenly I see myself as you must see me — a pretty little thing with a nice figure whom you wouldn't be ashamed to be seen with in the streets of Paris. That's a bit grim for me, you must admit. I can't prevent myself now from seeing you in a very different light. I can't stand the idea of you perpetually drawing comparisons between me and other women, running over my points, criticizing me — especially in front of people who have played no part in our relationship. You are too essentially honest not to see what I mean, not to realize, as I do, that there is now an enormous wall between us. I think I ought to ask your forgiveness for a whole number of things — for having been so demanding, so un-understanding (that's probably what you meant by the tight rein — I should like to have a good giggle with you over that, it is *so* untrue) — so incapable of admitting how

239

totally different we are from one another. What I used to think of in you as lack of sensitiveness was, really, just this wall . . . You don't see me as I should have liked to be, and, for that reason, you will never find with me that peace of mind by which you set such value. I am not a woman of the world — and that's what you need — not elegant, not brilliant. Now that I bow myself out, I leave them all to you — though there was a time when I should have dearly loved to be the one and only woman in the world so far as you were concerned. I am quite sure that if I want to be happy (at the moment, I can't think of happiness even as a possibility), I must avoid handsome men. Don't rap me over the knuckles for saying that. Among the many delights you have given me, not the least was, quite simply, that of watching you live. . . .

I hope that you can read between these lines precisely how much I love you — though for me to say that again borders on madness. In ten years' time I shall think of you less frequently — which, for me, is some sort of consolation, and for you an encouragement. I shouldn't like to have hurt you — and, so that you may not have any wrong ideas about me — let me say that I didn't do anything bad while I was in C. . . . No one touched me, no one kissed me. The worst thing I did was to let myself drink, just to see whether I could forget — result, zero — and to dance, because I enjoy dancing — that's all.

Would you like to see me tomorrow? Thanks for offering me your help and support — but I need neither. Still, one never knows. I've nothing much to give you now — except a frank look in the eyes.

LISOU

Monday evening, 27th November
I lay my head on your shoulder. I am afraid, my love, that I shan't know how to go on living when you are no longer here. I am so much a part of you now. I am listening to a splendid

240

Concerto by Mozart, for two pianos. Each note disturbs me like a stone dropped into a pond. I know it's idiotic of me to write to you this evening: there is so little I can say now . . . I am happy, and that has the effect of making me inarticulate. I'd go so far as to say that I am even terribly happy — I hope that I shall get used to that some day — but I don't think I shall. You give me so little time to get used to things. Every day and every minute something new is born in us — which is very lovely, don't you think? Oh, this music! I wish you could hear it with your head tilted back on my arm, and your eyes shut — just as you were the other evening. If you were happy I should be feeling so completely fulfilled, and so proud. There is something extraordinarily moving about watching an eyeless face — but I shall never forget how you looked when you opened them — I felt that you were all mine — that is what your eyes told me — and it is quite impossible that you shouldn't have been. Don't protest. I should like to describe your expression, because you couldn't see it for yourself — and some day I will, in a novel. It was a quite unbelievable experience to sit there watching you, and waiting patiently until you raised your lids. At that moment, all life flowed back, and then withdrew once more into the secret places. Nothing remained but my hand on your body. What is it you do, I wonder, that the least thing coming from you makes me in love with life? I don't suppose you realize how enormously important that particular feeling has become for me.

I wish you were here. I wish you were talking to me. I wish you were passing your hands over my body. My hunger for you grows more and more intense. It is raining, and I have just read an article by Claudel which I don't like at all. He is really antipathetic to me. There is no sincerity in what he writes, nothing in it touches my feelings — what has become of *l'Annonce faite à Marie?* — on the other hand, I listened this afternoon to a short play by Chekhov which was quite extraordinary — about an old drunken actor who goes to sleep in a theatre box and wakes up long after the audience has departed.

He wakes, and with him wakes his passion for the theatre, though he has never played any but clowns' parts. He takes the prompter aside and begins to spout whole scenes from *Hamlet* and *King Lear*, and splendid Russian poems, all interspersed with hiccups, tears and memories. He doesn't want to go home — he has no home, no wife, no child. The prompter listens, and keeps on saying — 'What a wonderful talent you have, sir — truly wonderful.' He realizes that, talent or no talent, he is sixty-eight, and has been drooling away on the same note for an age. He rushes away, half mad, and shouting for a cab. The whole thing leaves one breathless and with an aching heart. You can have Claudel's faded felicities for all I care! The Russians seem to be gifted with a sense of fatality which could draw tears from a stone, and, perhaps because of the seeming ugliness of their lives, an artistic taste and a depth of sensibility which are unique. They can handle tragedy without ever becoming either insincere or ridiculous. One finds it hard to forgive people for being ridiculous, and least of all the authors whom one loves — at least, that's how I feel.

Incidentally, Li. has asked me to tell you that she is engaged. She particularly wants you to know. What an adorable child she is! I wish you could have seen her drop into a chair with a sigh, and heard her say — 'Ah, my dears, my dears, what an adventure!' — her eyes all shining with happiness. Don't you think they make a charming couple? — there's no other word for it — and it suits them so well to be engaged. I hate the word as a rule, and still more the condition, which has neither rhyme nor reason, but for them, and for certain other people, I think it must be the most delicious relationship in the world . . . I had the greatest difficulty yesterday evening to keep from laughing when she described how her mother cried with emotion when she looked at her. What an odd reaction, don't you think? I can't see *my* mother dabbing at her eyes in similar circumstances. And, do you know, her parents are still 'making inquiries' — I thought that sort of thing went out with the last century — it really is very comic. I must write a story about it

(I do so wonder what would happen if the inquiries were unsatisfactory — don't you?) — it sets me thinking. I wonder what you would do if you discovered that my mother came of a long line of pastry-cooks, or that my father was a blacksmith — it is all very silly and absurd — because I should still be just the same Lisou. But it's another case of how one *feels*. I'm afraid I'm rather boring you — let's change the subject. What awful weather we're having, aren't we? Couldn't very well be worse. I wish you were shut up in a room with me, or I with you. I have a longing for things that scarcely bear thinking about, and can't be written down or spoken. If ever you publish my letters, what sort of a figure shall I cut? — 'My dear, it's the only thing she ever thought about! — you've only got to read her letters to see that — it keeps on recurring like the *leit-motif* of her entire life! . . . It's obvious, of course, that it was the only great love she had ever known. He was everything to her — just everything. . . .'

Meanwhile, my dearest darling, I love you utterly.

Lisou

LETTER TO MADAME C.

Friday, 15th December

Mummy darling — just a hurried word to tell you that I got the parcel which you sent by train, and the other three which arrived by post. They have given me real pleasure, and I simply don't know what to say. I thought I should faint when I saw the scent. You are the most adorable of mothers, and pander to my every vice. Now that I've got this scent, I swear I'll never use any other. It is exquisite, divine, unique — and I simply reek of it! I hope you've remembered to send a telegram to Dr. E. Heavens! to think I'm actually of age! Poor E. — he must be terrified! We're leaving on Friday or Saturday —

which entirely depends on whether I get a couchette. The only thing I've got to bother about is resting — Yves has forbidden me to lift a finger. So I loll in bed all day while he writes, telephones, rushes off to reserve our seats, and generally behaves like a madman . . . it'll be almost as nice as travelling with one's mother.

The weather's glorious: we're devoting a whole morning to saying goodbye to the chaps at C. . . .

You ought to be very grateful to Yves — he's being perfectly wonderful — though he looks on me as so much excess luggage: still . . .

See you soon. No matter what anyone writes or says, I'm definitely leaving. I've filled up all the forms, and my name's down on the list of departures. I feel quite drunk.

Thanks again for everything.

Love to everybody — especially Ninnouche — it'll be lovely to see her again.

L.

Sèvres: Sunday, 24th December

How odd it is, Yves, to wake up without feeling that you are, in some sort of a way, close to me — that's to say, either in the next room, or on the floor above, or much, much closer . . . It's something I shall never forget. And now I have a feeling that I've said everything I had to say — I'm stupid when I have one of these uprushes of love, and quite incapable of proving that it's *because* I love you that I am so stupid.

I hope this desire for your presence will grow less sharp with time, otherwise it's a poor look-out for me. It would be nice to think that you miss me a little, too.

I felt terribly depressed when I got home — from many points of view. It's curious how detached from them all I feel, how cut off. You are the only thing in the world that really matters to me. With the people here I seem to be living on the surface, and scarcely even there. My deep and secret self is with you. The conviction that that is so sometimes comes over me in the middle of a conversation. Do you understand what I mean?

10 p.m. I couldn't go on with my letter just now, because I was being continually interrupted: but at last I'm alone. They've all got things to do in the house before the guests begin to arrive. The whole business gets on my nerves a bit — probably because I'm tired. For the last few hours the atmosphere has been Christmassy with a vengeance! If only this damned house was rather less cold. None of the doors shuts properly, the parquet-flooring is warped, and there's a horrible smell of damp everywhere. I wonder if you're having it as cold as we are? What are you doing at this moment? I'm busy keeping the fire in. My brother has just brought me a branch of holly, and my sister is crying because there's a war on . . . Where is our tiny little *wagon-lit* compartment, now? — probably occupied by a grumpy old gentleman with a beard, or by two grumpy old gentlemen with beards. Never before in all my life was I so contented, so happy and so . . . oh, I can't find words for it. It was divine, and you were quite wonderfully as I want you to be. If one can only wait for moments like that, they always come, I believe. Actually, I'd rather not talk about it, it was too wonderful. The memory has been with me ever since we parted. I feel now that I can face this operation with complete courage. You have had the most marvellously cheering effect on me. I owe you so much — and I want to be in your arms, not saying a thing, just feeling your head on my breast and your hands on my body, just listening to your voice or your breathing.

Monday evening. Again, I spent most of the day sleeping. It's true I didn't get to bed till 6.15 this morning — not that I enjoyed the Christmas merry-making. I didn't, for one single moment, feel that I was on the same wave-length as the rest of them — if you see what I mean. The Americans were quite nice — a major of fifty, very quick in the uptake, almost like a

Latin, in fact — two very young officers, and an English private soldier. They danced well, but they're terribly pessimistic about the war.

Sèvres: Friday night, 29th December
Round about five, I walked as far as the woods. You don't like me to like my memories, but I had so many with me this afternoon that I felt weak at the knees. It is very depressing to be in a deserted wood alone (no matter who happens to be with one) at five o'clock in the evening. There was an enormous crow perched on a very high branch, and he twisted his head and looked at me every time I scratched at the earth with my foot . . . I had some make-up on my eyelashes which made them smart abominably. It was very cold. A number of bombers flew across the sky in single file, looking as peaceful as a string of oxen, each with a little light on its wing-tip. There are moments which ought never to exist, and this was one. What I hate is that one can do nothing about them. I felt so strongly that I might just as well spend the night leaning against a tree, and that it wouldn't alter a thing — or go home to bed. I need hardly say that I went home — not from any instinct of self-preservation, nor because I was cold, but simply because I felt I ought. I can't help wondering how different my life might have been if I'd had no family. Very different, I think. I felt an acute longing to be quit of the whole lot of them, without attachments of any kind, as my old friend O. Wilde puts it — you've never said, by the way, whether you like him or not. I do. He acts on me like a drug, and pushes me bodily forwards by both shoulders.

Why did you ask me those idiotic questions the other day? What sort of an answer did you expect me to make? I certainly don't know. You must realize that when I am with you I am a completely new person. Perhaps under conditions like that one can be? I always believe in those novels in which women

246

with lurid pasts become as little children when a great passion sweeps them off their feet (don't deduce from that that I am a woman with a lurid past! — far from it!). I believe that you can make me forget any life I may once have lived, any sentiment, any sensation I may once have felt. Everything stops dead at the point where you begin, and that's all that really counts. But you have got to be there, or I have got to feel in some way or other that you love and suffer from being without me. Once I lack that certainty I become capable of almost any idiocy. I have proof of that. There have been times when I have knuckled under — not to the extent of falling very far, because I don't like being involved in self-loathing, and because under the influence of self-love I am capable of doing many things. Seriously though, I have occasionally let myself go — and you have always fished me up again. But I know that a day may come when, for some reason or other, you won't — and when that happens, then . . . I shall do it with my eyes open . . . but I hope that I shall be brave enough not to tell you anything about it. . . .

I suddenly feel tonight that I want to confess a piece of dishonesty. Do you want to hear it? — whether you do or not, I've got to get it down on paper. You may or may not think it's important, probably it is perfectly trivial, I, personally, don't think it matters at all. It is just this — that once, before ever you came on the scene, a man did undress me and see me naked. That's all. Now that I've got it out of my system I feel both frightened and relieved — though which of the two feelings is the stronger, I don't know.

The life I am leading here is, I think, from many points of view, quite hateful. I long to get away. I could even find it pleasant to go back to the Sanatorium. I can't get used to the idea of being an invalid in my own home. But to whom can I tell that? I am surrounded by people who bore me, with whom I now have nothing in common. I don't need them, but there they all are, as kind as kind, and trying desperately hard to show me affection, just in order to please me.

The sooner I can get into the Clinic the better. Once I am there I shall have long, blank periods, and that's what I want — terribly. But I should like to be able to take this room with me, its scrabble of papers, and its old familiar objects. But I've got to get used to being without them — I have left half of them at X, the other half is here. There's not much here now, just a few books, and I don't want to leave any of them behind. I loved your visit, but you were different. There are days when I find it impossible to believe in your existence, in you, or in your words, days when I am just scared out of my wits. I've got a stove now — it looks rather like a child's coffin. It gives off only a moderate amount of heat but a deal of smoke. In the room over my head, my brother is taking off his shoes — bang! — and then again, bang! I can feel that his mood is one of disgust with everything. My mother's hands are terribly worn, but she swallows her troubles with amazing courage. My father has just put in a rather sinister appearance. Our three best towels have been scorched on the stove in his room — there *is* rather a curious smell, to be sure. I am ashamed of lying in bed and doing nothing. I must get away. The 5th January is a long way off. I keep on thinking of that fair, flabby-faced woman in the train. The way she looked at you made me feel embarrassed — and the little chap opposite her, so pleased and patient — and the two Americans, one so curiously childlike and handsome — I wanted to touch his hair. I suspected him of being frightfully sentimental — probably suffering from home-sickness.

I think of you in your pyjamas — looking even younger than you used to do when we came back from our walks in the mountains. How I loved you — and, like the fool I am, I could never think of anything to say. I think you are the most essentially masculine person I have ever met — that may seem a clumsy way of putting what I mean, but it is difficult to find any other. I love it when you hurt me, and when you say 'that's what I want' — why don't you say it oftener, and twist my wrists? — I hate soft soap.

Mauricette is asleep on my lap. I am feeling hot, and the

248

back of my head aches. I shall see the New Year in by myself. The family's all going off and leaving the key under the mat. When midnight sounds I shall kiss my hand and wish myself a Happy New Year — Happy New Year, darling, may everything be well with you, and all your wishes be granted — Happy New Year ... I shall feel vaguely frightened at being alone, and I shall hear noises. I shall probably lie in front of the fire and write a lot of shocking bad stuff on the blessings of loneliness. I am reading a screamingly funny book by Huxley, called — *After Many a Summer* — I'll pass it on to you, if you like. . . .

I must get up and go to bed — it's after 11. What joy to have the light!

Good night: don't come unless you'd really like to see me. I am really quite an understanding person, you know ... I'd like to forget that I spent three days and three nights so close to you. You're right — aren't I too young for you?

I'd like to bend down over your mouth, unknown to you, and look at it steadily until I started to tremble with desire.

Saturday morning. What's the news? — they're putting me on a train again for the Sanatorium: there seems to be method in their madness.

Oh, well, it's all right — only, don't be angry with me if I do something silly — that's all.

Goodbye for the present.

LISOU

1945

Letters

I had a quite normal journey — no one at the station to go with me, and Et. here to meet me. No, Yves, I hadn't foreseen that it would all be so hard. I'm just a chuckle-headed little fool. I have moments of something very like softening of the brain, and when that happens, I become really almost despicable. I did keep a stiff upper lip, though, for quite a long time, until I was in the train, in fact — but it was difficult. I couldn't help remembering the same journey three weeks earlier, your arm round me keeping me warm, and our periods of lucidity. Anyone would have had the same reaction in my place, but it's not a thing I like admitting. Even Et.'s presence filled me with gloom — and then, when I did get here, nothing waiting for me but the Hotel Terminus. Have you got a glimmering of what that return was like?

9.30. I have just come down from Do.'s room. Those young girls are quite charming. Their tenderness to me restored my confidence. How I would have loved to see you! I dread this delay of six months — or more — before I shall be able to. You will have changed a lot, and so, I feel sure, shall I. By that time you will have become completely re-adapted to Paris life. I shall always be a step or two behind, and then, I can't help thinking how different we are, you and I. All the same, I still want everything. But I realize now what worlds away our ways of living are. I have an impression that you feel it, too, and that it worries you a bit. I don't think I shall be really happy for a very long time, not till all sorts of things have been said and done.

How beautiful it all looks — just as it did that day when we sat together in the snow: the same sky, the same air, the same warmth. I pitied you a moment for not being here.

I thought about you in the train, and got to the point of wondering why and how you manage to have all the marks of someone who has been very unhappy. But it seems to me that you have every reason for not being so. I can so well imagine what you were like when you were small — very well brought up — carefully chosen friendships — and a scrupulous conscience. All so different from me, from us. But it is you who are the normal one, and that rather annoys me. I was conscious of the difference every minute during the time I was seeing you away from here. I particularly don't want you to think that my mother isn't fond of you. She, too, is frightened — frightened of becoming attached to you, as she did to others in the old days, and then having to undo all those relationships little by little. I spoke to her about you in the train. She hated you for the harm you had done me. She could feel it in every one of my letters, although I never talked to her about it. She can't forget all that, and, what's more, she has no belief in *us* — which I find curious. What do you want to say to her? — she'll be very understanding. No, Yves, I love you more than ever before, more than I shall ever love you in the days to come. I am more convinced of that than I was three days ago. The fact of finding myself alone under the threat of something very horrible, has given me a curious lucidity of mind. But I won't pretend that I don't expect an enormous amount from you during this period, and I wonder whether it is wise of me to do so. Don't hold that against me, darling: I have had proof so often that my doubts are well grounded. You are not made for someone who is suffering, and you might as well admit it. I feel less and less desire to tell you how and why I am unhappy.

If everything goes according to plan, Dr. R. will arrive on the 25th, and I shall be put on the operating-table next morning — his first case of the day. What would you feel if I told you that I am frightened?

Wednesday. Nothing from you. I had a little private smile at my own expense because of all the things I had been imagining — I expect so much. What do you want me to tell you? It's a lovely — an incredibly lovely — day. I am protected against the sun by a flowered dressing-gown stretched between the casements of the window. A red-haired housemaid called Eulalie has just come in with a high stool and a grey-checked duster — such a to-do about merely giving the electric-light bulb a wipe!

During my absence, my room-mate has been busy hanging festoons of pink everywhere — even on the overmantel. She takes great pride in them. I feel as though I were living in a German kitchen.

Now I am going to begin unpacking my trunks which are all piled up in the corridor. I've already found out a way to have a few words with Z. — oh, hell!

Goodbye, Yves, for the present. Kiss my hands.

Lisou

Thursday, 18th January

I'm afraid of being guilty of a refined form of cruelty if I talk to you about this wonderful weather. The splendour never ceases. At this moment the sky looks rather washed-out — there is no more to be said about it except that it is blue. The hollows in the mountain show pink and mauve. The general effect is one of an extraordinary delicacy. I am listening to a Mozart Concerto which harmonizes wonderfully with the quality of the air and with my own feelings. Rarely have I been so receptive of impressions. In addition to all this, I can see a crescent moon curved like a nail-clipping. In an hour's time it will have crossed the frame of the window, and be surrounded by stars. All very Baghdad, don't you think? The air is mild and clean. I enjoy this weather as I enjoy the feel of your hands on me. Now that I am back here, my state of mind is very different from what it was in the old days. I employ my time differently, and, I think, better. Besides, I know that the moment when I shall really begin to get well is only a week away. I find much comfort in the thought that next Thursday, in a different bed, I shall be lying quietly nibbling at my nails and thinking about the morrow. There are moments when the mere idea of that makes me feel positively sick with terror — and others when I overflow with happiness, when I try to make myself as passive, as nearly animal, as possible, when I think of nothing, look forward to nothing, get to grips with nothing — and that is the best state of all. In the last analysis, I am definitely not afraid. You mustn't be, either, and especially not about me. The mountain tops are glowing bright pink like peaches, and the valley is becoming blue and less remote. I do so hope it will be weather like this next week, so that the framed view in the window may console me for everything.

9.30. After dinner I went and sat with Ar, whose room has nothing of the sanatorium about it. I brewed coffee on her spirit-lamp. We drank it and found life good. Now I am back here with no intention of going to sleep . . . It's all rather silly, I suppose, but so nice. Tonight I feel absolutely happy to be writing to you so frankly and freely. It is as though you were here with me. Do. is an exquisite creature whom I much look forward to seeing again at some time, away from here. She is lovely to look at, and very, very sweet. She always kisses my hand when she leaves me. I feel as though she were to some — in fact, to a considerable — degree my private property. The way she looks after me is quite touching. She is planning to bring me a whole lot of delicious things 'afterwards' — including an enormous ice-cream!

I had a long talk with the lady doctor this evening. She thinks that I shall be moved into the surgical block on Wednesday, but that the operation won't take place until Saturday. My most recent X-ray, taken the day before yesterday, shows a quite extraordinary improvement — the extent of my cavern has diminished by half . . . it really is incredible! This last trip of mine seems to have done me good. I don't understand it, and I don't try to. I am glad I didn't come back in a sleeper: sharing it with her would have seemed very flat, fond though I am of her. I have so precious a memory of *our* evening, *our* night, *our* morning. You can't possibly realize what pure waters of joy I draw from that recollection. Neither of us will ever forget it, will we? And then, the journey from Lyon to Paris. From leaning so long against you I developed the most extraordinary degree of sensitiveness. The lightest touch of your hand aroused in me a crowding flurry of desires. I didn't tell you at the time, but when you slipped your hand under my coat, I was completely thrown off my balance. I remember how, in the morning, you leant on the bar of the window, and how, looking up from beneath your arm, I could just see your chin and your mouth. I think I must have sat there for at least twenty-five minutes, just staring at your lips, and never once wearying of the occupation! But I had better stop. If once I start confessing all my fantasies I shall find myself embarked on an endless series of letters. It would never occur to you, would it, to gaze at my mouth for half an hour without saying a word, and simply and solely because the memory of certain things produced a train of such violent sensations? All of a sudden I feel the most terrific desire to tell you every detail of the life I am leading each day, from A to Z. Apart from the fact that it would be quite impossible to do so, and that the result of my efforts would reach you in a hopelessly distorted state, I should be guilty of a piece of exhibitionism in the worst possible taste. This morbid desire of mine to 'tell' is really very odd. My catalogue of events would, in itself, have no conceivable interest. It needs a very high degree of artistic awareness to decide what is worth saying and what isn't. Montherlant got in ahead of me with a rather similar remark about human suffering. But I, in my simple-mindedness, have no idea which will affect you more deeply — to know that the sky is a stainless blue, that years ago another man took off my clothes and caressed my body long before you did, that I have been drinking genuine coffee, or that I am full of aches and pains — out it all comes higgledy-piggledy. You give me the most perfect example of the opposite state of mind, but I can't help wondering which of us is right, and, in particular, which of us in the long run is the most impenetrable. We shall remain, both of us, on our chosen ground — you entrenched in your silence, I in my confusion of incompetently collected scraps of information which, I am quite sure, tell you no more than what I want you to know. It is a pity that what you most love in me should be the *simplicity* of a young girl, because I am convinced that the *complexity* of a young girl is what will always be my dominant element. This, however, I will say, that I do become simple when I have been with you for an hour. When I feel that you love me, all my complications melt and vanish. It seems to me at such times — and only at such times — that nothing else matters. But how, when you are far away, how, when for a whole week, I am given nothing but one brief and hastily scribbled letter, can you expect me not to revert to my natural self? Of course I love you, but my love doesn't to the same extent fill my mind to the exclusion of everything else, as when we are together. Don't you think that the fault may be yours? You have let loose in me such a raging torrent of physical passion that, for the moment, nothing can stand against it. There is no doubt that the 'you' I most utterly and completely love is the you who holds me tight, who caresses me and kisses me and sets my blood galloping. That is why I get so impatient with your letters — they are so little like you, so little like what I want you to be. Yes, it *is* your fault. If you loved me in a more intellectual fashion, I should be different — and so would you. I don't want to be loved like that, but if I were it would give me so much more the impression that it is me you love. Honestly, I find myself wondering why — for what reason — you love me. The words are inscribed in black and white at the end of your letter — 'I love you, Lisou', and I can see you in imagination, sticking down the flap of the envelope — 'there, *that's* done' . . . Will you ever find time to write to me as I write to you? — precisely as though you were coming to spend an afternoon with me? You don't mind giving up four hours to a visit, so why not give them up to writing — knowing full well, as you must, that every additional line will be a joy to me, that each time you put down the word 'I', the joy will be increased, and that I shall bless you for being, in your turn, quite a simple person? It amazes me that you should have to your hand — knowing you have it — this means of making me happy, and yet not want to make use of it oftener. So there — the buried hatchet has been dug up again! Why don't you snap your fingers at me and at my perpetual twaddle, and tell me to talk about something else? Never again will I drink a bowl of black coffee at half-past nine at night! It is twenty minutes to twelve — I've got only a tiny scrap of candle left and an enormous quantity of energy to be expended.

The wind is getting up and making the whole place shake. I talked too much about the glorious weather — I think it is going to break tomorrow. The air feels strangely heavy. I've got my sleeves rolled up, most of my pyjama jacket unbuttoned, and my lips feel dry. My room-companion — who also partook of my accursed brew — is sleeping with one arm dangling over the edge of the bed, and her fingers fiercely clawing at nothing.

I read today the most deeply moving book that has been written since *Mauritzius* — Steinbeck's *Of Mice and Men*. It really is a perfect thing, complete, rounded, a world in itself. There is everything in it — power and poetry, health and drama, starkness and subtlety, a toughness which is never vulgar, genuine originality, and inexhaustible literary skill — really everything: thank you, Monsieur Steinbeck, thank you. . . .

Friday. Gracious, what a wind! Huge black clouds, heavy with threats of vague disaster, are rushing across the sky. What violence! what energy! Did you know that Romain Rolland had written a stage-play on the subject of Saint-Louis? — a really side-splitting tragedy! My mother and I nearly died of laughing yesterday evening — all the more because we could imagine the actors in the Studio, complete with woolly comforters and leggings, half dead with the cold: 'The day promises great heat — prithee, Sir Gontrand, wipe my face, I swoon: — let us within the tent' — d'you get the idea?

259

— and all interspersed with frequent shouts of ' — Sing we our warrior song!' — after which they start braying like so many donkeys — 'Back! back! soon comes the dawn, we'll slay the Muslim infidels!' — great clanking of armour, and much panting from Gontrand.

I have been advised to exercise my arts of seduction on Dr. R. I shall do my best. The only trouble is that I shan't see him until I am in my cell in the Surgical Block — whereas I am so much more attractive in my own room! I have managed to get rid of the pink festoons, and have unpacked all my own dear belongings — my books and papers and little bits of nonsense. I only hope they won't shove me off into one of the other buildings when it's all over. In spite of what you say, I should infinitely prefer to be here.

The sight of the fog creeping up from the valley has cured me of any wish to stay here for long. I have returned once more to the charge with my mother on the subject of Passy. Now that your devastating influence is removed, I think I am making headway. I can take care of myself on my own — you can be sure of that.

LISOU

Tuesday evening, 23rd January: 10 p.m.

I've not yet read Eluard, but I swallowed the *Song of Songs* at a gulp. It's the most lovely thing that was ever written; why did you never tell me? All the same, dear wretch, it was sweet of you to send me so many nice things. I have only one complaint, and here it is: there was absolutely nothing to say that they came from you. Never mind, there's a quite adorable engraving at the beginning of the book (you must have seen it), which is the best of all dedications, and I regard it as such although you didn't, perhaps, intend me to do so.

I've just glanced at Paul Eluard's poems. They contain a

great many very beautiful things, when his patriotism is not allowed to feed on over-definite facts, but I don't much like the way he has of always mentioning names, and of mixing politics with poetry. The two don't, in my opinion, go well together, and I should prefer a poet of his calibre to take his stand on firmer and less shifting ground (I keep on thinking of Péguy — always so new). There is one beautiful poem on Paris in her misery — it is called *Courage*, have you read it? Why, after that, must he go and lose himself in personalities — 'so and so has been killed' — no doubt the thought is excellent and redounds to his credit — but the poem suffers, to say the least of it. I find it all rather embarrassing, if you see what I mean. But I realize, too, that I have not yet got the hang of all this modern verse. There is something in it that I shall always find a bit baffling. I hope you don't mind my finding Eluard slightly disappointing? — to my mind there is much more genuine inspiration in Aragon, and much less that is trivial. Obviously, patriotic verse is a very difficult form, unless one is willing to let oneself go on the old flag-wagging lines. Can you tell me, roughly, how old he is? I haven't the slightest idea. I'll read him again tomorrow with rather greater application, and perhaps I shall find more in the book than I did tonight. Anyhow, it is time I went to bed. Tomorrow they are showing an old film — *Les Trois Valses*: I think I'll go, just to have a look at your beloved Yvonne Printemps, and try to find what you find so attractive in her. Dr. R. has wired to say that he is arriving by car on Thursday, which seems to fix matters for Saturday. Think of me, darling, when you read this. Why must letters take so long to reach you? — it really is exasperating. There'll be a crowd of people looking at me and listening to me. I have given up all idea of seducing Dr. R. now that I know I shall be carried into the operating-theatre completely naked — art will be at a discount.

Wednesday, 11 a.m. I've just heard that I am to go off to the Surgical Block immediately. Hmm: I have a feeling that R. has arrived, and that my zero hour is fixed for Friday. I know he's going to begin with me — it's all pretty beastly, darling, but you are with me, aren't you? Look into my eyes and take my face between your hands. Bend your head a little to give me a kiss, tell me to be brave, and say that you love me — you do, don't you? — in any case, I love you and take you with me. I am very frightened, but you would be proud of me because I am so calm and smiling that no one would guess. Doesn't that deserve a good mark? I need you so badly. I think how much easier everything would be, how much less hard to bear, if you were close beside me; if I could see your eyes and your hands; if I could touch your lips, before starting off on this adventure — if you had said to me — 'Lisou, think of *us*.'

I don't like this weather — warm, soft rain, with clouds half way down the mountains. The valley looks black and very close. I am waiting for the mail. I must fly now, darling: I've got my packing to do. I don't know where my mother is. I haven't had time for any reading this morning. Three of *them* — one, a negro — have been fussing me with a lot of preparatory bits of nonsense. I don't like negroes. It gives me the shudders to feel those black fingers with their pink nails on my skin. I am terrified that there may not be a letter from you — but that would be no unusual thing! Goodbye for the present, Yves.

Your - wretched - little - girl - who - would - so - much - like - you-to-be-with-her.

LISOU

Thursday morning, 25th January
I have been in the Surgical Block since yesterday noon. I think it better that I shouldn't write to you. It is all rather hateful, darling — I ought to have been conditioned to this sort of thing when I was young. If R. doesn't operate tomorrow afternoon, I shall have, for some perfectly idiotic reason, to wait until he is through with all the others.

I've got a blue linen thingummy, and a shirt, rather like one of yours, with flaps back and front. I am in the depths of depression and perfectly helpless. Last night I had an idea that I might be able to run away, but the corridor is lit from end to end all night long, and I heard noises. Anyhow, it wouldn't have done any good. I have no courage.

Probably because of my utter state of misery, Eluard made a profound impression on me this morning. I withdraw some part of what I said about him. Do you know this of Calderon's, to be found in *Poésie 44*: 'Do you not see that I tremble to find myself once more in prison? . . . for I know now that human happiness is but a dream, and I would enjoy it to the full while it lasts.'

Menu: tripe and beans — after which I eat some jam. If you were here I should fling myself into your arms so violently that you would see only too clearly that I can't bear up against the dread of what is to happen — bear up, I mean, alone — that is to say, without you.

Why didn't you stay on here? — I've a terrible bone to pick with you for being so far away, and for leading a life that has nothing to do with me.

Goodbye, for now, Yves — I intend to write to you tomorrow. Kiss me, Yves — so that the world may change and give me everything I lack at present. I love you, Yves — for always.

Your
Lisou

Thursday, 25th January: 8 p.m.

Uncertainty seems to be dogging me to the very last. I don't know for sure, even now, that the operation is to be for tomorrow. When I ask the nurses, they just spread their arms, and let them fall with an air of weariness. Nobody knows anything, and they are, all of them, worked to death. The only thing I want is to be able to say to myself — this time tomorrow evening it will all be over — as children do. Don't laugh at me. To think of it in that way is my chief source of comfort — to think of next week (such a close next), of next month, of next year, and to know that inevitably the whole business will be just a memory. Yesterday is already over — though I shouldn't say 'already' because nowhere in the world does time pass so slowly — it makes one groan with impatience . . . I am out of luck. There was no post today. When I realized that, I turned my face to the window, and I don't mind admitting that I cried — not merely because there were no letters, but because of everything. I wish I could cry in your arms — though if I were there, I shouldn't, it is true, have any reason for doing so. I have had a visit from the Chaplain — an odd sort of creature. First he stroked Nicolas's ears, then he sat down. I know now that the benches in the Chapel are made of concrete blocks, each weighing 120 kilograms, and measuring 10 centimetres in thickness; that the girders supporting the fabric are 12 metres long, 20 centimetres broad, and 40 centimetres thick; that the arms of the chair are too slender when seen sideways, and that the engineer is Dr. K.'s brother. I can tell you for certain that the heating will be on in time for the Purification. In view of the fact that he swallows a good half of all his words, and that the other half is more or less unintelligible, that is about the sum-total of the information I can pass on to you.

When he got up to go, he was obviously expecting me to say: 'Can I take Communion tomorrow, Father?' — but I didn't. I am rather sorry now, but somehow the idea of making my confession to him wasn't very inspiring. I really do believe my mind is going, Yves. I have to make an enormous mental effort not to forget a good half of what I put into my letters — can you remember?

I can't tell you how humiliating, how shaming, I find certain services which have to be rendered to people who are utterly helpless, as I am going to be. You will tell me that all that is of only secondary importance. I know it is, but I hate the thought. It is frightful to be so wholly dependent on others.

The Abbé P. has just left me. My dear, I seem to be a favourite with the clergy this evening! I very much prefer him. I learned nothing about the foundations of the Chapel, but I have discovered that all suffering is good, even when it is caused by a corn on the foot. Did you know that? — I am pretty sure you didn't! My Abbé's got a sense of humour — I had noticed it before.

My light's just going to be turned off. It's sheer martyrdom to know that the current is full on all night, but that one isn't allowed to use it. Besides, there's a glow-lamp which burns away until morning, and that makes it all the more exasperating. Still, I expect I shall be glad of it when I'm feeling bad. I can't stand suffering in the dark. I am as hungry as a hunter, and my stomach has got to stay empty until tomorrow.

What's really strange is the horror. . . .

Friday morning. I was about to say that what is really strange is the horror which nurses seem to have of open windows. I really feel as though I am doing them a personal injury when I push mine ajar. They're across the room in three strides; they fasten the latch, and then make off with a look on their faces as though they were thinking: 'Whew! that was a narrow escape!' They're a funny lot. I don't think I've seen the same face twice running, except Madame D.'s, who gives the impression of being nice but severe. A little old thing with bandy legs has just brought me the yellowish, reddish, blackish, greenish liquid which goes by the name of breakfast. 'Good morning, sir,' she said, very pleasantly. From the fact that I am in the men's Block it follows necessarily that I am a man — and there's nothing I can do about it. It really is quite beastly here, in other ways, too. If you ever visited any of the chaps in this building, or Sa., you probably remember that there is an aperture in the glazed panel of the door narrow enough to make it impossible for one to recognize anyone from the inside, but where everyone passing along the corridor stops for a peep. It may sound incredible, but it is true. You couldn't help laughing if you could see your Lisou performing her ablutions in full view of this aperture. I hastily wash one small portion of my body, and hurriedly put my clothes on. Then I wait until there's not a sound to be heard, and start all over again. The whole process takes anything from an hour to two hours, and I never shift my eyes off the door. The nurses never knock — what do you think of that?

Oh, God! — this liquid! — and to think that I mustn't drink anything else! It seems pretty certain now that Dr. R. will operate this afternoon. I think I shall be seeing him this morning. There are two chaps in the rooms on either side of mine — I don't know them.

I feel extraordinarily calm today. Sister has put her nose round the door to say that if things follow their usual course, I shall be operated on this evening, which means this afternoon, and that Dr. R. will probably come to see me this morning. The weather's of the peculiarly frightful kind that one gets nowhere else but here — fog, and packets of melting snow splashing against the window. Really, Yves, the people in this dump are unique. All the time I have been writing to you there has been a little man running round dressed completely in white, with a spencer (I think that's what it's called) dragging on the ground behind him. I asked him to open the window a crack — and I think he'll remember the incident all his life. He yammered away with an air of dithering stupefaction. Meanwhile, I nearly passed out completely for lack of air. They seem to forget that I am still a normal person. If I started to tell you all the odd things that go on here, I should fill pages — besides, I'm hungry — so . . .

If there is no letter this morning I shall have a pretty poor opinion of you. Not a line since Monday. That's a bit much — especially at this moment of all moments in my existence. The truth is, you're not such a model of disciplined common sense as you would like people to think. I can hear the trolley. I suppose they are coming up to perform the last rites — the aseptic robe and the final coat of mauve paint. Half my body is stained that colour, and it looks pretty odd. Did I tell you

266

that on my first evening here they shaved my back? — the effects are still visible. Seriously, though, how can you expect me to face what is coming if you don't give me a sign of life today? You entirely underestimate the vitally important place you fill in my life. Something perfectly idiotic and very unpleasant has just happened — they have taken away all my belongings — books, writing-pad, and even Nicolas — who has been flung into the bottom of the wardrobe. There's nothing of mine left. I fought hard to be allowed my lamp. They don't like leaving lamps in the rooms of patients who have just undergone an operation. I'm not very strong-minded . . . still . . . and this wind . . . I'm just going to do something about my face (I'm not allowed so much as a grain of powder) — the brutes! The fog's so thick that one can't see more than a yard. The place reeks of disinfectant. If I had a pistol, I'd shoot the whole lot of them — the fools! — and what makes it all the worse is that I am here for my own good. What irony! — there are times when life's harshness takes a fantastic twist. If I had a moment, I'd add a sentence or two recording my impressions of the medical profession, and of R. in particular. He has been at the Sanatorium since eight this morning, I gather, going through the case-histories. I'd better be saying 'so long' just in case he should toy with the idea of doing something round about noon. I'm angry with you for leaving me without a letter. Perhaps it's the fault of the postal authorities? — no, on second thoughts, I'm not angry with you. I have given my mother your address for the telegram — every possible precaution has been taken. Kiss the back which is about to endure martyrdom — kiss all of me. I am putting on a bit of an act — but I expect you know all the same that I am feeling slightly shaken.

I am going to read until they come. The faintest sound of a footstep sets my heart going nineteen to the dozen. The wind is dropping. It's rather like me — sudden violent fits of exasperation, then periods of calm — a characteristic of youth, I'm told. Oh God, Yves, how young I am!

Kiss me once more in that special way which sets my blood

on fire even when I think of it. I'm certain it is as powerful
as any pain in the world. Probably a moment comes when it
is intolerable — when one cries out. Give me that moment
before they drug me into besotted nothingness.

Truly, truly, your

LISOU

What a pity you can't see me. I've got a white band round
my head and it suits me wonderfully. Not so much as a single
hair is allowed to show.

I expect there will be a bit of a break in my letters now — but
whatever you do, beloved, don't let that make you mislay your
fountain-pen.

1 o'clock. They're not going to operate until tomorrow morning — Hell!

1.15. They've suddenly cut me off all food — perhaps that
means it *is* going to be this afternoon.

LISOU

Friday evening, 26th January

The sole reason they didn't operate today is that the post
arrived very late, and they couldn't decently carve me up until
I had had a line from you. Now they can go ahead. I have had
a few words with R. on the subject, and he's going to do it
tomorrow — but not in the morning. I told him I was a slow
waker and didn't want to be bothered with that kind of nonsense. So, it's going to be in the afternoon — 2 p.m. — and no
mistake about it. My legs are quite stiff as a result of all the
injections they've given me. I have seen the butcher who is
going to slice me up. They all came to see me this afternoon,
after having officiated on Am. for three hours. To cut a long
story short, I'm to be the last of the bunch. What do they think
I am? I suppose they're keeping me for the dessert course.
Physically, they're a bit disappointing, as people always are

268

when one has heard too much about them. *He's* as big as a wardrobe, fair, with blue eyes — a bit on the hearty side, and given to making jokes . . . I was terribly shy. He had with him a comic little fellow with a beard who kept himself modestly behind I. who was looking very red in the face, and E. whose skull seemed longer than ever. Having all these people around makes me feel rather like an expectant mother. Why are you running a temperature of 102° — it can't be the tooth that's causing all the trouble. If only I could do a bit of auscultating myself, I'd very soon pack you off to a mountain cure at about 3000 feet — with a hard climate, fogs for preference — near C . . . if possible — the whole to last two months, just time enough to let me get on my feet again. Darling, I'm sure it's all the people you see who make you ill. Don't have anything to do with them — there's only me. I loved your letter. Oh, yes, Yves, do take me away to quite other mountains. The idea of you in Paris frightens me — you seem to be so much caught up in that life again. It's awful to think that I, who need you so much, don't have so much as a glimpse of you for weeks on end, while any idiot you happen to find yourself next to in the Métro has the right to press against you in the crowd. It's absurd, and I foam at the mouth with rage! Beloved, I am thirsty for you, and I am thinking beyond the fear of tomorrow to all the marvellous moments which life owes us — but oh! what a long time to wait! — what a very long time!

I adore you — let me stretch myself out beside you until the morning, so that I may wake full of courage and wonderful memories. Good night, my one and only love.

L.

Monday, 29th January

Mummy will tell you about everything, and how it is that I am still in the land of the living . . . Didn't I tell you so? . . . write to me.

LISOU

Thursday morning, 1st February

At last, yesterday afternoon, something from you reached me. I love you for writing at such length, but hate the thought that you should have been left without any kind of a letter from Saturday until Wednesday — especially at such a time as this. I don't suppose you've ever been through an experience like that before — and it's only just beginning. So far as my heart's concerned, Dr. E. says I have come through well, but this morning the liquid has started to form again. I don't believe there is any limit to what the human body can stand in the way of pain — do you?

I can't write any more — but — I love you. I only wish you could be here.

LISOU

Monday morning, 5th February

Do you know, darling, I actually wrote the address all by myself? Oh, I love you for having written me such a long letter, and even for the parts in which you lectured me a bit . . . I wish you had gone on. I am still feeling so bad that my temper's foul. I think of you all day and all night, and, as soon as I shut my eyes, when my breathing's easy, I see you there before me, and you take me in your arms. Then the soporifics calm me down, and I think of all the wonderful moments I have had with you. For the first time in ten days I got a few hours of continuous sleep with the help of morphine — Oh, it was lovely! Why weren't you here to play with my fingers while I lay biting my lips? How terribly I have missed you, darling! When I think that twice I might have died all this distance away from you like the little idiot I am, you'll realize the fantastic things I'm capable of when you're not here!

I think they're going to take my stitches out this afternoon, and perhaps send me back to the Sanatorium at the end of the week. I shall be so glad. This room gives me the horrors — and reminds me of so much that was horrible — I don't think I shall ever forget. I still have fever all the time — up to 101.3 in the evenings — and liquid — and, worst of all, every time I make a movement I feel as though I am suffocating.

I can't get away from the loud-speaker — jazz, jazz, all day long. The light is so glaring that my eyes shut of their own accord.

My love, I am having a good deal of pain, and my moustache is all beaded with sweat. You've no idea the amount they make me drink — in the long run it becomes almost like a torture . . . I feel as though I shall never be thirsty, hungry, or sleepy again, that I shall never be able to bend my left arm, and that my back will never be smooth. You'll get some idea from all this how low I am. If I had to face all I've been through over again — I'd rather endure almost anything else. The books have arrived. I am rather painfully getting through *Strange Interlude* — perhaps because I am tired it seems to me to be pure Piran-dello. But I do love the violence of passion which seems to animate all the characters — there is something fine about that.

I am not strong enough to read much, and I'm afraid I shan't have finished it for some time — afraid, because I want to send it back to you. I long for a sight of you — if only I could lean against you I should breathe so much better, so much more easily. If you had been my husband you would have been allowed to spend some of those hideous nights on a chaise-longue next my bed — like mummy was. They have just brought me a letter of yours — it had an immediate effect on me. Don't you notice how my writing has taken fresh heart?

I've also had a long letter from my sister. What she says about looking forward to long evenings of dancing with moujiks made me laugh so much that I had to be sponged from head to feet. It is strictly forbidden to make me laugh — please note.

I loved getting your letter, but felt worried at the idea that when you wrote it you hadn't yet heard the bad news. But perhaps you had, and didn't dare talk about it in case I mightn't have been told. As a matter of fact, I realized what was up at the moment it all happened — I had a sort of a feeling — it was really extraordinary.

It seems that I've got to break my fast. Ugh! — how beastly it was! One of these days, a little later, I'll answer your long letters. Just for the moment I'm not up to it. All I want is to be in your arms, babbling nonsense — I've had so much more than enough of the whole hateful business. I think I'm a bit of a nervous wreck — and my heart keeps going at 130 or 140 night and day — it's positively disgusting.

I oughtn't to have had to live through it all without you . . . It's been too much for me, my dear darling, and I am rapidly growing into a chronic whiner . . . Kiss all of me — even my thighs, which have become like a couple of sugar-sifters.

I love you more than ever, and I hope that life has something in store which will make up to me for all the beastliness.

Your sore and sad little girl

LISOU

Wednesday afternoon, 7th February

I asked mummy to send you a line this morning. I can't bear to think, darling, that you should be without news of me. I was exhausted as a result of the tapping, and because I had had a rotten night owing to breathlessness. Don't you think that feeling of not being able to breathe is one of the worst things of all to put up with?

I have had a letter from you — you're really marvellous to write so often. The whole of my day centres round the arrival of the post — don't forget that — and when there's nothing, I am the most miserable creature in the world. Your talking of the future, of you and me, gives a little fillip to my courage. Do it often, please. It's the only thing I have to cling to, dear love.

No one would believe how tired I am — I've got liquid on both sides. For you a day is just a day — for me it is a terrifying sequence of minutes during which I think of nothing but the next breath . . . If you could have seen me last night, you'd have been really frightened. I shrieked aloud — I tore at my clothes — my ears felt completely blocked up — it was indescribably awful. On the whole, it is better that you shouldn't be here, that you shouldn't see me at my worst. I can scarcely read because of this filthy fever. I lie back on the pillows in a state of complete prostration. The slightest movement brings on the breathlessness — Oh, what a life!

8.30. Not being able to write to you makes me feel quite unhinged. Whenever I can, darling, I do — really and truly. I feel a bit rested this evening, and my back's not worrying me. Mummy's knitting by the light of the small lamp. There are some lovely flowers on the table (Vi. has been kindness itself. I've still got a long way to go). They won't let me have visitors yet. It has always been one of my boasts that I can get along very well without other people, but I do so long now to see a friendly face.

I'm looking forward to my next shot of morphine with frenzied impatience. I know I oughtn't to be so dependent on it, but it does put me into such a wonderful mental state for thinking about you.

Thursday morning. No letter! . . . boohoo! . . . All the same, I love you — so much that in spite of the pain I clasp both my arms round your neck and refuse to let go.

Your little girl
LISOU

Everything's going wrong today.

Tuesday morning, 13th February

In spite of everything, beloved, I must write to you — it's impossible for me to do without it — things can't go on like this. I am back in the Sanatorium now, in my old room. The wardrobe's been moved so as to make way for the wheeled stretcher when I'm taken upstairs for my medical. There was no vacancy in the new block. I'm rather sorry about that, because I really am terribly tired: 102.2° still in the evenings, and an oxygen tube stuffed up my nose. I haven't so much as put a foot to the ground yet.

It is a lovely morning, quite superb, such purity in the air. I do so long to have some natural sleep — like other people. I've had no sleep at all so far, except for a few hours under morphine. They won't give me any more . . . it's quite frightful to be without it.

I have been completely swept off my feet by *Strange Interlude*. I couldn't stop reading till I'd got to the end. I take back all I said about Pirandello — it's quite different.

I'd love to talk to you about all sorts of interesting things — but what?

No letter — traitor!

What a beautiful day — I can hear the characteristic sound of footsteps in soft snow.

Everybody is *so* sweet to me. The new nurse (she's pretty) calls me 'duck' and Do. feeds me out of a spoon. When I have one of my breathless fits they're all very frightened. Someone is playing the piano. Don't you ever go to a concert? — you seem to go everywhere else.

Oh, darling, I look so odd, and I'm sure you wouldn't like my appearance.

My skin's dead white, I've got enormous black goggles, and my hair has been cropped — they had to do that, but it'll grow again, I promise. With this oxygen tube I'm sure I should frighten small children into fits. But you are brave — everyone knows that — so come, all the same, and take me in your arms and carry me into the open air for a bit — then

274

you can put me to bed again and kiss me all over — *all* over. I am hungry and thirsty for you — and, would you believe it, I've forgotten the sound of your voice.

My love is as great as my pain.

Your

LISOU

Saturday, 17th February

You are leaving me in the lurch, beloved: I get scarcely anything from you now. I realize that this state of affairs is dragging on for too long, and don't blame you at all. I'm just emerging from a bad moral shake-up. I think the pneumo really looks like working. But the whole thing is becoming too much for me. I've hardly had any sleep — there I go! — complaining, complaining, complaining. . . .

Tomorrow I'm to be moved into the other block — this time it's certain. I rather think that the W's are there. I dislike the thought of going intensely, but what does a little vexation more or less matter? If only they can get this lung right again so that I can breathe. I don't care two hoots about the final result. Even if it means spending the rest of my life in bed that'll be better than the hideous time I've been through lately.

I won't go on with this letter. My morale's at a low ebb, and I should only bore you.

I wish I could see you instead of merely writing. I think that when I do I shall faint from sheer happiness.

Goodbye for the present, beloved. Think of me. I love you more than anything in the world.

LISOU

Sunday evening, 18th February

Beloved — all is over between us! I have fallen in love with the gentleman who comes round with the breakfast coffee —

275

and I am pretty sure that my feelings are reciprocated (so what is the good of trying to put up a fight?). That reminds me — will you be big about this and send me my saucepan back? Its intrinsic value is enormous — besides, I need it so that he can have something in which to heat up my elevenses. I hope sincerely that you will get the better of this disappointment, and not become a hopeless, broken-down no-good. You must try to build a new life (I know, of course, that you are elderly, still, you mustn't despair).

I'm only joking. As a matter of fact, I feel as limp as a rag.

I had a pleasant trip on my stretcher with that everlasting oxygen balloon between my knees. I don't like these rooms, darling. I knew they'd give me the jim-jams. Mine is gloomy — like all that's modern. To make matters worse, they won't allow me to hang a single picture on these monstrous pink walls. How interminable the evenings here will be — unless my neighbours take to paying visits. They can if they like, do you realize that? I fume with rage when I think that if you were here it would be the easiest thing in the world for you to come and see me. I spend my time imagining how the door might open, and you come in — to play with my fingers. Beloved, why am I still so tired? — 102.5's no joke. Don't be angry if my letters are rather incoherent. Ever since the operation I have had odd fits — there are moments when I seem to lose my grip entirely, when I seem to be swimming, floating, and not to know what I am saying. Do you realize that I've been in the same position for three solid weeks, and that it's impossible for me to change it? It's horribly painful, and the pillows are hot, and they slide about and fall on my head. Serves me right for always insisting on lying flat.

I'm in pain, darling — and all because I laughed. I remember you sitting in my room and caressing my legs. I was standing in front of you, and you said: 'My sturdy Lisou.' That made me think. I look awfully odd with my short hair. I'm just listening to a splendid concert. I'd love to be lying beside

276

you. Please make me not have any pain tonight — and don't forget all about writing to me — that would be too awful!

They're coming to deflate me. Yesterday I wanted to die. If I'd had anything sharp I'd have cut the vein in my wrist. I've had about all I can stand.

All the same, I'll love you to the last drop of my blood. Good night, man-I-love — I am yours for ever.

LISOU

Wednesday morning, 21st February: 8 o'clock

I'm beginning to get used to the long nights, and lie here thinking all sorts of serious thoughts (I *can* think a bit now). For instance, darling, I have been thinking something quite awful which you ought to know — and that is that with all this heart trouble I shall almost certainly be forbidden to cook up a child. No little Marc . . . do you realize that? I tremble with horror at the idea — and I feel that for you it must be as though half of me — and the best half — had been removed. Darling, darling, I am so dreadfully miserable when I think of it, and I don't know what to say to you. I might, of course, perform an act of self-immolation and say that I don't love you any more, but you wouldn't believe me if I did — and, anyhow, you have been warned. I feel like giving you a good dressing-down. For the last few days you have been writing me perfectly idiotic letters — or, rather, you have not been writing me any at all. But it would be ungrateful of me to complain. I could never have believed that you could write as you have done. All I can think of is my delirious happiness at sight of your enormous envelopes. Oh, Yves, I do love you, really I do. If I weren't feeling so low, I'd tell you how, and how much, but these cursed pleuras hurt like hell, and I was still 100.9 this morning — which is a pretty look-out for this evening — and that's why I prefer to write to you early.

277

The floor-nurse is an old friend of mine, and we're on very intimate terms. She's a Protestant, and walks with a sort of skip and hop. She has got a prim little mouth, and looks as gloomy as the tomb. She gets on my nerves because she's always wanting me to complain about the way she looks after me. She's one of the retiring sort — but she's got fingers like steel springs. When she helps me to sit up, or when she washes me, I feel like one of the lesser-known martyrs.

I've just eaten a whole rusk, with butter on it! — It was sheer agony. Luckily, I was listening to a military band all the time. Have I told you that I'm now without a single bandage? I hope you won't find me looking too much of a wreck. I haven't yet been able to see whether I've got one shoulder lower than the other. Anyhow, I can really move my left arm — look!

I think that the little noise I can hear is rain. My voice has gone, and I feel as though there were a sheet of glass between me and everything I look at. I long for it to be eleven o'clock, and for my mother to come — and the post.

I've suddenly begun to feel very uncomfortable — I must stop. When I shut my eyes I feel as though I were in a car looping the loop, and that makes me feel sick.

I'd give anything to be able to write you an intelligent letter — that'll have to be for another time. Kiss me hard — with your tongue in my mouth, all warm and living like a small animal. Oh, my love, how far away all that is, how far! . . .

Noon. Thank you, sir, for your epistle. Poor Sa. . . . please give her all sorts of messages from me when you see her.

Don't be impatient with me for writing — I do so love it. What can I say to you in a few brief lines?

It is misty and white, and the doctors stand by my bed wearily shaking their heads. I love you. That just bursts out of me — and you hug me tighter than ever.

Today I can do nothing but just be obedient . . . I've just had my pleura washed out . . . It was very painful, and I'm all in. So I can manage only a few words. Nothing from you this morning . . . The weather's appalling. There's an extra-pleural adhesion, just where it shouldn't be. I think I shall have to view the future quite differently — and so will you. It's hideous, darling, but there it is. I shall adopt a baby boy, and spend all my life lying down, and wear very pretty pyjamas. You will come and see me. I shall write and draw on a sofa in front of the fire. I shall spend all day reclining in front of the door of my chalet. I shall have innumerable lovers (not you).

Perhaps I shall contrive to be happy. I shall never see Paris again.

I am listening to a wonderful waltz, and the sky is a flawless blue. My cheeks are quite red. Have you any idea what it's like to have something beside one's bed to keep the pain away — and not to use it? — That's sheer, unadulterated virtue, that is! Oh, cover me with words and tender gestures. Goodbye for the present. Kiss the palms of my hands. They smell deliciously of lavender.

Your

LISOU

Monday, 5th March

Thank you, Yves, my beloved, for your letter. I haven't written to you much these last few days because I haven't been able to find a suitable moment. What with being pole-axed with morphine, or in pain, or too tired, I haven't had much time. I am taking advantage now of a lucid interval. Yes, the saucepan arrived safely — I send you my thanks, but only rather little ones. Ever since my mother has had the thing, she's been enjoying herself like a lunatic cooking up all sorts of odds and ends which I am supposed to swallow. Fortunately, I had the brilliant notion of developing a bad tongue. It is completely flayed, and I can only drink. In addition to which I've got orange-peel tied to my heels with little gauze bows.[1]

If you could see me now, you would be at my feet. I'm at my best when I've got the headphones on and there's nothing to be seen but the tip of my nose in an indescribable tangle of wires.

Oh, darling, I know I'm a coward, and that I ought to be able to put a better face on all this, especially when I think of what I shall have to fight against in the future. Forgive me — I really can be the most utter little fool — when I give my mind to it!

Take me in your arms. I'll groan and grumble and tell you of all the barbarous and agonizing things they do to me — and you'll have tears in your eyes.

Your little girl

LISOU

Friday, 9th March

Today, I'm in a good mood — which, with all these washings of the pleura, is a rare occurrence with me. They are quite sizeable operations. They last for half an hour, and are so painful that, when they're over, I am completely flattened out. I had one yesterday, so I am making the most of today. How are things with you?

I am really beginning to take quite a liking to my floor. It'll be a difficult business getting me to move. If only I could get up for a bit . . . Still, I *did* stand all by myself in front of the X-ray screen. True, I had to straddle my feet a bit, and I did have the rather uneasy look of a penguin who'd been stuck on top of a mast. Still, the great thing is that I succeeded in staying upright.

[1] This passage is quite inexplicable. Still, it is no part of the translator's job to suppress difficult passages, and if any reader can find a different interpretation of, or meaning in, 'les talons dans des pelures d'oranges attachées avec des petits noeuds en gaze . . .' I hope that he (or she) will tell me.—Translator.

Did you know that poor dear St. had died? We were together in the Surgical Block. Poor boy, I feel it terribly. So has Bl. Did you know him?

Yesterday evening there was a procession of young men in fancy dress. It went on till 10 o'clock and was great fun. Some of the dresses were lovely — much better than last year.

I've got to be deflated before taking my cure. Are you worried? I lay my hands on your eyes.

Your

Lisou

Sunday, 11th March

At this very moment, I expect, the day being so lovely, you are in the Avenue du Bois. There is a hint of mist between the trees, but everything is so fresh and so utterly unsullied, that one is thrilled to one's very feet with the joy of living. What bliss to go walking of a morning — especially a Sunday morning. Yesterday evening you went to the theatre. I can just imagine the scene in the intervals — the bar — the staircase — the family parties — the people who didn't understand a word — and, then — the true theatre-goers who came for the play. They always stand out a mile, don't they?

For me there is no Avenue du Bois, no memory of a good play, no amusing interval crowd. All the same, I am happy. N. told me that I had rounded the cape — but I'm taking that with a grain of salt, and understand him to mean that there is another cape to be navigated before I am clear. But I'm not going to let myself get excited — it'd only mean another 24-hour battle with my pulse, like after the operation. I shall never forget that time. I wonder whether you realize what I went through? — the awful feeling that one's heart is just about to conk out. Each time, I said to myself: 'Now I'm for it' — and each time an injection patched me up again.

I didn't mean to tell you about that — the words just slipped out.

I've got three magnificent red roses, some pinks, and an adorable little garden of primulas. Mummy grubbed them up a fortnight ago with moss round their roots, and they're growing beautifully. She has just come in now, and says I look like someone who's been making a night of it! — poor me!

This floor is a perfect dream of a place. I never leave it now. The people in the ward on my right have made me a toaster. I've only got to mention that I want something for it to appear. Yesterday I had some oysters — but no lemon. I let it be known, and three minutes later half a dozen lemons were delivered at the door! Y., among others, took no end of trouble. I assumed that expression of embarrassment which you know so well — and kept the lemons!

Do go and see Mauriac's *Mal Aimés* — it's most awfully good.

The nurse regards me as her prize patient, and pampers me deliciously. She's a different nurse from the one I had. Yesterday, she made me some fried potatoes — the real thing! I ate them with my fingers all the time I was playing draughts.

I'm looking up a bit, think of that! Instead of 102.2° at night, I'm making do now with 100.4°.

I don't know whether I told you a piece of news which they broke to me with infinite tact ten days ago — that the extrapleural liquid is septic. Doesn't that seem to you quite disgusting and absurd? — It does to me. I can't believe myself capable of such a thing. I gulp down all these horrors without turning a hair — all the same . . . Now I'm going to have a bit of a clean-up, using my left arm. The blasted fool has gone all stiff at the shoulder. My thinness has to be seen to be believed. Personally, I think it suits me very well — and so do the others.

I must break off now, and wash — which means splashing about in a basin — not much in the way of a bath. All the same, I find it enchanting. So long.

Monday, 1 o'clock. I've just been brought back from having a pleura drench which lasted a whole hour, and I find a letter from you waiting. In spite of my exhaustion I'm writing to you because I want to so badly. Here are five answers: (1) Yes, I am rather better. One of my cheeks is quite pink (the left one), and I get slightly more sleep without the dose being increased . . . (2) No, I'm afraid you're wrong to think that I can do without the oxygen. I've still got a tube stuck up my right nostril. (3) The level of the liquid is not sinking — merely behaving a bit differently and changing its consistency . . . There's a large pocket to find. They wash me out with my head hanging down and the whole bag of tricks. (4) Am I in pain? — of course I am — and I've had about all I can stand. I groan and grumble, but what must be must be. (5) Result of the operation? — not very cheerful — practically non-existent until they started with these drenches. Now, however, there does seem to be some definite progress — the adhesion is breaking down, and I'm going to have an extra-pleural. So much for my news.

I've just had a shot, so I'm literally half asleep.

Your
LISOU

Wednesday, 14th March
Not very happy today, because I've started to itch all over (I had only to write saying I was better for my evening temperature to shoot up to 103° — and I can't keep my food down . . . bad sign).

I told you I was itching all over. They tell me it's my liver — the nit-wit! I spend the time scratching myself, from my toes to my neck, from my tummy to my eyes, and it's really beastly. And that's not all. At night I behave like a lunatic, dreaming aloud and flinging myself about — so that I half wake up. It gives me quite a turn to catch myself at it. Last night I found I was gargling — the noise woke me — I did look a fool.

I've got to scratch the calf of my leg, so I'll say goodbye. My ears hurt — I can't swallow because I've got a diphtheric throat, and one of my heels is misbehaving — gout, I guess. Tomorrow they're giving me a pleura drench of 2 litres instead of 500 cm.[3] . . . I *shall* enjoy that! Apart from these little odds and ends, everything is going very well, and I remain, always, your little girl

LISOU

Thursday, 22nd March

Thanks for your letter, darling. The reason I didn't write is that I no longer have the free use of my eyes — completely gummed up for three days! Today I am like a little kitten, peering out of two slits. I don't know what it is they've smeared all over me, but it's awful. Three days ago Dr. E. decided to try Dagenan treatment. I needn't tell you the state I'm in — just about fit to be scooped up in a spoon. And it'll go on for another week . . . They plan to take me to Lyon for ten days or so to see what penicillin will do for the liquid in my pleura. It seems I'm a perfect subject . . . All the doctors here are very excited. I shall be the first case they've had. Y. went down in advance in the hope of finding some at C . . . Perhaps I really am going to get cured, beloved, who knows?

I'm being looked after now by Dr. W. Heavens! — how handsome he is, and how kind!

I had a very painful pleura drench this morning. I've never known anything like it, nor have I ever suffered such pain. And now my lung's full of serum, and I can't breathe.

How I do go on complaining!

It is wonderfully lovely and warm, but with you away, nothing counts.

Your brave but miserable little girl

LISOU

Thursday, 29th March

What am I going to do about making myself eat? I'm thinner than ever — it's quite terrifying — I discover bones in the most impossible places. I've just been interrupted by a visit from Dr. W., and we talked about you — he sees that you're told all sorts of things, and then, quite naturally, warns you not to make too much of them . . . (this is a side of things that I don't, as you may imagine, at all like).

I was 100.6 this morning, and foolishly took a tablet of Kalmine because of my back, with the result that I am now sweating like a pig, with a face as red as a peony. I am peeling from head to foot in the most extraordinary way — I can pull off great flakes of skin.

I'm waiting for Dr. I. to get back with news of the penicillin . . . I behave abominably at night. Last night there was quite a scene. My bell wasn't working, and I lay here shouting for an hour and a quarter — I was out of oxygen, and was terribly breathless. It was my neighbour who turned up at last — I cried with joy at sight of him. I am going through a perfectly foul time — though, seen from a distance, all this must seem nothing at all.

As to you — I just let myself go and shut my eyes (— you'll only have to press my nose and it'll just happen of itself).

Your little girl
LISOU

Friday evening, 6th April

I am feeling much better since they celebrated my twenty-second birthday by putting in a large draining tube. I've practically got no more temperature, and I'm hungry. To-morrow morning I'm off to Lyon with mamma and N. I'm supposed to stay there a fortnight. Dear love, do pray that this time I may be cured. *Of course* I'll write to you when I arrive.

Perhaps they'll put me in a room with twelve other people. The journey'll be rather fun.

I've just had a long visit from the Abbé P. I saw his blue eyes through the tulip stalks. He was quite wonderful, very simple — I dozed a little behind my goggles.

I love you. I've had a shot of Sedol, and feel a bit odd. The Abbé said that loving means the gift of oneself. Well, I have given you *my*self.

Oh, your eyes, darling! I'd love to be sitting on your lap and licking them. I'm feeling well — no pain anywhere, and I'm leaning against you.

Think of me, darling: 'My arms are the ivy that binds you to this world . . .'.

I'm just dropping off.

Your little girl
LISOU

Lyon: Wednesday, 11th April

Here I am in Lyon — this city full of memories — but it's not at all the same thing.

The treatment started at 9.30 on Sunday morning. At the moment I don't feel either better or worse. They push 20,000 units of penicillin daily into my left pleural cavity (and they propose to double the dose from tomorrow on).

Hospital life is not very attractive. The times of meals are really comic: breakfast at 6 a.m. — in complete darkness — me wearing an inmate's nightdress : lunch at 10 and dinner at 5. Method of locomotion — the nurse bundles one up in her arms — one is bumped and shaken in the most appalling way. N. comes to see me frequently, and this morning, much to my delight, Al. turned up (you remember that pink, finicky boy?) — he brought me some Marcel Prévost, and a whiff of youth. . . .

Don't assume from all this that I am happy, and that everything is fine. Of all my experiences, I think that this time in hospital is the worst — the good sisters, especially. The success

of the treatment seems to me to be still extremely problematic —
and I do love life so!

I can hear a lot of little tots who are suffering from whooping-
cough — it's frightful. Professor Z. is an odd creature with ugly
little eyes which sparkle with intelligence. He arrives, followed
by a crowd of attendant students, delivers a little lecture on
my case, and then withdraws, the others jostling behind him.
He is very kind. I like the way he calls me 'child', and the feel
of his hand on my neck — though it is there only in a medical
capacity.

That's all my news. What about you? Perhaps they'll send
on my letters . . . I should like . . .

Goodbye for now, my love. For your sake, I'll get well.

Lisou

X . . . Sanatorium: Saturday, 21st April

Here I am, back again on the heights. I left Lyon in a
hurry yesterday morning, the treatment being finished. In
other words, the result being nil, they let me go. Just money
thrown out of the window . . . This penicillin's just a lot of nonsense. But I'm glad to be back here. I liked the journey by
car. Not that the road was particularly pretty, but every now
and then there were marvellous twists and turns, a line of
poplars, a little lake, or a meadow with highly coloured cows.
I have a weakness for poplars . . . there's a sort of trembling
grace about them which seems to be the very essence of happiness — especially when the sun's shining. I got here after lunch
and was quite moved by the welcome everyone gave me, from
patients to doctors. People I knew only by sight ran beside the
car asking me how I was, and great big Bi. shouted: 'Well done,
Miss' — and so it went on, all the way from the paddock to
the top of the steps . . . There was such a general air of kindli-
ness, from nurses, doctors and everyone — such a change from
my arrival at Lyon. I can't tell you how awful that was — they

showed me into a room from which a dead man had just been taken, and his mother was still there, clinging to the bed, howling and moaning and refusing to budge, and there was I, waiting to get into it. She was in a state of nervous collapse — not a very cheerful welcome. And then, to keep my spirits up, I had a tetanus case next me all night, a man who screamed the place down in the most appalling way. All very delightful — and somewhere there was Montmartre, with you there, and not me (actually, I've never been to the place). I've had enough of being sick. What an idiotic word that is, isn't it? I think I'm better. Something seems to have woken me up, shaken me, though I don't know what. I'm going to begin to write. I found out yesterday that the Editor of one of the big weeklies is my cousin. I shall try him with some of my stuff. Dr. I. is back from Paris — quite unrecognizable. She has had a perm, and her hair is all in little curls. She's put red on her lips, and has been dancing in night-clubs, etc. etc. *Le Ciel est à Vous* is a very good film — all very healthy, but I didn't like it.

This letter of mine seems very sober and sedate. It's raining cats and dogs, and the storm's at its height. I've been thinking of you, with the result that I feel relaxed all over. I must go to bed now. I've got a bit of pain. I stretch my hands to you.

Your small beloved girl

LISOU

Saturday, 28th April

'Oh Life — accept me — make me worthy — teach me — '
There's nothing really in that to make one shed torrents of tears. Personally, I squeezed out one. Thank you for your letter. Send me as many papers as you like. I enjoy reading the papers, and the ones of your choice are certain to be good.

They've put me back in my old room. I'm impatient to be up and about so as to be able to set it to rights. Alas! the most recent analysis has again come out positive, which means

288

starting again from zero. That's no reason, is it, for being prostrated or wringing one's hands in despair? One thing, however, is certain: in spite of everything there's something in me which obstinately refuses to make the grade. What it is, or why, I don't know. This desperate fight is getting me down. What am I going to do, Yves? — go on fighting, I suppose . . . Whether or no, I am quite sure that I must stop this letter now . . . otherwise, it'll just become a catalogue of absurdities. So, good night.

Sunday. I am listening to a Schumann Symphony, and wondering all the time which of the Beethoven's is going to follow. I happened to tune in just now to a recording of *The Flashing Stream*, broadcast from the Théâtre Pigalle. You ought to go and see it — deputizing for me (it's the Fifth — the Victory — my favourite). I think the part of Ferrers was being played by Henri Rolland — I recognized his voice. I missed hearing the list of the cast. I love that play — it is so intelligent.

Like your lady friend, I should have loved to be behind you at the Rugby match. I can't help brooding on the fact that even your love has never given me the privilege of seeing so much as a crack in your façade. (But I *am* becoming more sensible and less demanding, aren't I?) L. has just got married. Don't you think it odd that someone should have taken my place so soon? — I do — and I find it mortifying — truly.

Monday. I'm just back from my medical which, in spite of everything, managed to be richly comic. I appeared before a crowd of entirely new blokes. I did my very best to look as intelligent as possible — which isn't easy when one arrives on wheels, when one can't assume an upright position, when one is hitched to a balloon, when Dr. E. says — 'Tomorrow, everything will be fine' — one racks one's brains for a quick and witty retort and nothing comes — not to speak of all those people sitting there in semi-obscurity and staring . . . I'd rather face a dozen Disciplinary Boards. When it was all over, the orderly treated me to some of the pleasures of speed in the corridor — I gave a great howl when we got near my door. I felt sure I had my ears laid back. Perhaps I shall be penalized — Ah, youth! youth! — but how miserable it all is, and how I should love to know what you are thinking at this moment. I feel as though you had been sucked away from me — miles and miles.

It's snowing fit to make one cry. No matter how far away you are, I pass my thumb along your lips with a pensive air.

LISOU

Tuesday, 8th May

If you're not feeling cheerful, *of course* it's no use pretending. All the same, it's — how shall I put it — rather hard for a person of my temperament to read what you write.

Oh, I *know* it's frightful to think of all these deported persons. Several friends of mine haven't come back. These poor creatures have suffered more in their bodies and in their belongings, through the war, than anyone else — and the return of the prisoners is often so heartbreaking. . . .

I can't write any more today. I am feeling a bit off colour. It's madly hot. I love the sound of ice clinking against the sides of a tumbler. Yesterday evening there was dancing on the terrace in honour of the Armistice. It was dark — it must have been rather lovely.

So long. I should like — no, that's absurd. Till we meet again, perhaps.

LISOU

Wednesday morning, 16th May

Dr. W. put in an appearance under the awning, not to ask how *I* was, but for news of 'Father R.' He seemed to be afraid that you might have been playing the fool. I pleaded complete ignorance — so he sent you friendly messages — and here they are.

I can't help wondering how many citizens were crushed to death in Paris on Armistice Day. According to the papers, it must have been an epic experience. But I'm not at all sorry to have missed it. I have always had a horror of crowds, though, in some ways, I suppose, it was worth some discomfort to see it. I should have liked to be able to watch from a great height, and am quite glad to have done so from a great distance. Here, we had a display of fireworks and a deal of noise on the terrace — and much singing of the *Internationale* by schoolchildren.

How beautiful Paris and the Quays must be just now. The mere thought of it all moves me to tears. You can't possibly know how out of things I feel at times.

I am listening to some good American jazz, and desires crowd in thick upon me ... I am glad to think that I am, to some extent, armoured against you. I wait for two days, and then my pain goes. You really are the oddest of creatures, and all this business of letters crossing and never getting answered doesn't help any. You make it impossible to let things slide. My lips are made for your kisses and for them alone — though, on second thoughts, perhaps not, after all. I suppose quite a lot of men kiss as you do? But, Yves, I am hungrier for you than ever before. May I say that? — do you give me permission to cling to your coat-lapels in order to tell you so? In any case, I can write in a letter that I love you so much that it's almost killing me — but that by calling in the assistance of my self-esteem, I *can* forget you. I have just found that out. I feel no scruple now about asking you to carry me in your arms. I'm weighing less and less, in spite of all the condensed milk in the world.

I have been moved to the cure balcony, where, as I've probably told you already, I sleep. Darkness has fallen. I can see the whole valley with the village lights. I remember once looking at those same lights with my head on your shoulder. My feet were in the snow, and I was gazing out between the tree-trunks. There is an immobility in the scene which takes away all idea of time. For people like us that is lovely, and there is something about the whole spectacle which is really beautiful. It is wonderful sleeping here. I have only one sheet. The shrilling of crickets is everywhere. I can hear the chaps to right and left of me talking. On one side, the problem of the existence of God — 'My dear man, if you'd read . . . it's all in . . . no, old man . . . yes, old man' . . . On the other, 'If I could lay hands on the . . . who fixed my shirt with sticking-plaster!' . . . It's all very funny. Away to the right there's a bald and bearded object with a — how shall I put it — an effeminate voice, who answers everything that's said to him in verse or by quotation. I lie in my bed tying myself into knots with laughter. He is very popular: his room is never empty. He's got the makings of a small-time cabaret-singer. Don't you want to go and see Rigaux? — it's the kind of entertainment I avoid, because when I start laughing the results are appalling and I can't stop.

Thursday evening. I don't seem able to finish this letter. I moved rooms again today, and that meant a full-dress expedition. I am always amazed by the number and importance of the various objects which I trail about with me. D'you know, I actually walked by myself for the first time this morning! I got the whole way across the room, and then collapsed into a chaise-longue on the balcony. Ever since I made this almost unbelievable effort I have had a nervous trembling in the hands — which accounts for this positively senile writing. I hope it may settle down with the passing of the years, because it makes me look like a half-wit. The great joke here, for the moment, is giving me full spoons to hold. I sugared my strawberries in that way this evening, and found it very convenient. Have you read Montherlant's *Mors et Vita*? — it is quite admirable. Everything he says about the war strikes me as being absolutely right. I should like to think it is. It strikes a long, resounding note for me. It is a beautiful piece of work, and he a really great man. His style is splendid. My bed here is turned the other way round, and I can't go and sleep on the balcony any more merely by ringing a bell. I feel terribly lost, and have got a bad attack of the blues. T. is coming over to see me at the end of the week from the house where he's been staying for the past eight days. He was with me when the armistice broke out — and was a real godsend. What are your brothers doing?

What was it that my mother told you? — how odious I am, I suppose, and that she can't put up with me any longer. I'd give a good deal to have her here now — but I don't tell her so because she is quite capable of rushing back at a moment's notice . . . I can hear a small baby crying — it must be the same one we heard that day at the foot of the waterfall. You told me once that you desired me — and I didn't blush! No, sir, I certainly did not! I'm feeling sad because Do. is leaving tomorrow for Paris. Do you think it would be a good thing if I went into that Sanatorium kept by Dr. M.? I am told it has a great park with huge trees — which makes it terribly tempting, doesn't it? I can fancy myself gracefully sauntering in the shade of centuries-old oaks, with a pencil stuck behind my ear and a notebook in my hand. I think I might even take seriously to catching butterflies — I hope you'll lend me your little net.

Heavens! how infuriating it is to tremble like this!

I must leave off now. I am living next door to a mad woman who's to be sent to an asylum. She has just been in to offer me her services. I find her rather fun, and she gives me a family feeling — It's stupid of me, but I just can't go on writing.

Have you seen Bagatelle and La Roseraie?

Kiss these idiotic hands of mine. Hold them tight.

> Your little girl
>
> LISOU

Sunday evening, 20th May

To go, or not to go — I am only waiting for a maternal message to pack my bags — or, rather, to have them packed for me — for the tenth time. If they don't cure me this time, I give up — wouldn't you? Dr. R. spent a few hours here, and I saw him. He suggested that I should go into *his* Sanatorium, which lies low, because of my heart and my breathlessness (you're right about the environs of Paris — they wouldn't do me any good). I told him that I thought it a good plan. It only remains to see whether the parents favour the move — and whether the dibs run to it. If their finances are in the same state as mine the look-out's not too good — though it's true, of course, that I do all sorts of silly things. For instance, I've had a case of bottled beer sent up from the village. I got it into my head that if I drank a bottle a day it might help me to put on weight. Besides, it's delicious. I am developing an unsuspected passion for this particular tipple.

Where is Lisou? Lisou has vanished, or will do soon. I shall *re*-instate myself in a *re*-car which will *re*-store a bag of bones to my mother, and then take me to a *re*-institution where a lot of *re*-doctors will *re*-treat me with *re*-systems — and the extraordinary thing is, Ladies and Gentlemen — that I have not yet ceased to be human. To give you one example among many — I walked as far as the next room, and, on the way, caught sight of my image in the window-pane. If I hadn't been clinging with both hands to my oxygen-balloon, I'd have gone down flop on the floor! It was the first time I had seen myself at full length. What I saw may have been somebody else — but it certainly wasn't me — you can take the word of a Lisou for that! Never look at me in a window-pane! I had the appearance of a — I don't know what — of a bedraggled tramp — a pair of pants much too large for me — legs like match-sticks — and playing the bag-pipes (my ox. balloon). Still, everybody found me charming — 'she looks so well — really a case of being raised from the dead — and how splendidly she walks — just look at her, she's actually moving!' (and move I did).

The sun was shining outside — not too fiercely, because it was his first appearance after a series of wet and misty days. My toes trembled with joy at feeling the cement surface of the balcony, and I hurriedly gripped the rail so that others shouldn't see my idiotic delight at being once more on my feet in the sun. I can't tell you the effect it had on me — though it was far from being a pioneer attempt to take my first steps — like everybody else I have often suffered from illnesses which make that initiation necessary. But today was a special occasion. I had got out of bed unaided, and then, oh, I don't know — the grass was very green, and the blue of the sky very tender. I forgot all my troubles for a while — I *do* have some, you know, and just at a time when what I most need is peace of mind.

Monday morning. Gracious, how beautiful this view is! You must envy my not being cooped up in an office.

There's a small wind blowing, just enough of it to set the cloths on the tea-tables in the garden flapping, and a few doors banging — all quite delicious . . . This morning I managed to drink some tea and to nibble two pieces of toast and jam. How I wish that my mother and you were here with me — you all relaxed and simple in pyjamas with your feet on the table. With one hand, my mother would hand you a cup of tea, with the other, point at me and say — using, I am afraid, a very vulgar term — that I was just a trollop. The tea would boil, I should protest, and you would read the marriage column in the paper — and the tea would go on boiling.

Say something nice. I'm due for a medical. You'll never know the end of my story, nor how the sugar-tongs were all awash.

You're sleepy — so go to bed. There is nothing I can do about it. I'm going for a stroll.

Tuesday, 29th May

This morning, feeling my end approach, I decided to enjoy life to the full — and ate a whole packet of chocolate . . . That explains why I look so thoughtful, and have that heavy expression which tells of the inner life.

295

Guess what I did with myself yesterday evening? — I went to the cinema. I did not take the same road thither as common mortals do. With my usual scorn for appearances, I witnessed the performance comfortably stretched at full length, with my head on a pillow, my feet under a rug, and my little oxygen projectile at my side. I'd have liked to stay longer, in spite of feeling tired. There are moments when fatigue gets so muddled up with excitement and nervous tension, that it's almost like a feeling of renewed energy ... The audience was a bit of a surprise — its composition, I mean. There were five faces I knew, including D.'s — all the rest a surprise packet of bobby-soxers who seemed to have got in by mistake. Several very handsome men — 'But they don't look ill at all' — I thought as most people do who come here for the first time. One of them had a beautiful jet-black beard, and eyes that cut one up into tiny bits. There was a sprinkling of unkempt and uncontrolled young fools who might have stepped straight out of the bar at the 'Colisée'. I found something unpleasant in the thought of such a completely new set-up, all in the space of five months.

I long to go for a walk ... The rain has stopped, and everything is smelling good. For four months I have been in bed — four months — without being able so much as to lift an arm high enough to take something off the table. It's frightful, darling! — but all that's going to change now. My heart's giving me trouble. Well, if it conks out, the end will come quickly — if not, so much the better. If I take care there's no reason why it should do the dirty on me. Just now, it's beating at 148. I always seem to have an unpleasant feeling in the pit of the stomach. They tell me it's nerves, and that the only thing to cure it is bodily and mental calm (and drenches, presumably).

You lucky dog to be able to visit the Trianons so easily! There's something a bit self-conscious about Le Hameau — all the same, it's charming. I remember a stream where I used to throw stones at the fishes, and all those weeping trees — so languishing. Oh, how I used to love it all! I am passionately devoted to trees. The streets must be brilliant now with little girls on their way to First Communion . . . I have so clear a recollection of my own First Communion, and of how amateurish I was, just like all the others. If I hadn't read somewhere — probably in O. Wilde — that 'all artists are dilettantes' I should have been in despair. Which reminds me — I had a visit today from a girl who's one of the patients here. She was trained at the Beaux-Arts, and is decorating one of the altars in the Chapel. She had thought out a magnificent composition, but the Abbé P. insists on having a Christ dressed like a working man entering a student's room, and a woman carrying a steaming souptureen! I must confess that made me a bit wild! She raged and threatened, but all to no purpose . . . He's dead set on Christ in overalls — but with beard and halo all complete. It's going to have an awful art-for-the-common-man look. It's rather surprising to me that the Abbé, who is undoubtedly intelligent, should have ideas like that, and should cling to them in the face of everybody else's advice. (I assume, naturally, that everybody else shares my views.)

It's now half-past five, and I'm going to play bridge as soon as the others turn up.

I must stop. I love you.

Your
Lisou

Friday, 8th June

Three cheers for Liberty! If you want my considered opinion, here it is . . . All that concerns my own liberty is sacrosanct. Until I came here, I had always done exactly as I chose. Thank Heaven, they were thoroughly sound on that point at home. So far as respecting the liberty of others is concerned, I have always tried hard, and the results have been magnificent, and, as you say, 'stunning'.

Your letter is chockfull of questions. They're so many that I feel terrified. You may not like answering, but you do love asking. I've sniffed at every fold, and I don't like what I smell. But that, I suppose you'll say, isn't my business. Your tone makes me tremble. I am inclined to give a very much wider reference to the phrase 'playing the fool'. It's nice of you to remind me that with an oxygen balloon and a pulse of 148, I've got a pretty thin chance . . . that's only too obvious.

Of course your girl friend is right. You ought to get married. It would simplify so many things for you. I was thinking about it the other day, and came to exactly the same conclusion. Just think, you would get all your darning, ironing and cleaning done for you (you'd better choose a pretty sturdy female because of all this standing about in queues). It might be as well for you if she didn't make too great a point of her 'liberty' — just to restore the balance. Be that as it may, I do hope, Yves, that all these proclamations about your love of liberty are not designed as a direct attack. I should hate to think that I weighed at all in the scales against your principles. If I do, tell me.

No, I am not sweet, I am not frivolous, I am not adorable. I am only profoundly discouraged — and that is due to physical causes. The thought that I shall be back at home in a fortnight terrifies, and, at the same time, enchants, me. I think so much about it that my heart is heavy. I have been so panic-stricken at the idea of dying here.

Good — I, too, have laid aside my rose-coloured spectacles. I can be a pretty pitiful creature when I set my mind to it. As Dr. I. so kindly said . . . everyone hopes I shall be well soon. . . .

Your
Lisou

P.S. The dentist has been to see me — the oddest of odd creatures, whom you must have come across. Every movement he makes is carefully considered. He told me that one of my wisdom-teeth was coming through and that he'd have to

cauterize my gum so as to give it room to expand. At that I
let out a quite inoffensive 'Good God!' — but it seemed to
knock him sideways. 'Invoke nobody, and move your tongue
over to the left' — said he, with majestic slowness. So I moved
my tongue over to the left, which clearly enabled him to see
further. This morning, at my request, they cleared my navel
with the vacuum-cleaner. It is a curious feeling, and I recom-
mend you to try it. I was rather afraid that it might turn inside
out like the finger of a glove, but not at all — It is now completely empty. I particularly wanted you to know that.

Thursday evening, 14th June

I should have loved to telephone you as soon as I got home,
but that is something which will have to wait. The latest
discovery is that it is quite impossible for me to make the
journey — some wretched question of oxygen. My struggles at
this moment prove how right they are. I shall have to wait a
bit until this particular trouble has been dealt with. Do you
know what it's like having to fight for breath? I wouldn't wish
my worst enemy to go through that.

Each letter that reaches me from home is like a smack in the
face now that I know I can't get away from here. All the news
of their preparations for my arrival makes me go pale with
longing. It seems to be God's will that my exile is to go on a bit
longer. (Mummy has had a telephone rigged up beside my
bed — think of that! I should have been able to talk to you
even in the dead of night.) I daren't write home counter-
manding everything — they would be so terribly disappointed.
I need my mother terribly. I am on the very brink of despair.
You have no idea what a haunting obsession this problem of
breathing can become.

Now that I have had a good wallow in self-pity, let's change
the subject. No, I have not yet sent anything to the weekly I
spoke to you about. Mind too tired . . . I've written nothing

that's the slightest good. Nobody can have any idea how
fagged out I am — almost incurably so, it seems to me. To
quote Dr. H. — no progress. You realize what that means,
don't you? I'm just not climbing back up the hill. It's a
whole week since I put a foot to the ground. Everything's
got to begin over again — everything. Good. Well then,
here goes.

Honestly, Yves, at this moment I am no longer an intelligent
being — as, no doubt, you have realized for yourself. I am going to wire my mother to come. I have just about reached
breaking-point.

Your little-misery-who-needs-you

LISOU

P.S. Fundamentally, everyone who wants to be free, can be.
Liberty is in ourselves. (There is, unfortunately, another kind
of liberty which depends on money — it is a very real variety of
liberty, and bulks large.)

Tuesday evening, 19th June
My faculties are so much in abeyance that I literally don't
know whether I have, or haven't, written to you in the last few
days, or, if I have, what I've been talking to you about.

Yves, I am neurasthenic — and it's a very odd state. I have
been acquainted with it before, a few days at a time — but
never to this extent. Nothing, absolutely nothing at all,
interests me.

The upshot of everything is that I am going back to Paris —
I think on the 30th — by car. I shall like that. But there can
be no question of my going home. I believe they've decided to
send me to the M. . . clinic. What's it like? . . . I rather think
Sa. was there. Did she have a room to herself?

The temperature here is tropical — added to which, I have
just had a visit from the Abbé P. He was almost as much

knocked-up as I was. There was a fly on his flushed forehead.
It rubbed its paws together and walked up and down as though
it had been in its own home. He raised his hand. It made a
half turn and then settled down in precisely the same spot. He
stood it for thirty seconds, then drove the creature away again.
It buzzed round for a bit, and then — plump! — back it came.
I was quite hypnotized. He left me, and then returned for his
breviary. I could have throttled him!

Will you think less of me if I stop there? I should love to talk
to you (no, listen to you) — but I can't go on a moment longer.

I drink great draughts of bromide — they have really very
odd ideas — that's probably why I am so idiotic.

I warn you, Yves, that I am returning in a deplorable condition — but I shall be most awfully glad to see you again and
very nervous. You'll see how little I can be relied upon to play
the gangster. I'm just about fit to be stuck up in a field of
vegetables to scare the sparrows. . . .

All the same, till we meet again

Always your
Lisou

Sunday evening, 24th June
There was a magnificent storm yesterday evening, beloved. Like a good, intelligent storm it waited until dark had
fallen before breaking. Since I couldn't sleep, I followed its
every phase. It was overwhelming — but quite thrilling. At
first, oddly enough, it was like a silent film — superb flashes of
lightning, but not a sound. Then, far away, a faint noise as of
someone pulling up a chair on the other side of the mountains,
followed by a tremendous blast of wind. This was the curtain-
raiser. A moon cut out of white cardboard was pinned to the
sky immediately facing me. It was an unforgettable moment,
because something was coming to an end, and something else
beginning. I could feel that, but there was nothing for it but to

wait . . . I had the sensation that my body had been turned to marble — and oh! the sweet sound of the first raindrops!

Then, bang! — a fierce and searing blow — the mantle of black cloud ripping apart — the rain, the rain — I felt like groaning with satisfaction — and the vast hurly-burly up above. I was so worn out as a result of having to play a part in these mighty manifestations of the Gods, that I went to sleep. How many wisdom-teeth have you got left? I only hope mine won't give me as much hell as yours did you.

I forgot to tell you in my last letter how much I feel for you in your sufferings. I may joke about it, but I know you must be having an awful time. Did you kick about wildly, as I did? They had to fasten me to the chair. I swallowed all the wads of cotton-wool, and when the dentist said — 'Spit' — I leaned over the contraption and did my very best. Oh, how hard I tried! But I seemed to get tied up in a long tangle of saliva which seemed as though it would never end — and *how* beastly my mouth tasted. My man was a little Jew with long, Andalusian eyes, and a melancholy expression (like all Jews). And then, the hanging about in the waiting-room with its inevitable bronze group. There was a bunch of glorious roses which seemed sadly out of place, a peach-coloured fitted carpet — a big picture (Prix de Rome) of a man with a haughty look and wonderfully moulded legs, leaning over the edge of a fountain, all in pale fresco tints — and four windows looking on to a square filled with pigeons and children. It's all so long ago. I had a purple felt hat and crepe-rubber shoes — a pleated skirt — and I sat with one leg curled under me — quite incapable of looking at the illustrated papers.

Wednesday. It's cool — What a day! Arrival of my mother — T.'s visit — and then, they told me of Erik's death. It all seemed like a bad joke. I can't believe it, because it was the wrong sort of death for him.

This letter will arrive before I do, I think — Oh, Yves, I'm going to see you again! . . .

The idea numbs me. It seems wild and mad — when? All

this comes at a bad time for you — Hell! I hope you'll come and see me as soon as you can. I gather I shall be seeing At. again — so much the better.

If things go according to plan, I shall be in Paris on Sunday evening. I only hope it won't be too hot.

I love you truly I do.

Your
LISOU

Paris. M. . . . Clinic. Thursday evening, 2nd August

I was nervy up to half-past seven, at which hour I dined with my mother — all rather gloomy. Still, I got quite a lot of food down, and you would have been pleased with me. You needn't be afraid that I shall make a nuisance of myself when you're off in your invalid chair, because I shan't. I'll leave you full in the glare of the sun for a good two hours, without even the hint of a hat — and when you're in the garden, I shall forget all about you for nights on end. The 'help' will say — 'Lord, ma'am, if we didn't forget to bring the master in yesterday evening!' You will be found wet with dew and covered with cobwebs — I can't help laughing in anticipation!

My mother seems better disposed towards me (there are times when she finds me very moody and irresponsible — but that state of affairs never lasts long).

I really am a sad sight when I'm on my feet — and I long to have you to lean on. After five minutes or so I'm literally trembling with fatigue, but I stick it out until I start going dizzy. I spent this morning arranging my flowers on the window-sill. I looked at the garden, and then at the trees. Over to the right I could see quite a long way — there was a faint breeze blowing, and all the branches were leaning over in the same direction — rather a pretty sight. A very handsome man was playing an odd sort of game with a big ball. I could watch the rippling of the muscles under his shirt. He was laughing a good deal — and I felt that life was splendid. But I don't suppose that when *I* get out under the trees, and have my feet firmly planted on the ground, I shall bother my head about a poor girl at an upstairs window who may be finding life splendid. Most people's lack of interest in their fellows is rather saddening.

Friday evening. Honestly, I no longer know what to talk to you about, and that's the truth. Put yourself in my place and you'll see what I mean. I am beginning to feel as though I had been chopped into little pieces. If I talk about myself, then, according to you, I am being 'self-consumptive'.[1] If I don't, I am being shut-away and secretive. If I am in pain or gloomy, and say so, it's because (better face the fact) I want to be pitied ... Hell! If I refrain from saying anything about my condition and my doctors, the reason — you suggest — is because I have become besotted by illness. If I *do*, then that's because the thought of tuberculosis has obsessed me to the exclusion of everything else. If I write and tell you that some of the things you say are profoundly wounding, I'm merely dramatizing myself and showing a lack of humour. If I keep mum on the subject, I suppose your unspoken comment is 'what an insensitive little silly she can be!' etc. etc. ... All this must seem quite idiotic to you — typical Lisou stuff — all the same it's true.

Where we went wrong this evening was to start arguing when I brought up 'him and me' as illustrative of something. I don't suppose you much liked my taking up the cudgels for T. quite so energetically. But it wasn't him so much I was defending, as his way of acting. He's the sort, you see, who can be perfectly frank, can observe the rules of fair play, even in his attitude to life. You can take my word for it that life hasn't spared him up to now, and I can see nothing dishonourable in his wanting to tell me all about it. Life is such a filthy business, so full of lies and tricks of every kind, that there is something rather splendid

---

[1] There is a play on words here which cannot be rendered. What she says is: 'quand je parle de moi, je suis "moitrinaire". . .' the word being (presumably) her own private distortion of 'poitrinaire' — or consumptive.—Translator.

in this determination to tell the truth, the whole truth, and nothing but the truth. All that, I have learned from him. I wonder if you realize what a love like ours could be if, in addition, there was between us some such mutual understanding and shared knowledge? It would, I think, be a thing of cloudless beauty. I know it will never happen, and to that knowledge I am resigned. I love you so much that, fundamentally, such considerations have long ceased to have the slightest importance — though the fact remains that we shall each of us die shut away in a little private world which is a pity. One must, I think, love *enormously* for such a growing together to be possible — at least, that's how it seems to me. There are things I could never have put into words in the old days. I would rather have died, for instance, than let people jump to the conclusion that I loved somebody. To have admitted that I was happy would have been sheer torment — stupid, nonsensical things like that. Now that I do *really* love I can see that it is all damned silliness to think in that way. What frightens me is finding in you the very attitude which I myself once adopted towards people about whom, as I now realize, I didn't care two hoots (you'd better re-read all this). Anyhow, hell! — we shall go on endlessly arguing without reaching a conclusion. What's at issue is something very deeply lodged in our two selves, and whatever we do it'll never be changed. We must just face the fact that we are different. After all, it *does* add zest to our relationship, and creates, I suppose, a sort of balance.

All I want you to realize is that there is nothing contemptible about T. (I'd probably defend your point of view just as violently, if somebody began criticizing you to me).

I'm tired — but, oh, I forgot — that's one of the things I mustn't say. No, no, I feel very well, very, very well. I shall sleep soundly, and I haven't an ache or a pain anywhere. But I am going to be perfectly sincere — with your permission — and say that I long to have you take me in your arms (I'm a pretty woman) — to feel your mouth come nearer and nearer, move about my body, stop, then move again. Oh, Yves, I do so wish you would kiss the inside of my left thigh . . . Really, nothing else matters but that — all the rest is nonsense. The day on which I shall be able to offer you a sound, healthy and presentable Lisou will be one of the happiest of my whole life. I say 'one of', because I foresee many wonderful days in the future.

Good night, my Prince.

Saturday morning. What I'm going to say will make you jump. I am taking the liberty of telling you that you're looking tired. If coming so far means additional fatigue for you, then you must come less often. I know it involves a long and tiresome journey (I'm not saying this with the slightest implication of bitterness. *Of course,* I'd like to see you every hour of the day or night).

Needless to say, I've given much thought to what you said yesterday evening. We must both just stand our ground — because I, too, am quite certain that right is on my side.

In any case, beloved, if you have reached the point at which you believe in nothing and are doubtful of everything, I do at least hope that your faith in me is unshaken.

Saturday evening. I am glad, and, at the same time, miserable, that you have decided to go off somewhere each week for a complete rest . . . It means that I shall have terribly little of you. I feel wildly frustrated to see you looking so tired and to know that there is nothing I can do to help — and it's an additional hurt to have the knowledge that you can find rest and refreshment far from me. I get so much and give so little — I realize that only too clearly — all the same, I belong to you utterly.

I don't think I shall resume the experiment of writing to you. It would mean that I should have to keep a strong hold on myself, and the thought of that fills me with horror.

Oh, my sweet, I love you! — I love you!

I lie all soft and gentle in your arms. I want to hear you, too, say that nothing else matters. One of these days I will give you all the tranquillity, all the peace to be found in the whole world.

P.S. Something is worrying me — and that is that you don't seem to believe that I *want* to get well, or that if I do it's because of 'us' at the end of the long road. I won't tell you all I have done to make the future come true, but, believe me, I've done a lot.

What do you want me to say? When you turn up here I am terribly happy, but you do have such an extraordinary way of sending everything toppling down. I sometimes wonder whether you really believe all you say. If you do, it's awful: if you don't, then you say it merely in order to hurt me, and that's awful, too. But, maybe, you don't realize what you are saying. That is what I tell myself, and, as you can see for yourself, I quickly forget it all in your arms. Your Lisou's not one to nurse a grudge. The only satisfactory behaviour is not to take these things too seriously. They are just so much childishness.

M. . . . Clinic: Friday evening, 10th August, 1945

The first night of peace is falling upon the earth — a great event, whatever you may say — but all I get is an impression of silence, nothing more. As my brother says, I have a 'keyhole view' of the outside world. But you must needs mark this letter of mine with a cross — it will rank among the lesser historical documents. But you'll be the only person able to read it. On the whole, I think it better that it should remain as something which Marc can show later on to his schoolfellows — 'Here's a letter my mother wrote to my father on Peace Day, 1945. They didn't make much of a fuss and bother about it, you see — so why should we have to mug up all that nonsense about Potsdam and the Atom Bomb . . .' Poor Marc! — don't go flabby, my darling. Your mother was a vain and superficial woman, and your father was probably deep in a game of bridge, and losing a fortune. Tomorrow he'll go fishing. With your permission I'll get into touch with him again. So long, my pet.

Hullo, Yves! — I rather think you're celebrating on the q.t. I can just picture you tilting your chair back, raising your glass, and laughing. Oh, nobody in the world has ever been loved as you are loved. I'm in the inside pocket of your jacket at this very moment. I am being very quiet, and I can hear what you are saying — and also the sound of your heart, which is thumping away like anything. Perhaps you are thinking of me — yes you are! You are thinking how lovely it was, when I was strong and healthy, to hold me pressed to your side — how you used to stroke my leg, and how you would take off your glove the better to feel my skin — it was sometimes so cold that I would catch my breath. My ear-rings and my comb used to fall off into the road. By the time I got back it would be 7.8, 7.10, 7.12 — and Z. would look at me as I walked down the dining-room. It all seemed to me wonderfully strange in those days.

Yes, there are some superb bits in Valéry — but I detest that bit about the 'pecking sails'. Every stanza is magnificent except that one.

Good night, beloved. Fold your arms about me, and keep me safe.

LISOU

M. . . . Clinic: Wednesday, 22nd August

I wish you could see eye to eye with me about this. It is extremely difficult to be ill in public, as I more or less am, just now. Everyone proffers advice, and, in the long run, the whole crowd get on my nerves to such an extent that I feel I'd like to pack up all my little bits and pieces and just go to the devil! All the same, I longed so hard to be back in Paris, and now I'm there, there I'll stay, and even you with your considered opinions won't make me budge. Enough of all this nonsense! Don't think I can't see your point of view. I understand you so well that it goes to my heart. If, like you, I was up against somebody who, I felt convinced, was doing nothing to hasten her recovery, I should feel just as exasperated as you do. More so, indeed (with me, everything is always 'more so'). I know you want to see me up and about again without unnecessary delay. I know, too, that all this is no more fun for you than it is for me . . . But what you don't seem to realize is that, in the last analysis, it's I who am right. The future will prove it. It's awful for me to have to talk to you like this, beloved. I wish you could look at it sometimes in that light, could bring yourself to think how much rather I'd like to be able to say — 'In three months I shall be out of here, in four, *I'll* be coming to see *you*', etc. etc. But it's you who say all those things for me, and it doesn't seem to occur to you that for me to hear them is sheer torture. At the time my mood is part fury, part gloom, and it's only later that, thinking it all over, I know that I should have behaved in exactly the same way if I had been you. It is a dangerous, delicate, subject, because really it depends neither on you nor on me. Be that how it may, I want to make it quite clear that, so far as I am concerned, you are completely free. You have every right to grow pensive over an attack of 'flu which looks like going on for so long (I didn't dare write to you about it last week). But don't be angry with me, and don't treat me like a little noodle. Put yourself in my place, as I put myself in yours.

My own true love, my hopelessly adored one, think of me often — very often. I live on memories and hopes. Do you remember one freezing evening when I held your head tight between my knees? — the sky was a mass of stars, and I could never have believed . . . There are moments when I can recapture those sensations merely by dwelling on the memory — but it's all over very quickly — and I feel that my thoughts must be plainly visible on my face for all to see. I love you, Yves. I long for so many simple things, and for all the others which, I feel, are waiting for me in the years to come. The good God can't hold it against me that I am sometimes arrogant.

He has a way, in His dealings with me, of somewhat exaggerating.

Tell me it's true, and then treat me as though I were a beautiful woman.

Yo te quiero

LISOUTCHKA

M. . . . Clinic: Sunday evening, 16th September

I am happy this evening. I am so longing for life that I feel I could pull the framework of my bed to pieces — But is God on our side?

Oh, beloved, nothing better has ever been invented than the sound of your voice saying — 'I love you.' It strikes roots of joy into every part of me. It is sweet. There is nothing in the world remotely like it. *I* love *you* — for always. You do know that, don't you? — for always. Were I to die now, at this very instant, I should have put the essential truth into words.

Good night, my executioner — I am sensible, I am controlled.

LISOU

M. . . . Clinic: Friday evening, 28th September

A small boy came to see me today. He hurried past the porter's lodge for fear of being nabbed. He is tiny for his age. He told me all sorts of exciting stories. When he goes back to the Lycée at the beginning of next term, he'll be in the top form of the Lower School. He dislikes the idea intensely. He is an amusing little creature, with large, projecting ears and a big mouth, but his eyes are magnificent, almond-shaped, with a guileless expression in them to which his every movement gives the lie. I like him enormously. He fished a small pot of honey out of his pocket for me. It was, he told me without the flicker of an eyelid, an 'issue'. He much admired the way the

gardens are kept, and hoisted himself on to the window-sill
by his elbows in order to look at them. 'That's an awfully good-
looking coat,' I said. 'Yes,' he replied, 'and I've got trousers to
match.' Would you believe it, he's in sole charge of a garden,
and has had a lot of success with his tomatoes . . . on the other
hand, he is much bothered by parsley which, he tells me, grows
like a weed. He is planning to reduce the size of the bed in
which it is planted. He has just got back from Saint-Georges —
an impossible journey, my dear. The 'little ones' (his sisters)
behaved abominably. But what intoxicating memories he's
brought back with him! They found a fishing-boat, launched
it, climbed aboard — sixteen of them — and left the rest to
chance. There were all sorts of excitements — shells to explode,
powder, mines . . . But the real marvel was the ship. They
had made themselves oars and a sail, and went bathing in the
open sea. Those who could swim pulled those who couldn't
back on board. Sometimes, with a bit of luck, there were a few
extra guests in the stern, and then the boat would capsize. He
spluttered with retrospective excitement in telling me about it.
Just as he was leaving me he said how delighted his mother was
not to have had to sugar her last lot of pear jam — but the
trouble they'd had with the maid! — what times to live in!

This infant's name was Antoine — it suited him about as
well as a forage-cap would suit a rabbit. He swears like
nobody's business . . . still . . .

So, you're feeling a bit fed up, beloved — or so I gather from
what you say. How much greater your peace of mind would
have been had I never set foot in the Sanatorium at X. . . I
love it when you talk about the place. You always say — 'up
there'. You can smell the immortelles, can you? — so can I. I
wonder when I shall see again my lovely smooth stretch of sea-
shore. You can have no idea how big it is. Nowhere else have
I ever had such a sense of grandeur as there, on stormy days,
when I turned about and saw the slim, small point of the church
steeple away at the far end, and thought of my bed, my table,
my family. No matter how loud I shouted in the wind, the dogs

could never hear a thing. So I yelled at the top of my voice, the first things that came into my head, and it was wonderful. What did I think of in my bed at night? In all probability I told myself that my 'fate' would be a stocky little man with fair, curly hair. . . .

Have you ever looked at Dubuffet's pictures without feeling frightened at the thought of all the lunatics there are at liberty? (I mean Dubuffet — and also the gentleman who must have said 'that's really tip-top stuff — we must arrange an Exhibition — the chap's a genius'.) It's the greatest piece of spoof of the century, and you'll never persuade me it isn't. When I think that people like that are being 'exhibited', I am plunged in universal doubt, or, rather, I am completely flabbergasted, and just give up.

That article made me see red — the aggressive instinct is waking in me again — so I'd better leave off. You can't possibly know how soft and tender your eyes can be at times — I feel exactly as though I were dissolving in them. My arms are cold — but I love you, oh, so much!

Your
LISOU

M. . . . Clinic: Friday evening, 12th October

There's a mass of things I want to tell you, but when you are with me I have neither the saliva in my mouth nor the breath in my lungs which would let me put anything into words. In the first place, I do understand why you were annoyed with me for not at once reading the article to which you had drawn my attention in our magazine. If the situation had been reversed, I should have felt no less indignant than you. I have no excuse. But I did read it this afternoon. Whether because of what you have told me about L. M., or because of what emerges from the article — probably a mixture of the two — I realize to the full what a really remarkable person he must have been, and envy you your good luck in having known him. Those fragments of letters — they amount almost to a journal — are quite admirable in their sincerity. I feel that they are just what letters ought to be. It's a wonderful thing, don't you agree, to be able to get the feel of a person from a few written lines? Whatever he says, whether he is joking, making bitter reflections, or sudden, spontaneous judgments — one hears the note of absolute truth. It is rather odd, you know, that a man should feel constrained to take up his pen and write — 'I looked in at the butcher's at a quarter to three, and asked for a beefsteak. He gave me two *escalopes de veau* . . .' etc. What is even more curious is that one can read two or three hundred pages of that sort of stuff without ever feeling bored for a moment. (I find him encouraging, from many points of view.) Have you got any letters from him? Who is La. who wrote the article (very well done, and pleasantly simple, in my opinion)?

I'd like very much to know what you think of his poems. I am such an ignoramus about poetry, that I would rather not express an opinion. I have got a blind spot so far as that particular literary form is concerned. For me, one of his letters is worth ten of his poems. All the same, some of them are very moving. I like his attitude to life, his determination to take it as it comes and discard what is ugly. I don't know your own views on the meaning of life — forgive such big words. Personally, I am quite sure that salvation lies in the love of beauty. That, I feel sure, is how he felt — and there is beauty to be found everywhere (I am pretty well convinced that you don't realize that. Your particular brand of scepticism proves it).

I find that there are millions of things I have to tell you — but we have plenty of time before us . . . I love and adore you in your tender moments, and would willingly be hanged for you. You had better make the most of that, because you won't find two women in your life who will say as much! Like a little goose I drank my sleeping stuff a short while ago, and can scarcely keep my eyes open. Good night: I belong to you entirely, even when I'm in a bad mood, even when I get on your nerves. You always have the right to come and take me in your arms. . . .

Oh, Yves, happiness is hard to come by. I am full of my desire for you, and I don't blush to admit it. There is no question now of a child . . . I could wish that our legs might do battle — just once in a while. Meanwhile, I am going to knit you some gloves: would you like that?

Saturday. Well, the blow has fallen, and it seems I've got to be moved again next month. If there is no more in this suggestion than there was in the Saint-Cloud one, I can go on sleeping soundly at night. If it is more serious, then I don't like the idea at all. Oh, if only a time would come when I could pack my bags and write the home address on my labels! They seem to be having a proper fun-fair there at the moment. They've got an old lady (very, very old), Françoise, who's sleeping in the attic, Hélène's American, who's dossing down on a mattress, and T., who is sharing a bed with Jean-Jacques. In addition to all this, one of my aunts is expected daily with her son . . . The meals, I'm given to understand, have to be seen to be believed. Mauricette sits on mummy's shoulder, the old lady's at loggerheads with Françoise, who, in her turn, quarrels with Hélène, who's billing and cooing with her Richard, who yawns and stretches and exasperates mummy who unloads her ill-humour on papa, who is irritated by the old lady who wants a little silence so that she can listen to the music which Jean-Jacques is trying to get on the radio, and which deafens everybody. Oh, how I should love to be there to add my note of serenity to the general hubbub. . . .

M. . . . Clinic: Saturday evening, 20th October
I have a whole lot of things to talk to you about, as usual. In the first place, I don't know whether you understand what I said about your friend Br. I had no intention of wounding

314

you when I gave a frank answer to your question. I've never known any people of that kind (with the exception of L., who was a bit inclined that way, and whom I couldn't stand). I have never been surrounded by people for ever talking of women, of 'going to bed with' . . . of so-and-so's legs and so-and-so else's breasts. It's not my fault if that sort of thing gets my hackles up — or, rather, has the immediate effect of striking me dumb, so that I make myself as small as possible so as to offer the least amount of sensitized surface. The reason is not only that I don't understand that sort of talk, but that I am embarrassed by it — I feel a crushing weight of discomfort. What is more serious — I shall never be cured of feeling like that. I know that if I were at a dinner-party where that kind of conversation was pushed to excess, I should be quite capable of laying down my napkin and vanishing. Just now I shot the most bewildered glances at you, though nothing particularly bad was being said. It was no use my coiling up and trying not to be noticed — what I wanted was a raft to cling to.

Heavens, Yves! — don't you regret ever having known such a little silly?

(This letter was never sent, but was found among Elizabeth's papers.)

Z. . . . Hospital: Wednesday, 31st October
Beloved, if only I could bury my face in your shoulder so as not to see and not to hear all the ugliness round me. You can't realize . . . I can imagine myself in 36,000 appalling situations, but never in anything worse than this organized hideousness. . . .

Truly, I long to be able to talk to you, and to be just the little idiot I have been for the last few days. You would say: 'Lisou?' — and that would be enough to make me drop a tear — a bigger tear than you have ever seen.

I can't describe the impression of horror that haunts me — it enters at every pore of my skin. I'd rather you didn't come to

315

see me, you might share the feeling, and it is quite bad enough to have it myself. I keep on wondering why I should have to go through all these awful moments — on top of everything else.

I arrived under the sign of the 'bird'. I could hear them everywhere in the trees. I got the orderlies to open the skylight of the frightful ambulance — and now, here, the sparrows perch on the very eiderdowns and dance about with insolent insistence if one doesn't at once feed them crumbs.

Apart from all that — it had never occurred to me that women could reveal so many horrors.

Thursday evening. To continue. I lie with my eyes shut and think of the way you reproach me for never talking enough. Here you would find as much as you could put up with in the way of talkative females. Come and rescue me, beloved — hold out your two hands to me — I need you, and I make no bones about saying it! Do you know that when thirty women are gathered together, there is nothing to be heard but an unending catalogue of ailments and miscarriages . . . This exhibiting of all the intimacies of married life is quite appalling. . . .

(This was the last letter that Elizabeth ever wrote. It was found among her papers after her death, which occurred on the 13th November, 1945, in a Clinic to which she was transferred from the Hospital.)